Designed to Blossom

A Creative Workbook and Foundational Course in Human Design

IT'S TIME TO LIBERATE
YOUR INNER WISDOM KEEPER!

ROSY ARONSON, PHD

"In Human Design I am a Projector. I am here to direct others, guide responses. I amplify other's energy! I absorb, expand, and reflect the energy of others. Projectors need to be at peace with their true self, who they are. Think of the Projector type as one that helps guide others in using their energy, to use it. Projectors are creative. They are natural leaders. They make wonderful innovators and guides, helping others to focus their energy in the 'right places.'"

"Projectors value accomplishments and successes. Others are moved by projectors. Projectors have an inner authority. They read other with intrinsic natural ability. They are an accurate and powerful in their keen analytics. Their inherent ability is being deeply attuned with others." As a 'projector' you know it can be a blessing and a curse. The blessings win out, however,"

Seal Pup
PRESS
Berkeley, CA

For permission requests, write to the publisher, addressed "Attention: Permissions Coordinator," at the address below.

Seal Pup Press
PO Box 138
Berkeley, CA 94701
sealpuppress.com

Writing and design by Rosy Aronson
Cover design by Kim and Rosy Aronson
Artful exercises by *Designed to Blossom* course participants
Muse Consulting and Editing by Pam DeLeo
Key words and concepts related to *The Spectrum of Consciousness* by Richard Rudd's *The Gene Keys*, Gene Keys Publishing © 2009

Author's Note: *This course offers an introduction to the Human Design system through my uniquely creative, eclectic and psychologically-integrating lens. Should you become interested in a formal training in Human Design, or in becoming a certified analyst, please check out the resources provided at the end of this workbook/course.*

Ordering Information: This workbook/course is available on Amazon and **wisdomkeepers.net**.
For the online version of the course, go to: **designedtoblossom.com**

Designed to Blossom/ Rosy Aronson, PhD—1st Black/White Edition
ISBN 978-0-9970230-4-6

 Look for this icon! Wherever you see one, there's a free instructional video for you at: **wisdomkeepers.net/DTBvideos**

Also by Rosy Aronson

64 Faces of Awakening (artwork)

The Wisdom Keepers Oracle Deck (full color, and black & white limited edition)

The Wisdom Keepers Inner Guidebook (paperback edition)

The 64 Faces of Awakening Coloring Book

64 Faces Projects (global outreach)

Designed to Blossom Foundational Course & Creative Workbook in Human Design

Designed to Blossom Resource Book

Walking a Fine Line: How to Be a Professional Wisdom Keeper in the Healing Arts

A Tale of Serendipity (Part One of The Wisdom Keepers Adventure Tales Series)

Praise from Designed to *Blossom* Enthusiasts!

"*Designed to Blossom* is a unique experience that will set you on the right track, rejuvenate you, reconnect you with the intimate parts of yourself, allow you to forgive yourself, discover the hidden cultural patterns that limit and define you.

Cataclysmic, re-knowing. Rosy will love you like you've never been loved before, accept you as you've never been accepted before. Rosy is a tour de force, her insight, her imagination, her connection with the deepest parts of you will enable you to paint with words, to draw in the colors of life, to reconnect with your passion, to be more than you've ever thought you could; to draw when they told you not to, to sing when they told you not to, to believe when they told you not to, to flourish when they didn't think you could. Rosy and *Designed to Blossom* are a priceless gift. Give yourself the gift of a lifetime."

~Yasmin, Writer

"Rosy's *Designed to Blossom* Program opened a portal of creative self-discovery that I never thought possible. It provided a supportive container while I explored my inner terrain, enabling my process to unfold in a playful and magical way. I felt an inner dance of shadows and light as it weaved together a tapestry of my truth and authenticity, shedding layers of old conditioning while enhancing my gifts. Rosy trusted me, the process, and her loving presence was felt throughout my journey. She didn't waver, and slowly through this amazing process, I learned, and continue to learn, that *anything is possible*. I will always feel grateful for Rosy, her presence, her Program and the sacred container it provided."

~ Judith Snyder, Holistic Licensed Therapist, Certified Yoga Teacher and LifeForce Yoga ® Practitioner, Lover of Creativity, Play, and Sacred Movement.

"A true Human Design master is part knowledge-expert, part artist, part therapist, part facilitator. Rosy is all of these and more. The promise of Human Design is to shift the 'stuck places' and experience relief, new freedom, a sense of possibility and/or transformation. With compassion, rigor and an amazing capacity to track the complexity of experience, Rosy was able to offer me a very accessible framework and in-the-moment tools that help me make choices more easily, express myself more authentically and experience a sense of aliveness and alignment that are unprecedented in my 56 years (and ohh, so many therapy sessions!)."

~Susan Strasburger, RPT, PhD, Integrative Coaching and Counseling, Living with Presence

"Playing with Human Design and Rosy was one of the most encouraging, affirming, enlightening and fun experiences I've ever had. This System of discovery acknowledged who I am based on how I was designed before any of this crazy world's conditioning got in the way. It changed my life to start seeing myself through truth-glasses rather than cultural, societal, familial or trauma-based ones. Human Design was the perfect prescription to help correct my self-vision and move me toward 20/20. My gratitude abounds…"

~Anissa Matthews, Purveyor of Passions and Worshipper of Life

"As a magical mentor, coach, artistic midwife, and celebrator of what's blossoming in an individual, Rosy Aronson has cleared the dust from my eyes and set my feet on solid ground time and time again. She has a gift to see deep into one's soul and usher us into our greatness. I would not be this currently 'blossomed,' and constantly still blossoming version of myself without her acute wisdom and generous joyful support. I would encourage anyone wanting to step more fully into the highest version of herself to experience Rosy Aronson and *Designed to Blossom*. Rosy is a magically inspired, creative, and powerful force of nature on our planet at this time!"

~Jenny Karns, author, healer, creator of Remembering Our Magic Telesummit: A Healing, Empowering, and Global Peace Project

"Rosy Aronson's *Designed to Blossom* program was the perfect intro into Human Design. She distilled Human Design's complexity into fun, accessible, lessons and practices that helped me start living my design and trusting myself in new ways. We continued to work together in a coaching relationship that has expanded beyond Human Design. But I look at the work we did together in the *Designed to Blossom* program as the foundation of our work, where I began learning how to trust my generator belly response rather than my mind. Over time this practice has transformed my life by releasing me from pressures and those nagging "shoulds" that weren't serving me. Human Design can feel overwhelming and complex. If you're looking for a fun, interactive, and creative approach to learning it, I highly recommend you consider the *Designed to Blossom* program!"

~James Alexander, Truth Seeker, Writer, and Spiritual Coach

"Rosy possesses the rarest sort of genius, and she puts it to still rarer use. Part supportive counselor, part wise interpreter of the soul, part clear-eyed intuitive, Rosy is the sort of ally in life I wish everyone could experience. The whole world would be the better for it. In a world where, it seems, only the most conventional and obvious skills and life paths are encouraged, her commitment to naming and supporting subtler gifts and needs is vital. I'm always touched by her insight, empathy, and boundless understanding."

~Siona van Dijk, Writer, Facilitator, Clinical hypnotherapist and Literary Dilettante

"Rosy is a lighthouse, illuminating the way for those who seek knowledge of self. She is like a compass guiding you back home, and once there, can never stray away again. I was looking for a Human Design facilitator through the internet and I found Rosy's name. I was immediately attracted to her energy and spent several days researching Human Design. I have participated in the *Designed to Blossom* course and worked with Rosy privately for quite some time, and I have to say she really is one of the most dynamic women I have ever met. Her intelligence, professionalism, passion, integrity and expertise are exceptional. She has a gift of combining all her wisdom and knowledge into her work. Thanks to Rosy and this course, my life has blossomed, and through an understanding of my Design, I have become more empowered."

~Sandra Rojo, Certified Wellness, Health and Life Coach, and Healer

"Rosy is not only an expert on Human Design but a true artist in the way she personalizes the work and gives it voice. I have invested in many workbooks and coaches for personal growth and development and my experience with Rosy was by far the most valuable for what I learned and could immediately apply to all aspects of my life, relationships and business. Until understanding my Human Design I tended to make things so much harder than they needed to be. With Rosy's guidance, I was able to start to trust my rhythms and ways, and have had incredible gifts appear in my life. Just thinking of my sumptuous Human Design experiences with Rosy brings sunshine, flowers, and fresh air into my being! She is a sparkling gem. I cannot recommend Rosy's work highly or deeply enough!"

~Karyn Amore, Catalyst and Muse for Your WildSexyFree Life

"Learning about my design from Rosy was an amazing experience of being fully appreciated and praised for all the parts of myself and life experiences I held in contempt and judgment. Not just facts and figures, but the way Rosy interpreted and delivered the Human Design information is what was so impressive and therapeutic to me. Very powerfully, intuitively, empathically, compassionately and so joyfully, Rosy told me the story of myself; introducing me to my long lost Truest Self. Rosy completely reframed my perspective regarding my life's journey, purpose and accomplishments. I discovered I was more on track than I thought and very creatively fulfilling my Life Purpose mission. Not only am I right where I'm supposed to be but ahead of the curve in many ways. For the first time in my life I am able to accept and fully embrace my creative ingenuity and allow 'not knowing' and trusting the unfolding of life's process to be my Muse rather than my Nemesis. Thanks, Rosy. You are truly an amazing gift to all the lives you touch."

~David Scheel, natural Empath and Change Agent, facilitator of True Self Re-membering and Embodiment

"Rosy and the *Designed to Blossom* course changed my life in a profound way. The brilliant creative exercises engaged me at a deep level, and passed the chatter of my mind. I've been in therapy for years, explored several spiritual paths, studied many systems of self-understanding, and had many different kinds of Readings. I had actually received an HD Reading by someone else, but the information was dry and lifeless. Rosy makes Human Design deep, alive and juicy, full of love, respect and humor. I had been anorexic for decades when I started the *Designed to Blossom* course. While doing an exercise that focused on my body, I drew a tiny stick figure behind prison bars. Looking at that drawing, a deep, unknown desire to free that stick figure arose inside me! For the first time in 40 years, I felt ready to let go of my anorexia. Of course, the letting go didn't happen overnight. But the profound shift in consciousness that I experienced in the *Designed to Blossom* course, set me on the road to true recovery. I am now fully recovered and feeling fully alive and in my body, at last, which I now experience as beautiful! I consider my connection to Rosy and the *Designed to Blossom* course to be one of the blessings in my life."

~Jackie Goodman, a whole, free, alive human being

"This Human Design information can be confusing. But, shared with someone rooted in Love and Integrity such as Rosy, it begins to open, maybe…unfold…who we are. Working with Rosy, I just felt recognized…that's me, described in a new language! It comforted me, revealing an inner guide and self-trust I had never really dared to rely upon. Listening, I relaxed into who I am, and found myself…loving…the uniqueness of me! My relationships immediately took on more fullness. I came to this planet with the unwavering belief that each person has everything they need already 'installed.' Human Design is a way to discover what we have within, and how it can be reached and expressed to give shape to the life we live."

~Brett Diethert, Imaginist, dreamer, poet, writer

"I'll tell you now of Rosy, Compassionate and Wise—
Who's always in my Corner, Exposing all the Lies
That I in Years of Living Believed about my Self.
She Gently and with Humor Uncovers all the Wealth
That's been Hiding in the Basement under Years of Self-Neglect.
While Vacuuming and Dusting, she showed me—Self-*Respect!*
The Journey is Ongoing, and my Blossom's Just Begun
To Open, and to Fragrance the World with Joy and Fun.
What lies ahead is Foggy, a World yet Unexplored.
Technology seems Baffling, but I am Moving Toward
A Place that will be Perfect for my Projector Soul
To Flourish and to Open as an Integrated Whole.
How rare a find is Rosy! Her virtues know no end,
A Coach and Guide and Counselor, and my Eternal Friend!"

~Margaret Blackburn, Mother, Grandmother, Wife, Teacher, Energy Worker, Musician, Author (and Angel)

 Look for this icon! Wherever you see one, there's a free instructional video for you at:
wisdomkeepers.net/DTBvideos

To the many brave, trusting and devoted ***Designed to Blossom*** participants
who over the years, dove into this material with their whole hearts, provided me with invaluable
feedback, and consistently encouraged me to make this creative and
empowering process available to more people.
You'll see their brilliant creations sprinkled throughout this Workbook.
From the bottom of my heart, THANK YOU!

A special Thank You to Ra Uru Hu, who channeled the Human Design transmission,
turned it into an easy-to-understand system, and made it accessible to people all over the world.
He believed that this profound material was meant to evolve, expand and awaken the planet
through the unique, creative and empowered voices of its students.
Deep gratitude to you, Ra.

To be yourself in a world that is constantly trying to make you something else is the greatest accomplishment.

Do not go where the path may lead, go instead where there is no path and leave a trail.

—Ralph Waldo Emerson

Table of Contents
 Free instructional videos available at: wisdomkeepers.net/DTBvideos

Look for this icon! Wherever you see one, there's a free instructional video for you at:
wisdomkeepers.net/DTBvideos

My Story

I was born into a warm, creative, self-sacrificing and slightly neurotic Jewish-American family. From the day I burst out of my mother's womb, I was a 'highly-sensitive' being. Despite years of twisting myself into pretzels, attempting to 'succeed,' be selfless, pleasing and invisible all at the same time, I continuously flew in the face of personal and cultural conditioning.

While studying Transpersonal Psychology and Social Change at the University of Michigan, I expanded my world view and struggled for the rights of any potentially oppressed people I could get my hands on. At the University of Seville in my Junior Year, I met a tall, blonde, anarchistic (and considerably 'woo woo') Danish artist who turned my relatively conservative academic life upside down.

Instead of going down the expected care-taking Ph.D. track, I moved to Denmark to explore my artistic dreams and reclaim the creative muse within who had always existed, but was never prioritized.

(I had learned early on that to earn the right to exist, I had to find a way to serve others that could be intelligibly talked about at dinner parties!) It was never my plan to stay in Denmark, but I did—for eight years (seven without the blonde! But that's another story!). No longer burdened by conventional "American" conditioning, I joyously followed my instincts and partook in a rich buffet of 'alternative' experiences.

As I shed the weight of cookie-cutter expectations, I discovered myself—and even managed to transcend a life-long pattern of sacrificing my needs and suppressing my light in order to protect the people I loved.

After an unbridled year of art making and exhibiting my work, I longed to reintegrate my love of embodied learning and artful service. I trained and became certified as a breathworker, and then continued my education at the Institute for Art Therapy (where I met my wonderful husband, Kim).

By 1991, I was happily self-employed and the co-founder of the Center for Water Rebirthing in Copenhagen.

As my private practice evolved, I worked as a Jungian-inspired art therapist, creativity workshop facilitator, and supervisor/teacher for alternative healing professionals who longed to incorporate the wisdom of depth psychology into their work with clients. In response to the challenges and pitfalls I witnessed in alternative learning and healing communities, I wrote a book called <u>Walking a Fine Line: Being Professional in the New Age</u>.

In the mid 90's, Kim's hunger for adventure joined my growing desire to return 'home' as my empowered, authentic, culturally and spiritually liberated self. We sold our Danish home, packed our bags, and moved back to the States—settling close to the place where I grew up, in the Northern suburbs of Chicago.

Despite my great expectations, returning 'home' to the States was NO PICNIC! I was surrounded by family and friends who loved me. But they had no clue about what I'd been doing all those years abroad, or how my experiences had changed me. To my utter dismay, none of my European credentials or professional experience were recognized in the States.

If I wanted a life like the one I had in Denmark, I'd have to start ALL OVER.

As my new disturbing reality sunk in, and meaningful job search failed miserably, I began to panic. Desperate for work, I accepted a job for which I was entirely unqualified, and which was located (don't think I don't get the irony here!) just across the hall from my father's pediatric practice. I became a…DENTAL ASSISTANT! (You read right! The dentist I worked for was not your ordinary dentist. She was bright, hilarious and a devoted wiccan! I came to love her dearly.) As the months—and years—passed, and I finally learned the difference between Bicuspids and Molars, memories from my liberated 'past life' drifted into the remote corners of my mind.

> *I'll never forget the moment I was standing by a patient's side.*
> *The woman looked up at me, dressed in my powder blue mask and smock,*
> *and in all sincerity asked, "So, Rosy, is your dream to become a dentist one day?"*

That kind, innocent question ripped to shreds any last illusion I had that my life made sense. When I got home, I had a total and complete melt down. My poor husband held me while I sobbed, and sobbed, and sobbed. How could this have happened? I had spent the past 15 years on a path of uncompromisingly courageous course towards authenticity. And yet, here I was, living in an American suburb, holding a Spoon Excavator in my hand, completely unrecognizable to myself and everyone around me. That night, I looked in the mirror, for a good long time, and then it hit me.

> *I had devolved! I had become Rosy the 17-year-old!*

There she was, looking right back at me, still living close to her parents, feeling, thinking and doing all of the things that helped her survive her child/teenage-hood.

I was:

- Sacrificing and ignoring my needs, wants and instincts for the sake of my relationships
- Trying to please and win the approval of my parents
- Buying into all of the materialistic, external-success-oriented values of mainstream US culture
- Feeling like a freak and a failure
- Saying 'yes' when I felt a 'no'
- Beating myself up (not to mention my body) with binge eating and brutal self-talk
- Hiding my light
- Mentally agonizing over every move I made

It was as if all of the personal growth work I had done had vanished the moment I set foot in the States.

No matter how authentic and untethered I had felt abroad, I had no clue about how to sustain 'True Self-hood' in my home land.

One thing I did know was that I couldn't genuinely blossom as myself until I consciously and courageously released myself from the grips of those old, buried, crushing conditioning messages, telling me who I was and how to be.

The journey back to my authentic life took a long long time… and it involved a lot of trial and error!

But I learned so much. Not only about myself, but about what it truly means—and requires—to claim and live one's own life.

I also learned how *not alone* I was in my lostness. Many of us are living lives that don't feel like our own. Lives our parents wanted for us. Lives that our educations supposedly prepped us for, but we no longer relate to. Lives that kind of "just happened." Like the Talking Heads song, we find ourselves asking, "How did I get here?!" Instead of blossoming, we find ourselves wilting—feeling trapped, confused and hopeless. Many of us become paralyzed by our overly analytic minds, or caught up in a chaos-creating cycle, making one emotionally charged decision after another. This is why I've become unwaveringly committed to making the "path home to self" easier, more enjoyable—and hopefully *much smoother*!—for others.

In this Workbook/Course, I've taken two of the most essential, empowering and practical ingredients that have helped me blossom in my own life, and woven them together.

Ingredient #1: The Creative Process

I am absolutely convinced that I wouldn't be the resilient, adaptive, persistent and faith-filled person I am today if I hadn't spent so much time engaging in the Creative Process. It's through the Creative Process (I'm not talking about creating fine art here) that we learn how to feel comfortable-enough in the unknown.

Blossoming authentically requires that we 'hang in there' even when it's highly uncomfortable. It asks that we trust something deep—often invisible—within ourselves, even when the pressures and expectations of the world are mounting all around us, pushing us to get our acts together and become Impressive Success and/or Pleaser Machines. Creativity also invites us in. Whenever we let go of a 'Life Should' and enter a playful space, we give ourselves the opportunity to explore (even get absorbed in) our rich, fertile inner world. For service-oriented beings especially, there is no greater medicine.

I want you to receive this creative Workbook/Course as an invitation to explore fun, hands-on and experiential ways to access your truth, even if that means trying something new, not doing something perfectly, or graciously bypassing your mind. You don't need to be or even want to become a fine artist to have fun with the experiential invitations. NOT AT ALL! (Though I have a hunch you're probably much more creative than you think, when you finally let go of what you've been taught about what creativity looks like.)

Ingredient #2: Human Design

While the Creative Process preserved my spirit, I'd have to say that it was an unexpected and enthusiastic encounter with Human Design that grounded—and ultimately allowed me to fully embrace—my authentic life.

For those of you who have never heard of Human Design, it is a mysteriously practical, relevant and life-changing system for understanding, honoring and liberating your uniqueness, brought into the world and comprehensively developed by a man named Ra Uru Hu. In its essence, Human Design is a practice of Self-Trust.

One of the biggest gifts of Human Design is that it helps you learn how to put something ELSE in charge of your life than your logical mind. It gives you:

- something to turn to when you feel pressured, overwhelmed or overstimulated
- a more natural, ease-filled way to move through this world, and…
- an authority inside of you—a TRUTH compass—that is consistent, reliable and unique to you

Over the years, I've found that systems or tools -- like Human Design -- are most helpful when held lightly with the flexible hands and open ears of an 'artist' who listens.

In the end, this is all about you learning how to **trust yourself** and your *Inner Wisdom Keeper*, how to become the authority in your own life, and how to honor your unique timing—no matter what anyone else is saying…me included! So, please don't think you've got to swallow what's in this Course/Workbook whole. Think of it like Buddhist meditation, or a fun personal science experiment. Try it out for yourself, and see if it works!

Finally, one of my deepest intentions is to form a bridge between traditional Human Design and some of the beautiful transpersonal work being done by Richard Rudd (through the **Gene Keys**) and Werner and Laura Pitzal (through **Integral Human Design**). Richard Rudd is a teacher of world mythology, an award-winning poet and the author of *The Gene Keys: Unlocking the Higher Purpose Hidden in Your DNA*.

There is of course one more absolutely essential ingredient to any blossoming journey.

A village of compassion!

I'd never be as "blossomy" as I am today without people who believed in, encouraged, challenged, listened to, cheered on, unconditionally loved, and sometimes not-so-gently nudged me out of my Insecurity Shell.

I am forever grateful to my friends, family, mentors, role models, clients, students, and fellow bloomers like you… It is ultimately through our relationships that the value of our own lives is reflected back to us (no matter how society looks at what we do, no matter how invisible we may feel at times, no matter how ridiculously our work is taken for granted), especially during those multitudes of moments when we can't see it ourselves.

I want to encourage you to surround yourself with personal support and a community of compassion as you enter into and move through this experience. Consider 'blossoming' together with a group of friends. Share your experiences, expressions and epiphanies with the people you feel most safe with, who know you well, and who genuinely celebrate in your blossoming. For a more intimate and personal feel, consider adding the online *Designed to Blossom* self-study program to your process, where I present the material in lovingly crafted videos, using music, creative illustrations and my genuinely heartfelt presence!

I once received a fortune cookie that said, "Put yourself proudly in front of the world and declare your place."

This is what I want for you. And this is what I offer: a love of uniqueness, and a deep faith that there is a place here in this world for all of us. You too. I would be so honored if together we can help you find a way to blossom into your absolutely unique and lovable self… so that you can enjoy, relax and serve from your perfect place in the Garden.

Love,

Rosy

It All Starts with a Bud of Intention

Reconciling the We with the Me

During my beloved sister Marilee's travels to India, she spent some time living with a family. They showed her exciting places and showered her with hospitality—food, attention, care, the works. My sister found herself repeatedly expressing her gratitude. Until finally her hosts advised her to stop saying *Thank you* so much. They said, "Why do you keep saying *Thank you*? You don't thank your body for chewing or breathing, do you? So why should you thank us? We're not separate; we are One."

I was so touched when I heard this story and felt its profound Truth. We are all indeed interconnected, each of us a part of the same sacred whole. When one of us suffers, we all suffer, just as when one of us offers a gift of service, we all benefit… including the gift giver!

At the same time, upon receiving this important reminder, I couldn't help but notice another (slightly less enlightened!) part of me feeling a tinge of embarrassment. I still found myself wishing (and waiting) for *Thank you's* in my life. A chronic over-giver, I tended to forget, compromise and neglect myself in my efforts to serve the people around me. A little appreciation lovingly sent in my direction went a long way.

If you can relate, you know just how possible it is to get so caught up in all that you're doing for others that you don't even realize how empty your cup is. If your work is the forever-mounting and never-ending kind (like care-taking and relationship-maintenance), or if 'what you do' isn't easily seen or valued by our materialistic and achievement-obsessed culture, you may have an especially hard time justifying self-care to yourself. Prioritizing your own needs (your First World problems), honoring your true passions, and risking disappointing others, can feel selfish and 'unspiritual.'

If you've been on a self-development journey, you may have another problem. You may find yourself so overwhelmed with the task of tending to old wounds and manifesting personal desires, that you have little surplus for anything else. You may feel at times, like your nose is permanently stationed in your navel, and your true calling is wafting right overhead…into the mists of a distant unreachable future.

At the heart of the **Designed to Blossom** journey lies an essential paradox and inquiry to explore:

How can we find a way to honor our interconnectedness and serve this beautiful world of ours, without losing ourselves in the process?

How can we truly get to know, trust and honor our unique selves, without becoming so self-absorbed that we miss out on the chance to make a positive difference?

We don't want to get so swallowed up and sucked dry by the to-do lists and relationships of our lives that there's nothing left to give. And we don't want to get so caught up in our inner growth ambitions and personal dramas that we abandon our soul's calling to share our gifts with the world.

Believe me; if this crazy, wounded world of ours needs anything, it needs your cup to be full, and that you generously share what's in that cup—with yourself and others!

You could say this **Designed to Blossom** journey is an invitation for all of us to find our own unique dance between the Me and the We. To celebrate the relationship between Uniqueness and Unity. To cultivate the greater Garden by honoring and empowering each of its flowers (you!) to fully bloom!

Please don't be fooled!

This journey may at first appear to be "self-centered" in nature, but this couldn't be farther from the truth. You are entering into a profoundly generous Rite of Passage, designed to lead you to a new way of being human, of serving the planet, and ultimately, of *LEADING*—the kind of leading that is surrendered, trusting and unforced. The kind that will naturally guide you to join with other kindred spirits, in budding, synergistic and collaborative groups.

One more thing: If you long to become a flourishing flower, or a full-fledged member of a thriving collective Garden, you may have to do some serious letting go. There are some things—in yourself, your way of operating in the world—that may need to fall apart. This letting go will likely require courage, a willingness to feel, and a great deal of gentleness towards yourself.

I also recommend that you:

Stay open to surprise! *(You are very likely much more magnificent than you ever dreamed.)*
Remain flexible.
Get creative!
Most of all, remember that you're not alone. We're all in this together!

Here's how it works!

This *Designed to Blossom* course has been designed to unfold like a multi-petaled flower. As you move through, you'll be guided—petal-by-petal—through a fun, educational and creatively-inspiring path.

Get ready to:

- Fully embrace all parts of yourself, and enjoy the abundance of energy that naturally flows your way when you stop fighting your true nature

- Access and **trust** your natural Truth Compass, your *Inner Wisdom Keeper*, no matter what is going on around you

- Discover new (even fun) ways of making decisions with grace and certainty

- Liberate your mind from rigid life agendas and "goals," without giving up your dreams and desires

- Know what people and places are actually healthy for you

- Explore whether you are a person who actually thrives from "making it happen," or someone who's beautifully built to receive and respond

- Discover the surprising ways your body is designed to guide you in making the very best choices

- Stop the constant self-judgment and nagging self-doubts that are keeping you stuck and afraid to be who you really are

Remember! To bloom big and strong, flowers need time, love and attention. Thus, the more heart and soul you put into this adventure, the more you'll get out of it.

How to Get the Most Out of Your Experience

MAKE SURE YOU HAVE A COPY OF YOUR HUMAN DESIGN CHART!

You will need your accurate birth data to receive a Human Design chart. This includes your birth date, your location of birth, *as well as an accurate birth time*.

There are many places online to get a free copy of your Human Design chart. Just google "Free Human Design chart."

If you purchase the online version of the *Designed to Blossom* self-study program, you will receive a special 'Blossoming Bodygraph,' along with over 65 lovingly crafted videos presenting the material in this Workbook/Course in fun, creative ways. Just go to: DesignedToBlossom.com

Follow the Flower's Unfoldment

I've designed this Workbook/Course to unfold in a particular way... for a reason! From my experience as an artist, counselor and Human Design/Gene Keys professional, I've found that the healthiest blossoming journeys begin when we're nice and grounded, and when we feel relaxed, open and connected to who we are and where we're at...right now. Before you learn more specifically how you are designed, I'd like to first plant a few *permission seeds* for the creative process, and help you get a lay of the land in your own life.

You'll notice that each Petal begins with a Teaching, and ends with an Invitation.

Think of the Teaching portion of each Petal as your chance to receive information, and the Invitation portion as your chance to integrate the information, and actually apply it to your life through a creative or practical experiment (this is where the juicy rubber hits the road!).

I REALLY ENCOURAGE YOU TO GET YOUR FAVORITE KIND OF JOURNAL FOR THIS COURSE!

Throughout this process, take time to jot down notes, make little doodles, and record insights as you go. I highly recommend creating a Blossoming Journal just for this course. Human Design tends to sink in more and more over time. Having a place to return to as you integrate this knowledge can be so helpful!

(This beautiful journal was created by a *Designed to Blossom* participant!)

KEEP YOUR CREATIONS SAFE AND CLOSE BY

Throughout this journey, you will be asked to concretely explore what you are learning through creative processes. Find a safe place for these Self-maps so that they can act as personal touch-stones for you, and so that you can return to them as the Petals unfold. As you weave in more and more information about your unique Human Design, you will likely find these personal creations/explorations to be very helpful.

TAKE YOUR TIME

This process is meant to be enjoyed and to have a life-long impact. It is said that it can take 7 years (or more) for this information to become a deeply embodied part of one's life and way of living. So, there is no hurry. Relax. One discovery and experiment at a time. (I do encourage you to take this journey in the order it's presented in this Workbook.)

FOCUS ON YOU FIRST
(and then indulge your curiosity about others!)

One of the most wonderful gifts of Human Design, and what I consider one of its most globally healing aspects, is the way it helps us understand and accept others for who they are. That said, especially if you tend to lose yourself in others or in unhelpful comparison traps, I strongly suggest that you start with a strong focus on your lovely self. Later, you can always partake in the rest of the Human Design buffet provided in this Workbook/Course. (My hope is that by the end of your experience, you'll be really good at knowing what to eat from 'life's buffet' and when!)

CONSIDER FINDING A BUDDY
(or an intimate group of dear friends)
TO DO THIS WITH!

For some of us, having an ally as we move through a self-exploratory and empowering process can make all the difference in the world. If you go through this *Designed to Blossom* together with a friend or a group of friends, you can share the creations you make and the insights you gather. You can encourage each other to keep going when you're tempted to jump ship.

You can also **get to know** each other so much better! Especially when you begin to learn about your unique designs. I've found that my Human Design-informed friendships and relationships have a particularly deep, respectful and permission-giving quality to them. Lord knows my relationships with my husband Kim and my daughter Maya have been immensely helped by this information and practice.

KNOW THIS IS JUST A BEGINNING,
AND THAT IT'S MORE THAN ENOUGH!

Designed to Blossom, amongst other things, is an introduction to the extremely deep and rich system of Human Design. I've studied this system for a long time, and still feel like I have only scratched the surface myself. There will be more for you to learn at the end of this experience, if you are interested.

That said, I've done everything in my power to include enough information here so that you never have to take another Human Design course if you don't want to! You'll learn everything you need to know to put this information into practice. In the end, it's through your own personal experiment that you'll find your way.

First Invitation

Begin Your Journaling!

Take a moment to write down in your journal (and/or the Intention Box right here!) your deepest blossoming intention. What aspects of your life are most in need of blooming? What aspects are blooming quite nicely already?

SEE Yourself

Entering the Heart of the Flower

A CASE FOR CREATIVITY

As mentioned earlier, the creative process has been an essential part of my life. Years of puddling around in paints, making silly sounds, and flipping words like pancakes, helped me become as resilient, adaptive, persistent and faith-filled as I am today. It's through *creativity* that I learned how to feel comfortable (as comfortable as one can ever feel) in the unknown, and through the *creative process* that I came to know myself. Just being allowed to explore my inner world, with no agenda other than play, was quite a profound medicine for a 'We-oriented person' like me.

As an artist, writer and counselor, I'm a big believer in "other ways of knowing." (Human Design is a great example of a system and practice that encourages alternative ways of accessing truth.) Whenever working with people, I love to weave into the process at least a little bit of playfulness and creativity. I often find that those who are willing to loosen up, make a little mess, and have some fun (and invite their inner critic to take a nap), tend to get so much more out of the experience, whatever it is.

VERY IMPORTANT NOTE:
This is not a self-study course for fine artists!

The creative invitations you'll be receiving are not requirements to create fine art, to make something beautiful, or even to be skillful. Not at all! (Interestingly, professional artists can have a harder time letting go of their conditioning and just expressing themselves, for the sake of self-discovery.)

If you've never 'made any art' before,
you might be at an advantage!

The Gift (and Value) of Artfulness

● *Art & the Creative Process can be delightfully Problematic.*
It can teach us a great deal about having and solving problems.

● *Art Opens the Door to our Imagination; it's full of Surprises.*
It automatically puts us in touch with the unknown within us, and around us.

● *Art helps us Loosen up and Learn how to Play: Art has No Goals.*
As the artist/philosopher Paolo Knill says in one of my all-time favorite quotes, "There is a sacred, worshipful quality in any activity which has no goal other than to be a playful manifestation of life, as when a tree plays with the wind or a child plays with her toes."

● *Art helps us get Comfortable with Discomfort.*
Even when we're looking the unknown straight in the eye, feeling uncomfortable or working with potentially confusing, emotional or overwhelming material, we can learn not to run away. We can learn to approach what might otherwise be a scary process with curiosity, Openness and a spirit of playful experimentation.

● *Art connects us with Resources we didn't know we had.*
We may tell ourselves we're not creative, that we can't paint, or collage, or sing a song, or write a poem. Then, we make a collage, or a doodle, or color in the Petals of a flower... In the presence of that solid, visible picture or expression, we can no longer deny our creative potential.

● *Art gives us Opportunities to experience Mastery.*
Every time we take a risk and survive, every time we try something new and it works, every time we turn a mistake into something interesting, every time we build on or improve upon something we're creating—in the sense that it feels more true and right to us, or closer to some essence that we're longing to communicate—we learn something about our capabilities. We feel more masterful.

● *Art can hold everything—Diversity and Paradox.*
A single canvas can hold all colors. A dance can contain all movements. A song can contain all sounds. A work can express all feelings. A single flower can hold many Petals. There are no bounds. We can even experience joy and liberation while painting our despair and imprisonment. Art gives us a very embodied experience of *Unity*, of moving beyond duality...from the *This or That*, to the *This AND That*.

● *Art is Physical. It engages all of our Senses.*

In fact, art is the only dream that is physical. When we paint a painting, or dance on the floor, or map out our passions, we can actually experience a physical release in our bodies. Emotional change becomes visible, felt, real in a way that can't happen when we're just 'talking.' Some say that the more senses we take our explorations, intentions and visions through, the more we bring them into consciousness.

● *Art is Physical, and it can be Shared.*

Through art, we can connect directly with the inner experiences and emerging expressions of others. We can actually experience *Creative Insecurity* together, which can make the unknown feel less lonely and scary, and the exploration of it more playful and rewarding. This is why I'll be inviting you to share what you create, or what you've been exploring with the people in your life…so you can experience the positive ripple effects the 'We' will feel because you've taken time to explore and enjoy your 'Me'!

● *Art Helps us learn how to Let Go of Control.*

Since we can't predict what's going to come out of a creative process, we are forced to surrender, to suspend the critical mind. We have to enter a play space, where no one is the expert. We simply have to release control. We're forced to wake up and become more fully engaged in whatever is emerging. The more engaged and less attached we are in relation to what we're doing, the more easily we attract kindred collaborators.

● *Ultimately, our relationships can become the Art itself.*

We realize that what truly matters is the attitude and spirit of creativity that we bring to all of our interactions with the people and communities in our lives.

Finally, art evokes LOVE. It feeds the Soul.

When we fully engage in an arts process, we can actually fall in love. If Love does anything, it makes us courageous, open, and permeable. It makes us willing to hang in there, even when things get uncomfortable. We simply can't help ourselves, just like we can't with our own lovers! Over time, as we tend to our creations, we learn what it means to care about ourselves, our lives, our Truth. Ultimately creativity puts us in touch with something larger than ourselves. We fall in love with Life itself—the pain, the pleasure, the hope, the despair, the grace and grit of it all!

Your First Invitation
Get Ready to Make Art!

I invite you to begin by making it as easy and fun as possible to make art.
I recommend gathering together any or all of the following materials:

- a Blossoming Journal
- big poster-sized paper
- sketching paper
- old and/or inspiring magazines you're not attached to
- glue sticks
- markers

- crayons
- water color paints
- brushes
- pastels
- glitter
- feathers
- whatever floats your boat

Dedicate a Blossoming Space for your upcoming creative explorations in your home. (You might need to get extra creative if you've got a small space!)

Write a little note to yourself that says something like, "This is about being yourself, not being perfect. Remember to have fun!" Stick the note up on the wall, or inside of your sacred play space.

"See Yourself" Invitations
#1: Your Blossoming Check-in Flower

Now that you've dedicated a space for blossoming, and gathered some materials, I'd like to invite you to do a **Blossoming Check-in.** This is your opportunity to take stock of how your *Life Flower* is doing right now, at this point in your life. (If you've done this before with me in some other context, do it anyway! The state of our blossoming is always changing.)

If you don't have a lot of time, or want to start with a 'quickie,' use the flower on the following page. You might want to take a picture or make a few copies of this flower, in case you want to do this again. A Blossoming Check-in makes a great weekly/monthly practice! (A more in-depth invitation will follow.)

 Feel free to write arising insights in your journal!

Do a Blossoming Check-in!

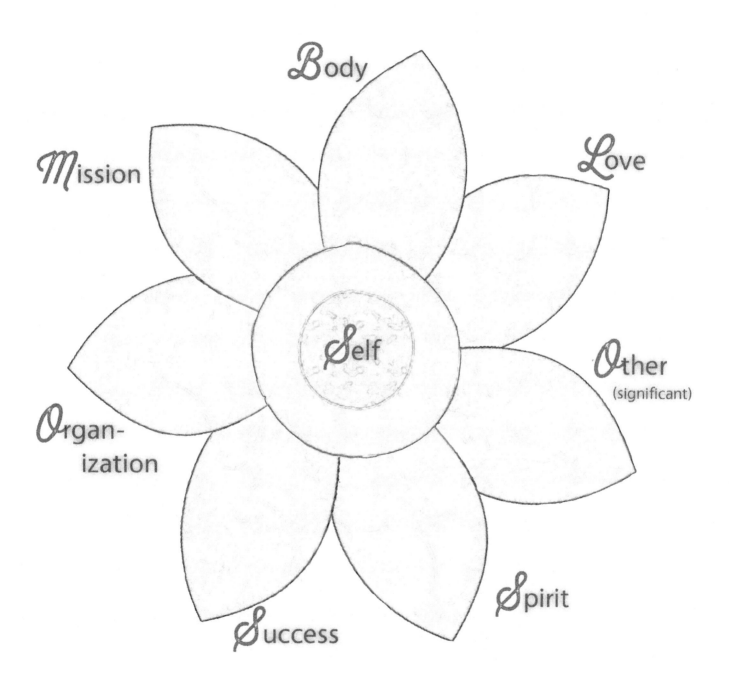

IF YOU WANT TO GO BIG!

Begin with a simple contemplation

Start by imagining a flower, with your "self" at the core, and then 7 petals all around that core. Each petal is here to represent a main area of your life (that is in need of warm light, replenishing water and supportive soil).

When you think of the flower, think of it as holographic, in the sense that the health of each petal has a direct impact on the health of the whole flower.

When you think about balance, don't think 'perfect balance,' or 'static balance,' since there is no such thing. Think of a constantly moving, 'dancing balance,' where we want to make sure there are no areas of total neglect!

Create your flower

Take out a large sheet of paper, or cardboard, and a bunch of crayons or colored markers. Allow the extra space to inspire you. Use an array of colors, evocative words, meaningful phrases or quotes, and powerful symbols to 'flesh out' your flower...so that what you create really means something to you.

Start with a relatively small circle in the middle of the page. Draw 7 larger petals all around the middle. Next to each petal, write a Letter and a word. (For some 'possible meaning' inspiration, check out the B.L.O.S.S.O.M. Glossary.)

Quick B.L.O.S.S.O.M. summary (more on the following page)

- **B** for Body
- **L** for Love (for your friends, your families, communities and the earth)
- **O** for significant "Other" (or your longing for that intimate or Inner/Divine Other)
- **S** for Spirit (which includes *fun*, *creativity* and *deep relaxation* inside of your own skin!)
- **S** for Success (not just the money-making kind)
- **O** for Organization (both inner and outer)
- **M** for Mission (our purpose for being here... which we may or may not have a sense of, and which is a wonderful mystery, here to unfold just like a beautiful flower)

(Feel free to use other categories that feel more useful or relevant to you, or to add more petals if you like.)

B.L.O.S.S.O.M.

**Here's a very loose and basic BLOSSOM GLOSSARY, to help you orient yourself.
Feel free to use the definitions and/or approaches that feel most meaningful and relevant to you.**

S
for SELF

At the center of your life is your beautiful, lovable, worthy **SELF**. When contemplating the state of your "self," you might want to percolate on one or more of what I like to call the **"THE SEVEN SELVES"**: Self Love, Self Care, Self Confidence, Self Awareness, Self Trust, Self Centering & Self Acceptance

B
for BODY

There are so many ways that we can care for and enjoy our BODIES. Eating well and exercising are just two of them. What are the ways that you nourish and connect with your body? (i.e. Cuddling up under the covers, receiving massage, going for walks, doing yoga, taking vitamins, playing with children, kicking a soccer ball around, taking a bath, making love, eating ice cream, putting a heating pad on your belly, etc.?)

L
for LOVE

Here, we're looking at the ways LOVE is felt and expressed in relation to your family, friends, spiritual family, your larger community, even the earth. (I know; it's a lot of territory to cover!) I invite you to look at this Love Petal in one of two ways: 1) with a broad & general stroke (i.e. How much of your LOVE is flowing out towards others in your life—as opposed to towards yourself?) Or, 2) with a finer comb (i.e. How is your love for others distributing itself these days?) For ex., your kids may be getting lot of LOVE, but your friendships not so much.

O
for OTHER

Here we're honing in on SIGNIFICANT OTHER... If you are in a committed relationship, this is your chance to take a look at how you and your partner are doing these days. Perhaps you have more than one significant relationship to contemplate. Or perhaps you're longing to focus on and cultivate a deep relationship with your Inner, or Divine Partner. Again, feel free to use a broad stroke, a finer comb, or make adjustments so that this feels relevant to you. (Some RELATIONSHIP themes to keep in mind: Friendship & Fun, Spiritual & Creative Connection, Parenting Alignment, Romance & Intimacy, Emotional Support & Empathy, Equality & Respect, Independent Support Systems, Authentic & Transparent Communication, etc.)

S
for SUCCESS

In our Western culture, "SUCCESS" is often linked to external results—status, money, achievement, profession, etc. And yet, there are many ways to be and feel successful, You might find it useful to explore your relationship to our culturally biased definition of the word. You might want to separate SUCCESS into 2 sections: Outer & Inner. Or, you might want to go with even more categories. Whatever feels most relevant & illuminating to you right now!

S
for SPIRIT

"SPIRIT" means different things to different people. I'm interested in how you connect with whatever it is in your life that puts you in touch with Love, Peace, Deep Relaxation, Meaning, and/or a sense of being part of something bigger. Maybe for you it's all about NATURE, or yoga, or meditation. Or creativity, inspirational reading, spacing out, being silly, being of service, being with people you love, going to church/synagogue/mosque/sweat lodge, etc. Maybe your business is your spiritual practice. You get the idea. Whatever works for you, I want to know how it's working!

O
for ORGANIZ-ATION

Here, I'd like you to look at the ways in which you feel (or don't feel) your life is ORGANIZED. This can involve your external environment—your home, your office, kitchen, kids' rooms, etc. It can also include your internal environment. How much order, or chaos, do you experience in your inner life—in your mind, heart, spirit?

M
for MISSION

Here I'm talking about a deeper sense of purpose. It doesn't even matter what you're actually doing in the world, whether you have your dream career or not. This is more about how connected you feel to your reason for being here on the planet, whatever that is ultimately. (Hint: Chances are your MISSION is big, yet simple... and potentially applicable to many situations!)

Let your flower become a life mirror

Now fill in your flower according to how fulfilled you're feeling in these particular life arenas. Have fun with the process. Remember this doesn't have to be a work of art, just a loose, **honest** expression of how you're doing these days, how 'bloomy' (or 'gloomy') you're feeling. We want it to be as accurate a reflection of how you're feeling at this point in your life as possible.

Take a contemplative gander at your flower

Take a moment to sit back, relax and take in what you've created. Stay open and curious.

A few questions to ponder

- As you step back and look at the whole flower, what do you see? Is there a pretty even distribution of color? Or is your flower lopsided, with some petals overflowing, and others nearly empty?

- What are the areas of your life that are receiving the bulk of your attention and energy? What areas could use a little more love and care?

- If there were one petal on your flower that is calling out for your attention, more than any other petal, what would that be? For now, just **be** with the insights and reflections you receive. No need to apply any pressure or make any plans. Just notice the petal's need and hear its call. Stay open to its invitation. Notice in the coming hours or days, whether you feel more naturally drawn towards tending to that aspect of your life…without effort.

 Jot down any insights you receive in your Blossoming Journal.

(And check out the fabulous *Blossoming Check-in Flowers* made by former *Designed to Blossom* participants on the next page!)

Medicine Doctor's Orders
Regular Blossoming Check-ups Recommended

Doing a quick Blossoming Check-in can be a wonderful way to start your day, week, or month. It's a quick way to touch base with yourself, and to orient your subconscious towards greater life balance, without having to push or force anything to happen. As mentioned earlier, feel free to make copies of the Blossoming Check-in flower on page # 19 so you have a bunch to use in the future.

Keep your flower in a safe place!

You will be returning to this flower later, as you begin to explore your unique Human Design.

Share your flower with someone you love and trust!

There is power and healing in letting others see your flower in all of its glory—whether it's perfectly symmetrical, or totally lopsided (more likely!). This is your chance to be witnessed, embraced and supported by others who love and accept you as you are.

INVITATION #2: Your Passion Flower

For a long time, I saw the fact that I had so many different passions as a major handicap—something that made career-related decision-making a living nightmare, and left me feeling "mediocre-ly" good at too many unrelated (even opposing!) things.

Thankfully, I've finally surrendered to and learned to embrace my multi-faceted flower nature. Even though the petals on my Passion Flower may seem unrelated, even though it's not always clear to me how I'm meant to prioritize or synthesize it all, I celebrate that they all belong to me. Together my passions create a ***whole***. No matter what I 'do' or manifest in the world, they are always present...through my presence!

Now, let's explore the unique tapestry of passions that YOU ARE.

Here's a way to think about it

Think of this particular flower as a multi-petaled home for all of your passions. This time, instead of seeing each petal as a main life arena (e.g. Body, Love, Spirituality, etc.), see each petal as a sacred container for a particular passion or gift that you have. Feel free to add or take away a petal, depending on how many passions feel 'petal-worthy.'

Keep in mind: Your passions don't have to have anything to do with each other. You can put a cooking petal next to a belly-dancing petal, next to a creative writing petal, next to a horticultural gardening petal, next to a corporate diversity training petal, next to a staring-into-space petal. If it's a genuine passion, give it a petal!

There can be such a power in gathering up all of your passions and plopping them into one place, so that you can see your wondrous multi-faceted parts, reflected back to you as a **whole**!

(Please don't even attempt to figure out how to turn the perfect passion-weave into a million-dollar career that's going to save the planet. That's not up to your mind to figure out...as you'll soon see!)

Time to Get Started!

I want this to feel both exciting and fun for you, as well as doable. If you'd like to start small and easy, use copy or draw the Passion Flower in the Workbook/Course. Otherwise, GO BIG! (Instructions and loads of Inspiration to follow, provided by kindred *Designed to Blossom* journeyers!)

YOUR PASSION FLOWER

Use the Passion Flower above to explore the passions of your life.

Passions can be big or small, serious or silly, solitary or social, societally acceptable or dangerously taboo, extra-ordinary or seemingly mundane. Your passions may (at least on the surface) have nothing to do with each other.

Whatever they are, make sure they're represented.

Are you up for a DEEP DIVE into your PASSIONS?

I invite you to GO FOR IT! Give yourself a chunk of time. Use a combination of art materials and media that you enjoy (e.g. watercolors, crayons, pastels, markers, pencils, feathers, ripped-out images from magazines, tooth picks, etc.) You might want to focus on words rather than color and image on this one.

It's totally up to you. There are no rules here. All that matters is that you genuinely care about your exploration, that you're up for a genuine encounter with your passions.

Since there are infinite ways in which we can feel and express our passions, I thought I'd share a whole bunch of Passion Flowers, all made by wonderful *Designed to Blossom* participants, like you! The sky's the limit!

Have some fun... and remember that you are a wholly unique Passion Flower. Nobody in the world is just like you.

SOME INSPIRATION!

My daughter Maya and I did this process together some years ago, each of us choosing our own unique approach. She created a big Passion Collage, and I created a small Passion Puzzle!

And now... here's an abundance of Passionate Inspiration
from *Designed to Blossom* Participants! Feast your Eyes!

Time to Reflect on your Passion Flower and write in your journal.

- Which passions get the most of your attention?

- Which ones feel least realistic to 'pursue' professionally?

- What would your parents have to say if they were to take a look at this flower?

- Your siblings? Your friends? Your boss? Your spiritual mentor? Your therapist?

- Which one of your passions feels most acceptable to society?

- Feels most risky?

- Is most fun?

- Is most challenging?

- Feels most alive right now, at this time of your life?

- Are there any 'shoulds' that are disguised as passions in this flower?

Have a conversation with someone about your Passion Flower.
See what happens!

Spend an hour this week dipping your toes into the passion petal that feels most alive for you. If you're already doing it, pick another, or spend an extra hour doing it, or taking it to the next level.

Remember to keep your flower in a safe place,
and share it with someone you love and trust!

BE Yourself: Petal One

Why is this Self-Love/Life-Purpose Thing So Hard?

I mean, we know everything up in our heads. We know we want to make a difference in this world. We know it's not healthy if we get too caught up in the *Me*, or get totally lost in the *We*... We know we need our lives to be (relatively) balanced, so we can be both connected to ourselves and others.

We also know we bring passions and gifts that could be used in service of a Life Purpose.

Still, we feel overwhelmed, confused, stuck, frustrated, unfulfilled and/or not-good-enough. Why is this?

For one thing, many of us make the very common mistake of thinking we should be able to 'figure it all out' in our head and then 'make it happen' with will power. Those of us living in the Western (or Western-dominated) world are especially under the influence of a manifestation-obsessed culture. If we haven't achieved our ideal careers, perfect relationships or radiant bodies, we suffer. Many of us end up blaming ourselves. We must not be working hard enough, or disciplined enough. We must be too lost, too confused, or not mentally focused enough. We must not feel we're worthy. We must be lacking the talent, skill, faith or the inner fortitude necessary to succeed.

It doesn't help that in school, we're discouraged from following non-linear paths and surrendering to the Mystery. Instead, we're taught to think our way logically into the future—deciding on a major or 'track' before we've barely hatched, and then pursuing our careers of choice, by pumping up our resumes with ambition-driven (not necessarily passion-driven) activities and experiences.

No wonder many of us have trouble following through on things we've started, and end up with a plummeting self-esteem. Either that, or we stick with the straight and narrow, become successful in the eyes of society, but secretly feel unfulfilled.

Of course, "Just do it!" messages don't only come from the mainstream culture, *Nike* commercials or our educational systems. We 'seekers' get them in the alternative world as well. Whether attending a spiritual/alternative workshop, seeing a coach or watching "The Secret," we are often fed this particular line of thinking: that to get the life we want, we must first think up a dream, and then manifest it.

Please understand. I'm not saying that the laws of attraction or the power of the mind aren't great. They are. Nor am I saying that the quality or frequency of our thoughts and attitudes don't have a tremendous impact on our lives, our physical reality, and the way we receive, perceive and interact with our experiences. They most definitely do! What I *am* saying, however, is that the "Make your dreams come true" approach to life is often based on an underlying assumption that may be worth questioning, or at least *holding lightly*. The 'our minds always know what's best for us' assumption.

I don't know about you, but the contents of my mind aren't the most reliable! On the one hand, my mind always wants to know. It always wants to be in control, have a plan, and have my life all wrapped up in a bow. On the other hand, it's a messy mass of contradictions. (They don't call it 'monkey mind' for nothing!)

Here we all are, walking around with our parents, teachers, peers, bosses, institutions, cultural leaders, business coaches, flashy celebrities, and global opinion trends speaking (sometimes whispering, sometimes screaming) to us through the 'shoulds' in our minds—telling us what to do, and why *not doing it* would be a bad, even dangerous idea. Usually the 'shoulds' contradict each other, making our task of 'figuring out' what to do even more impossible.

THIS is why I'm about to invite you to explore your own conditioning (past and present). Before entering into the world of Human Design, I can't think of a more essential exploration.

Your Conditioning Flower

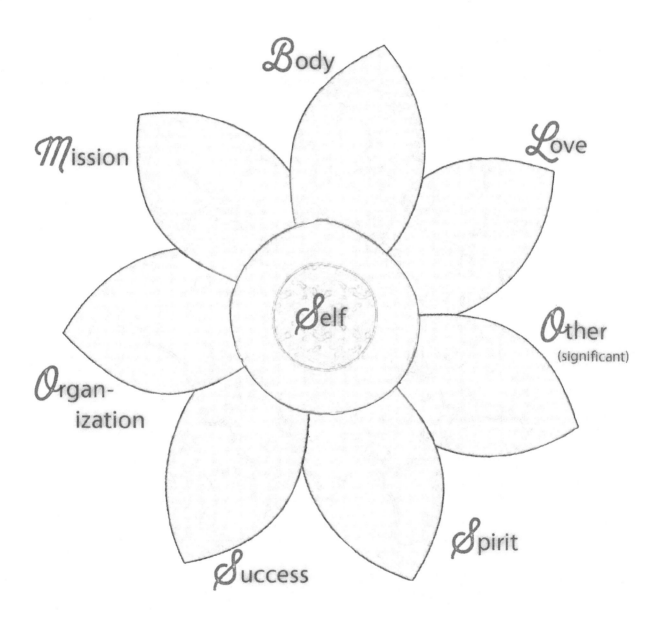

It is time to create the last of the foundational flowers—your **Conditioning Flower**—and to look at those potent conditioning messages that have seeped into your brain and body, and had you convinced that you're supposed to be someone you're not. (When it's time to get started, use the flower on this page or GO BIG! Instructions and Inspiration to follow.)

Before you get started...

A hot cup of compassion and a few pancakes of patience are in order. Unless you live in a cave (or aren't human), you're bound to bump into a plethora of confusing, contradictory and not-very-helpful conditioning messages—ones that you have very little control over. They're bound to have an impact on you. Please don't expect them to vanish into thin air, or yourself to develop complete immunity. Just be grateful that you're courageous and willing enough to learn how to hold these stubborn messages lightly, even when they're holding on tight! Before you know it, *something much wiser* will be guiding your decisions from behind the scenes, as you surrender more fully to your uniquely 'wild and precious' life, as Mary Oliver would say.

This exploration is so important, and I encourage you to give it the time and space it deserves. You may want some time to contemplate and gather, before sitting down to create your *Conditioning Flower*. As always, you can choose to go small or big, simple or complex. It's up to you.

Step 1: Open your awareness

As you move through your day or week, adjust your attention outwards, towards your many environments. Tune into and register the multitude of images, messages and pressures coming at you, pushing you towards particular (possibly contradictory) ways of manifesting yourself in the world.

At the same time, adjust your attention inwards. Notice how the outer pressures you're identifying have turned into inner 'shoulds.'

Step 2: Let the Blossoming Check-in Flower deepen your process

Just as the petals on the *Blossoming Check-in Flower* represent aspects of your life that are in need of love and attention, they can also represent life arenas where you've received core conditioning messages. Your entire flower has been influenced by conditioning.

 *Questions to inspire your process:*
(Feel free to jot down notes in your journal.)

● **SELF (in the middle of the flower):** What were you taught about having a *self*? What was your 'self' supposed to be like? Were you supposed to be 'good,' 'normal,' 'special,' 'intelligent,' 'successful,' 'invisible,' 'non-threatening,' 'competitive,' 'passive,' 'courageous,' 'unemotional,' 'witty,' 'loud,' 'soft,' etc.? What were you taught about your 'gender'? Which experiences and expressions were allowed, and which ones weren't?

- **BODY:** What have you learned about your *body*, what it's supposed to look like, and how it's supposed to feel? What purpose it's supposed to serve? What have you learned about caring for your body, or not caring for it? Who were you taught your body is meant to support, please, serve or impress?

- **LOVE:** What have you learned about building and maintaining *loving relationships* in your life? What were you taught about friendship? About family? About being a part of a social, professional or spiritual community? About what your role should be within them? Or not be? What were you taught was necessary (e.g. to express, to hide, to highlight, to minimize, to compromise) in order for you to belong, or be approved of?

- **(significant) OTHER:** What messages have you received about *romantic relationships*? About marriage? About sexuality? What have you believed you should manifest in these arenas? What was considered OK? What wasn't? Was not having a partner not even an option? Was monogamy a must? Who would be considered an ideal partner? Who wouldn't? What kind of person did you learn you had to be in order to attract a worthy partner? If you're not in a partnership, or are considering leaving a relationship, or are drawn to polyamory, what might the world think of you?

- **SPIRIT:** What have you learned about *spirituality* in your life? Were you supposed to be spiritual? Or was it taboo? Were you expected to embrace a particular religion? Or be an atheist? What have you learned that a spiritual life was supposed to look like? What and who contributed to your current definition of, approach to and relationship to *spirituality*?

- **SUCCESS:** What did you learn about *success* growing up? To be considered a *success*, what did you need to do, or achieve? Today, how much do you think you have to create, produce, or earn in order to deserve that title? How many people have to know who you are? Who in particular has to see you as a *success* for it to really count? Are you actually allowed to be successful? Are you allowed to *want to be* successful? Are you allowed *to know* that you're successful? Are you allowed *not to feel* successful? Who is it safe to succeed around? Who isn't it safe to succeed around?

- **ORGANIZATION:** What have you learned about living an *organized* life? What did you learn as a child about being messy or disorganized? Clean and orderly? How 'together,' efficient and streamlined do you think your life should be? What should your drawers and closets look like? Your computer screen? How disciplined should you be when it comes to your calendar, your exercise routine, your domestic tasks, your communications, your social life, your financial books, etc.?

- **MISSION:** As a child, what kind of a *life mission* did you learn was respectable and worthy (if you were taught anything about having a *mission* at all)? How big and impressive did it have to be? How small or non-threatening? Who was your *mission* supposed to serve? Today, what thoughts do you have about your own *life mission*? How do you think it should get expressed? Who needs to believe in it, be invested in it? Whose expectations does it need to fulfill?

Step 3: Time to Hunt and Gather!

Now that you've had the chance to contemplate some (or many) of the conditioning messages you've received over the years, and their impact on you, it's time to begin the process of creating your *Conditioning Flower*. (Inspiring examples to follow!)

I invite you to start by gathering all sorts of things—words, images, pieces of advice, old pictures of yourself and central people from your life, anything that feels intuitively relevant to this exploration. Rip out images or phrases from magazines that strike a conditioning chord (e.g. "Just do it.", "Better to look good than to feel good.", "Stand out. Be special.") Write down words or phrases you see on TV ads or in movies. Have a chat with a parent, or someone who's been a big influence. Let the conversation jog your conditioning memory. (Even an uncomfortable conversation could be very useful here!)

Remember that this isn't only about gathering obvious conventional messages; it's also about gathering messages you may be receiving from more 'hip,' 'green,' 'healthy,' and 'spiritual' sources. As long you are experiencing a message as a pressure or a should, or as a pull in a direction (even a positive one), include it. Notice which petals are super easy to find images for. Also, notice which magazines (if you're collaging) tend to really get to you... where the sore places are... (I was amazed at how much conditioning I've received in the Body petal, and how impossible and contradictory those messages have been!)

Don't worry about organizing anything just yet. Simply find a place to gather it all together—in a journal, box or corner of the room.

Step 4: Time for Sorting & Placing!

Now that you've gathered your conditioning messages in one place, it's time to do a little sorting and placing.

Take out a large sheet of paper (or any size you like or your journal!), and draw the outline of your *Conditioning Flower* (with the same petals you ended up using for the *Blossoming Check-in Flower*).

Jot down the word for each of the petals (e.g. Body, Love, Other, Spirit, Success, Organization, Mission, etc.), so you know what to put where. Remember the 'self' in the middle! Once you've prepared your canvas of petals, find the words, phrases, cut-out images and objects you gathered, and place them inside of the petals that feel most right. Have fun with the arranging.

And now for some fun examples from former *Designed to Blossom* participants!

Let them inspire you. Remember to do this in your own way. (If you notice yourself comparing your flower negatively with other flowers, then you're likely witnessing a conditioning gremlin in action! Make sure you find a way to include that 'not-good-enough' message, however it manifests, in your flower!)

Now complete your flower!

A few markers, a little glue (and some inspiring music!) should do the trick.

When you're done, reflect upon your experience. Share your *Conditioning Flower* with a friend, or someone you trust.

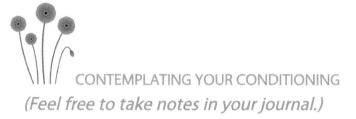

CONTEMPLATING YOUR CONDITIONING
(Feel free to take notes in your journal.)

Take a moment to think about the various ways you are exposed to conditioning messages.

How do these messages, pressures, opinions, thoughts get access to you? Is there a particular medium that tends to get under the skin? (i.e. TV, magazines, etc.) Are you particularly vulnerable when it comes to a specific sense? (i.e. sight, smell, touch, etc.) Are there certain people (known or known of) who tend to have more power over you than others?

Are there ways that you actually go out and look for this stuff?

Do you buy certain magazines? Do you watch or listen to commercials? Do you gravitate towards certain sections of the bookstore that aren't really good for you? Do you often find yourself looking for images, articles, posts, tweets, newsletters and web sites that reinforce certain beliefs—about how you should look, what you should be doing, etc. Do you choose to spend a lot of time with people who have the kinds of opinions and values that don't support or understand who you are?

Are there ways you might have more control over
the conditioning influences in your life than you think?

Could you watch less (or no) TV? Could you get rid of cable and just watch pay-on-demand, so you don't have to deal with commercials? Are there things you usually seek out and buy, that you actually don't have to seek out or buy—magazines, products, etc. Could you make different choices at the grocery store, the clothing store? Could you drive a different way home, so you don't pass by the same horrible billboard every day? Are there people in your life who you could spend less time with? Are there boundaries you could be setting that you're not setting?

Pay attention to the conversation in your head.

As you answer these questions, notice all of the reasons your mind gives you for NOT setting healthy conditioning limits. For not cutting back on, or protecting yourself from unhelpful influences. Is it telling you that you might hurt someone's feelings? That you might miss out? That you might bring on a conflict? That you might not be liked, or trusted, or respected? That you might not be productive enough? That you might not be seen as informed, intellectual and educated? That you might not be seen as beautiful, desirable and attractive?

You know the voices. You know what they tell you.

Once you've spent some time contemplating and journaling, take a deep breath. Please reserve a big dose of compassion for yourself. I mean, if you've got eyes, ears, a working nose, or a sensitive heart, it's impossible to avoid this stuff.

Rosy's

THE HUMAN DESIGN SYSTEM
AN INTRODUCTION

I hope that now that you've spent some time at the very heart of your flower, you've become more visible to yourself. With your Blossoming Check-in Flower, you've given yourself the chance to simply look at your life as it is—at the places that are thriving and getting lots of attention, and the places that are withering and neglected. With your Passion Flower, you've gathered together all of your core passions into one wonderful place, so you could see them together as a whole, even though your inner experience of your many parts may not always feel so organized or harmonious.

With your Conditioning Flower, you've given yourself the opportunity to take a long hard look at the forces in your life that have had you wondering whether BEING yourself is enough, and whether you're actually OK the way you are. You've seen how the conditioning forces that make you question who you are come in all shapes and sizes, and in all kinds of ways. Whether they show up in you through a TV commercial, a magazine ad, a parent's off-hand remark, a partner's annoyed look, a spiritual teacher's lesson, they can be sneaky little self-sabotagers!

They get you to doubt yourself. They get you to say 'yes' when you mean 'no,' and 'no' when you mean 'yes.' They push you to please, when it would be more appropriate to set a limit. They get you to feel guilty, when you're actually doing something healthy. They shove your own needs and wishes all the way to the bottom of your to-do list, making everything and everyone else seem so much more important. They confuse you, and get you to agonize over the decisions you make, and to trust everyone else's opinions over your own. They throw you so off center, that you forget what being centered and grounded even feels like. They convince you that the only way to solve your problems is to figure everything out in your head, and then use your Will to fix it. They especially get you to believe that your mind is in charge of your blossoming.

Here's the thing: Our minds aren't built to be in charge of our blossoming. It's not up to our minds to choose what kind of flower we are, but to *surrender* to what kind of flower we are.

This is where Human Design comes in... a system that I've found so incredibly helpful in my own life, and one that I've used for years to empower clients, students and the people I love to truly trust themselves... and to make decisions that are deeply aligned with their true nature, and right timing, as opposed to all of that conditioning noise.

As I've shared before, it's one thing to know up in your head that you want to blossom, or that there's an area of your life that's begging for more attention, or that you have a bunch of passions that are waiting for their Life Purpose. It's an entirely different thing to know what to do about that, as well as who to do it with, how much of it to do, when to do it, and when not to do anything at all!

Even if you know you want to be of service, that doesn't mean that your mind has a clue about how you're supposed to do that, what form that service is meant to take, or what form is actually going to make the best use of your gifts and leave you feeling most fulfilled.

 Human Design is an incredibly practical and precise way of putting each of us in touch with our Inner Wisdom Keeper, that place we can turn to for Truth—that part of us that we can trust to make our decisions in life, and to honor our own right timing.

The Human Design system came to this world in a highly mysterious way in January of 1987, on the Mediterranean island of Ibiza, to a Canadian-born man who at the time was named Alan (Robert) Krakower. While professionally he'd been an entrepreneur, magazine publisher, advertising executive and media producer, (and was quite the skeptic in terms of all things spiritual), he ended up having an intense mystical experience over a period of eight days and nights that would change his life forever, as well as his name! (From that time on, he would be called Ra Uru Hu.)

During what could only be called a 'revelation,' Ra was given an enormous amount of detailed and scientific knowledge about the mechanical nature of 'the human being' and the universe. It was this information that eventually formed the foundation of Human Design. Despite his skepticism, and the fact that he wasn't all too crazy about being the recipient of such an enormous and unasked-for universal download, Ra's keen intelligence, aptitude for physics and talent for making 'the complicated' simple, made him the perfect person to bring this system into the world and give it a form.

For twenty years (until his death in March of 2011), Ra traveled the globe, giving countless readings, teaching thousands of classes, and ultimately developing a vast and comprehensive training for Human Design enthusiasts and professionals through Jovian Archive, Inc. Today there are people all over the world, practicing and benefiting from Human Design, offering their unique flavor of this practical wisdom to clients and students, and helping Human Design evolve and expand in all sorts of fascinating ways.

Ra often said that Human Design doesn't require that we believe in anything. At its core, he felt it was a logical system—here to be tested, verified and experimented with, not swallowed whole.

Despite its mysterious origins, in the end, the Human Design system is all about helping you understand how uniquely you're designed to grow, live and blossom. It's not just about having your own 'Type' that describes your personality. It's about having a way of understanding your unique way of moving through the world and making decisions. It's a way of literally understanding how your aura works, so that you can work more consciously with the phenomenon of relational chemistry.

The more you understand your true nature, the easier it gets to access that place inside of you that you can turn to for Truth—that part of you that you can trust to make your decisions in life, and to honor your own right timing... no matter what anyone else is telling you, not even your own mind.

A Few Examples

Let me just start with a few examples of how different you can be from someone else, depending on your Design.

You might be designed to rely on your intuitive 'hits' in the moment when making decisions. Like it is with me, it may be super healthy for you to be spontaneous and instinctive, even animal in your movements through life. Or, you might be designed to be SLOW... to 'feel out' people, situations and opportunities over time—maybe even a LONG period of time—before knowing who and what is right for you. Or, you might be someone who is primarily relational, which means that WHO you're doing something with is ten times more important than what you're doing, or where you're doing it, or when you're doing it, or how quickly you're doing it. For you it may be all about being 'gotten' and recognized by someone, and being invited into a situation. These are just a few examples.

I can't tell you what a relief it was for me, when I first encountered Human Design, to learn just how different we all are. This knowledge has helped me so much in my marriage, with my daughter, with my friends... and all of the clients who have felt drawn to integrating Human Design into our work together.

I've designed this whole Workbook/Course in order to help you get—not just intellectually but IN YOUR BONES—that what works for you isn't necessarily going to work for me, or your friend, or your lover, or your client, or your colleague, or your student, or your kids. By the end of this Workbook, I want you to be downright celebrating that fact!

Let me start by giving you a bit of background about Human Design without getting too technical:

Human Design is a system that weaves in modern science (quantum physics, biochemistry, genetics and neuro-gastroenterology—the science of the 'gut-brain') with some of our most ancient systems for understanding the universe and our own nature (the Zohar/Kabbalah's Tree of Life, both Eastern and Western Astrology, the Chinese I' Ching and the Hindu Chakra system).

YOU ARE SO MUCH MORE THAN YOU THINK YOU ARE!

If Human Design celebrates anything, it's that you are not just your Mind, but a deeply interconnected combination of Body, Mind and Spirit. It opens the door to your *Inner Wisdom Keeper* by honoring and celebrating the unique marriage between what is conscious and unconscious in you, between those things you have at least some control over, and the many more things that you don't (like breathing, and hiccupping, and who you're attracted to!).

Human Design is not a one-size fits all system.

A well-trained Human Design Analyst could literally sit you down, and talk to you about your Bodygraph for about 2 weeks without running out of material. There are Types, Profiles, Authorities and Centers (and all sorts of elements representing aspects of your being). If you really go deep into your Design, you'll uncover layer after layer of information. Human Design is pretty complex. At the same time, when it comes to the practical application of this knowledge, there is so little you actually need to know.

My Intentions

I'm here to give you enough information about your Design to be able to start trusting yourself and blossoming. (But not so much that your poor head gets swamped with a fascinating yet inapplicable bundle of facts and information.) My other intention is to use a language that feels warm and inviting. Finally, I want to help you integrate this information into your actual life by inviting you to experiment and play with what you're learning.

An Invitation to Relax

Please Don't Confuse the Map with the Territory

While you move through this Workbook/Course, I really invite you to relax and receive, and trust in your own listening, wisdom and life experience. Keep your mind as open as you can to what you're learning. If something doesn't resonate, or it doesn't feel permission-giving, empowering or enlivening, just let it go... at least for now. If there is truth in something for you, then it will feel relevant to you at some point in the future. If not, let it dissolve like a raindrop in the ocean.

Human Design is a system for understanding your nature, and the way energy moves into and out of you in relation to a very complex environment. Even more than a portal for understanding, it is an invitation to experiment. I want you to discover the usefulness of this for yourself—on your own terms, in your own way, in your own timing.

As the transpersonalists say, let's be sure not to confuse the map with the territory. Your Blossoming Bodygraph is like a map of you and your life, but it isn't you, and it isn't your life. It could never be. You are something far more magical and wondrous and ever-evolving that any system could ever describe. OK, so let's take a deep breath and get ready!

LOVE Yourself: Petal Two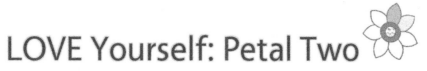

Your Unique Kind of Flower

By now you should have a copy of your own Human Design chart. (If you have purchased the online *Designed to Blossom* self-study course, you also have a copy of your Blossoming Bodygraph.) Along with your chart, you should have received information about your Type, or the kind of flower that you are. (If you don't have a chart yet, this is the time to get it! As mentioned earlier, it's super easy to get a free Human Design chart online. Just google "Free Human Design Chart" and a bunch of options should pop up. Charts usually come with the basic information about the Design, enough to be able to enjoy the rest of the material in this Workbook/Course.)

Your Blossoming Bodygraph Details

> Write down your basic Human Design elements here (and in your Blossoming Journal).
>
> TYPE (of flower):
> _____
>
> OPEN CENTERS:
> _____
> _____
>
> DEFINED CENTERS:
> _____
> _____
>
> AUTHORITY:
> _____
>
> PROFILE:
> _____

Some like to think of 'Type' as the particular kind of biological form (or 'vehicle') that we happen to be living (and driving around) in. You could say we all are cells, belonging to certain groups of cells, and we're living inside of a single living organism, otherwise known as Planet Earth (which itself is living within an alive cosmos). Although each of us 'individual cells' is extremely unique, each CELL GROUP tends to share certain characteristics and life themes, or a certain way of moving through and serving the planetary body.

I like to think of the different Types as different kinds of flowers (or Flower Families) in our great cosmic garden. Using the Garden metaphor, we can belong to the Generator Flower Family, the Manifestor Flower Family, the Projector Flower Family, or the small yet potent Reflector Flower Family.

Just as it is with 'flowers' in nature, some of us tend to thrive with certain kinds of food, climate and environment, while others of us do better with others.

In Human Design, we say that each Type comes with its own Strategy. It follows that each Flower Family has its own healthy growth path. Our strategies are what ultimately lead us to the proper nutrients—the people, environments, opportunities and experiences we need to thrive. When we follow our Flower Family Strategy, we're basically learning how to keep our 'flower bodies' healthy and how to sprout and unfold our petals naturally. From a Human Design perspective, this means learning how to make good decisions, how to recognize when we're on the right and unique path, and how to surrender to the flow of our lives.

People often say that learning about your Type and Strategy is like receiving a manual for your life, or like getting a set of instructions for how to grow your particular flower and keep it happy and healthy.

When you learn how you're uniquely designed, you learn how to nourish your body (and brain!) so that it can operate at its very best… and ultimately, so that it can take your 'soul' for the fascinating, flowing and life-affirming ride it's meant to have.

I'd like to introduce you to the four main Types in the Human Design System,
first from a flowery perspective!

(Of course, there is endless variation within each Type. There's a whole spectrum of frequencies through which you can express your essence. Type is only one of many aspects of your Design, and what makes you YOU. There are even Human Design teachers who are questioning the whole validity of Type! In my work with clients and students over the years, I've found the process of learning about and experimenting with Type way too useful and transformative to not share about it generously with you.)

There's a whole chapter devoted to each Type (or Flower Family). At the very end, you will find a plethora of experimental invitations to help you dive into an experiential learning process. Feel free to focus on your own Flower Family, or to explore the entire rich and diverse garden. Remember, this is all about honoring yourself and your unique way of doing things. You can trust your *Inner Wisdom Keeper* to guide you through this process.

A little aside: Although there's a refreshingly straight-forward quality to official Human Design Lingo, words like "Type" can make Human Design sound like an emotionless, cold and mechanical typing system. I've found Human Design to be a profound practice, even a spiritual practice. Please don't be deceived or turned off by the language. I promise that there is warmth, juiciness and creativity to be found in this world, if you give it a chance!

THE GENERATOR FLOWER FAMILY

Imagine a garden as big as the world, and in this wide and vast garden are a bunch of colorful flowers, of every shape and size, all swirling about in the breeze. They're bright and attractive and have a way of attracting all sorts of beings to their garden. When something or someone particularly exciting passes them by, or approaches them, they just light up, and start moving!

Open and responsive in their nature, these flowers are always ready to say 'yes'—to dance with the wind, to hum along with a hummingbird, to hop on the back of a butterfly, or to build a dam with a passing beaver. These flowers are happiest when they're working and using their playful, communicative and juicy energy to make this world a more beautiful, rich and exciting place to be. They have a special affinity for bees, because they're a lot like them... in that they love to work, create, build, collaborate and make honey out of life. However, not everything or everyone makes them come alive. If they're not careful and respond to too many opportunities that aren't really right for them, they can end up more like frustrated worker bees than satisfied and flowing flowers.

A Big Welcome to our BLOSSOMING GENERATORS!

If you're a part of the GENERATOR FLOWER FAMILY, then you are an infinitely creative, energetic and productive Buddha being. You have an enveloping aura, taking everyone and everything in. You came to this world to be absolutely authentic, to be deeply satisfied by your work, and to be respected for the valuable energy that you naturally bring to your relationships, jobs and environments.

Generator Flowers like you make up approximately 70% of the human population. You're everywhere! (Which is a really good thing, because this world needs a whole lot of people who are capable of perfecting and building things in increasingly efficient ways!)

There are two kinds of Generating Flowers—the *Pure kind* and the *Manifesting kind*.

While Manifesting Generators tend to be more intense, and Pure Generators tend to be more fluid, all Generator Flowers are here to **RESPOND FIRST**, and **ACT SECOND**. This is so important for you to understand... and ultimately practice.

Respond first. Act second!

Generators like you are here to be BUDDHA BEINGS. This means that before you do or initiate anything, it's always wise to check in with your highly intelligent and energetic gut-brain first. You were built to respond to opportunities that come your way, not to go out and make opportunities happen just because you think they're good ideas. Believe me; waiting to be initiated by life, waiting for life to come to you, isn't always easy... especially when we're living in a totally manifestation-obsessed culture.

But it's SO WORTH IT!

If you're a Pure Generating Flower, you're here to live one of the deepest truths in life, the truth that everything reveals itself over time, that it's all about going with the flow, listening for the underlying rhythms and cycles within you and all around you, and trusting in your own resilience. When Pure Generating Flowers like you are really living from this place of trust, they act as stabilizing forces for all of humanity. You have the potential to become deeply aligned with your own inner pacing, with the natural rhythms around you, with the earth, and the seasons. When you're aligned, you help the rest of us ground... which during these days of cell phones, email, texts and craziness, there are few things more important.

If you're a Manifesting Generating Flower, you're likely quite a dynamic person. You were born with a wonderful hybrid potential, in that you've got the stamina of the Pure Generator combined with the potency of the Manifestor, all wrapped up inside you. It can be especially hard for you to wait to respond, and for the right timing to use the full force of your potent energy. It's so important that you learn to rein yourself in. Once you start something, you can be unstoppable... even if you're heading off of a cliff, or building a super impressive life that's going to make you miserable! Manifesting Generators can be stubborn and obstinate at times, but you can also attract that quality in others, especially if you're ignoring the signs and pushing through... instead of relaxing and allowing life to come to you, and turn you on.

Whether you're a Pure or a Manifesting Generating Flower, you're still essentially a GENERATOR. When Generating Beings push too hard *trying* to make things happen, or spread themselves too thin doing things that don't truly excite them, they can really end up feeling frustrated and/or angry, even like slaves. They can either wilt from misusing their energy, or they can become so stiff from stress that they've forgotten how to wave in the wind and enjoy the garden. When you're letting your mind make your decisions for you, even if that mind of yours has wonderful values and very respectable goals, you can end up meeting a great deal of inner and outer resistance too.

All of you Generating Flowers, in the end, are really here to learn the same beautiful lesson: to relax, be patient, and to trust that when you allow life to come to you, life simply *flows through you*.

In the end, for you, *response is the easiest path of all,*
and *life is designed to be an eternal adventure!*
RESPONSE is your essential STRATEGY and way of moving through life.

Some Famous Pure Generating Flowers

Meryl Streep, Oprah Winfrey, Greta Garbo, Madonna, Margaret Thatcher, Meg Ryan, Einstein, Dalai Lama, Bill Clinton, Carl Jung, Elvis Presley, John Lennon, Mozart, Deepak Chopra

Some Famous Manifesting Generating Flowers

Hillary Clinton, Marie Antoinette, Mother Teresa, Yoko Ono, Jackie Onassis, Janis Joplin, Jimi Hendrix, Clint Eastwood, Sigmund Freud, Friedrich Nietzsche, Martin Luther King

THE PROJECTOR FLOWER FAMILY

Imagine beautiful, magnetic and delicate flowers with a penetrating gaze. They can see everything going on around them, and are overflowing with wisdom. They each have an unusual scent, one that can be picked up from miles away. There's nothing these special flowers want more than to get to know other flowers, to make this world a better place, and to participate fully and joyfully in life. Nothing makes them come alive more than being and sharing deeply with other flowers.

Not every flower can see them and their beauty, however. Not all flowers are ready to receive a Projector Flower's wisdom. Only those who truly need a Projector Flower's gift will see them, will smell their one-of-a-kind fragrance. When people do see those gifts, they simply can't help but invite Projector Flowers into their lives and into all sorts of exciting adventures that make the Flowers come ALIVE! When Projector Flowers can embrace and trust the power of their scent, magic becomes the natural way of things. They make their contribution to the world, without having to get all caught up in stress. When they don't trust the power of their scent, they can end up bending and twisting their stems in all sorts of uncomfortable directions, and flapping their petals around to a point of exhaustion, just to get some (well-deserved but often unfruitful) attention. In the end, they're a lot like the rose from the Little Prince. Here to be deeply loved and cherished, and in the presence of that love, to come alive and spread even more love around the globe!

(When they're not coming alive, they're meant to rest, radiate and have some fun!)

A Big Welcome to our BLOSSOMING PROJECTORS!

If you're a part of the PROJECTOR FLOWER FAMILY, then you are a bright, curious, energetically sensitive being who is deeply interested in others. You have a very attractive, penetrating aura that goes right into the core of people. You are here to learn, to interact, and to facilitate the doing of others, as opposed to do, do, do yourself. You're also here to be recognized for your true gifts, to understand the nature of systems, and to guide and integrate the energy of the people around you. You are very likely highly skilled and extremely intelligent. You can bring so much integration to groups and insights to individuals.

More than anything, you need TRUE ALLIES.

You need to be seen for who you are and invited by people who see you—and I mean really see you—in order to live out your Life Purpose or make your ultimate contribution. Unfortunately, most people like you are taught early on to initiate your life based on ambitious mental agendas. Many of you end up feeling exhausted, invisible and/or deeply bitter. Some of you have been so 'not seen,' that it's hard to believe that you'll ever be truly recognized for who you are, and all you know. If you can relate, then you might often make the mistake of either withdrawing into invisibility, or trying too hard to be seen by the wrong people. When you push yourself and your perspectives on those who either aren't ready to receive them, or just don't have the capacity to appreciate what you have to offer, it can be so devastating. The last thing you want is to be seen as interfering or annoying, or to make people feel uncomfortable.

This is why the main Strategy for you is to **wait for the invitation**, especially when it comes to the major decisions in your life.

This means waiting to be invited into
An intimacy, a relationship/friendship, a career/calling, or a place to live.

'Waiting for the invitation' is like a healthy screening process for you. It ensures that your highest potential is appreciated, your knowledge is wanted, and that your guiding talents are going to benefit those who truly need them.

When you are awakened, you live a life that is based on the deepest kind of TRUST.

A few famous Projectors

Queen Elizabeth II, Barbara Streisand, Marilyn Monroe, Shirley MacLaine, Demi Moore, Elizabeth Taylor, Princess Diana, Barak Obama, Nelson Mandela, Mick Jagger, Osho, Woody Allen, Fidel Castro, James Joyce, Brad Pitt, John F. Kennedy, Hugh Hefner, Karl Marx

THE MANIFESTOR FLOWER FAMILY

Imagine a big and bold Dandelion... standing alone. You can see this flower's yellow brilliance from anywhere. The mere sight of it is awe-inspiring. This is a Manifestor Flower, and it is free to grow where it wants to grow. You may even find a Manifestor Flower growing in impossible places. This is because it is powerful, and protected, and destined to make an impact. When the Dandelion is ready, it will exchange its yellow petals for a glorious mane of fluffy white buds... and these life-carrying buds will ride the winds of change, planting seeds of potential all around the world.

This flower must be free. No one can tell a Manifestor Flower when it's time to glow, or when it's time for its buds to blow. Its job isn't to follow and micro-manage each and every bud on its journey, but to give the buds the best start that it possibly can. The other job of the Manifesting Flower is to make sure the world is ready for its creative babies, by letting the world know they're coming, and making sure they're headed in a direction where they'll be most helpful and welcome. Other flowers might find the Manifestor Flower a little intimidating at first, but if they can respect its need for freedom, their lives will be deeply enriched by its catalyzing spirit!

A Big Welcome to our BLOSSOMING MANIFESTORS!

If you're a part of the MANIFESTOR FLOWER FAMILY, then you are a freedom-loving, potently energetic, and rare warrior being (only 8% of the population) who is designed to be PROACTIVE, to lead and to have a big impact. You were born with a powerful, self-contained and provocative aura that can either hold people at bay, or let them in selectively. You are the only kind of flower that is actually here to act on your own, to initiate projects, relationships and experiences, and to get balls rolling. You can be deeply empowering to others, especially when you cultivate good listening and communication skills.

Historically, members of the Manifesting Flower Family have been the leaders of the world, although the top-down leadership style often used by Manifestors in the past is losing its hold, as other forms of co-creative, energetically attuned, movement-backed leadership styles are gaining momentum. We feel this in the big paradigm shift reflected all around us.

Adult Manifesting Flowers like you are not here to be told what to do, or to ask permission. When you feel controlled, manipulated or unable to move and act freely, you can feel powerless and angry, and either do your thing in spite of everyone around you, and be perceived as 'not very nice,' or you can hold back, and become deeply repressed, turning your anger inwards against yourself... thus not being very nice to you.

Manifestors like you need to learn that it's OK to say 'no.' You also need to learn how to honor your big 'yeses,' and to inform others before you go ahead and take action—especially the people who are likely to be impacted by your actions. When you don't inform the people in your life, you can be met with great resistance and a lack of cooperation.

When, out of an understanding of your own impact, you show basic human courtesy and take the time to fill people in on your dreams and plans, you can inspire an astounding amount of cooperation and enthusiasm from the people around you, and of course, manifest wonderful projects, creations and achievements in the world.

Some Famous Manifestors

Susan Sarandon, Jennifer Aniston, Elisabeth Kubler Ross, Frida Kahlo, Al Gore, Adolph Hitler, George Bush, Johnny Depp, J. Edgar Hoover, Krishnamurti, Jerry Seinfeld, Richard Burton, B.F. Skinner, Jack Nicholson, Robert De Niro, Tom Cruise, Ra Uru Hu (the man who brought Human Design into the world)

THE REFLECTOR FLOWER FAMILY

Imagine an extremely rare hybrid flower who is half like a chameleon, and half like a canary! This is a Reflector Flower. Wherever you put Reflector Flowers, they will reflect back to you their environment. If they are surrounded by blue, they'll mirror back blue. If they're surrounded by beauty, they will radiate beauty. If they are plopped in the middle of a toxic coal mine, they'll be the first to keel over.

Nothing matters more for these flowers than being in the right place. For when they're in the right place, they experience and emit the absolute best in themselves, and everyone around them benefits. The process of finding the right place, and the right people, and the right direction in life isn't always easy or quick for Reflector Flowers. They need lots of time, space and opportunities to explore each situation from a variety of perspectives and moods. Finding their truth usually requires a combination of relaxing solitude... and constructive conversation with exceptionally good (agenda-free) listeners. Cultivating patience is ALWAYS WORTH IT! While all of the other flowers grow best in the light of the sun, Reflector Flowers thrive in the light (and follow the rhythm) of the MOON!

A Big Welcome to our BLOSSOMING REFLECTORS!

If you're a part of the REFLECTOR FLOWER FAMILY, then you are the rarest of all. Your kind makes up less than 2% of the entire human flower population. You are a deeply open, receptive and sensitive being who is able to take people in, enjoy the feeling of being surprised, and cultivate tremendous wisdom. Life moves through you all of the time. You are a deeply DIGESTIVE BEING.

Just because life is continuously moving through you doesn't mean that it all 'sticks.' Reflectors like you have what in Human Design is called a "Teflon" aura; it is designed to take everything in, yet keep nothing at the same time. (There are many in the Human Design community who believe that Mata Amritanandamayi (Amma), also known as 'the hugging guru'—is a Reflector. There are a few others who are questioning this, but it doesn't really matter. I still think of her as a fabulous example of the potential of a Reflector. Just think of this woman. She's able to hug thousands of people in a single day, some very sick people, without the slightest trace of burnout or "infectedness.")

Finding the right environment, the right community, the right collective 'meal' to digest and reflect back, is so deeply important for you. You are always going to reflect the environments—or the quantum field— that you're in. Environment is everything! If you're in an environment that isn't right for you, you can experience your life energy dissipating, and feel very disappointed.

At your most awakened state, you are designed to have entire communities revolve around you! In fact, you are here to transcend what most of us experience as a personal agenda. You have the potential to actually **be** a place. A beautiful, loving, inspiring and transformative place where others can't help but emerge as their glorious selves.

Some Famous Reflectors

Rosalyn Carter, Sandra Bullock, Amma (?), Vladimir Horowitz, Fyodor Dostoevsky, H.G. Wells

THE SCRUMPTIOUS SCIENCE OF SURRENDER

Now that you've been introduced to your Flower Family, let's go a bit deeper in the world of Type, and get some basic Human Design lingo under our belts.

As you can see, Human Design boils the human population down to four main Types: Manifestors, Generators, Projectors and Reflectors. (As previously mentioned, there are two kinds of Generators—Manifesting Generators and Pure Generators. I'll get more into that later.) Each of these Types has a particular Strategy for living that can enhance health and well-being, as well as minimize resistance and emotional suffering.

According to Richard Rudd, one of my favorite Human Design transmitters, as well as the poet/mystic/author responsible for the *Gene Keys* (which I'll share more about later), each Type is designed to surrender to something.

I love this focus on surrender, because it flies in the face of what so many of us are taught. For me, the biggest gift you'll receive from learning about your Design is the realization that you are here to SURRENDER. Also, that there is actually a particular way in which you finally break free of all of those 'shoulds' you've got running around in your head, trying to determine who you are and what you're supposed to do. A way to liberate your *Inner Wisdom Keeper* that actually feels fun, exciting, playful... and unique to you.

While it's always good to have an evolving vision for yourself, and the intention to make a loving, positive contribution to this world, you actually don't need to have a clue about where you're actually headed, in order to get there. I can't tell you how much of our time is wasted trying to figure all of that stuff out.

One of the biggest things to really get is that Everyone is here to surrender:

- Manifestors are designed to surrender to FREEDOM.

- Generators are designed to surrender to the NOW.

- Projectors are here to surrender to the OTHER.

- Reflectors are here to surrender to EXISTENCE itself!

As John Lennon would say, "Life is what happens when we're busy making other plans." That's actually how it's supposed to be!

Now, I'm a Generator. A Manifesting Generator (which will mean more to you as you move through the Workbook/Course), with a particular kind of truth-telling device that's extremely intuitive and spontaneous. Time and time again, I've found that through surrendering control, and to the now, good things have happened in my life. Service has happened. Love has happened. Authenticity has happened. Connection and exciting collaborations have happened. Just naturally. All I've really had to do is just kick back and enjoy the ride.

THAT'S WHAT WE'RE ALL DESIGNED TO DO! It doesn't matter what kind of Type you are, or what exactly you're here to surrender to. No matter what, letting go of mental control is likely to be a healthy thing for you.

Of course, sometimes inspiration requires a strong intention, and sometimes great effort. And prep-work. And planning. Even struggle. Sometimes, I turn into a ravaging pit bull wrangling with a beloved toy, but the toy is beloved. It has to be. There is a deep surrender that comes with any act of passionate devotion. That's the key. This is not necessarily about creating a struggle-free life. It's about making sure we've got the just-right struggles for our blossoming mission.

If I'm not engaged with something I love, something worth the wrestle, if I can't feel some wind at my back (whether it's in the form of inner excitement or outer support), then I'm just pushing the river. I'm trying to force myself to go where I'm not built to go, or to be someone I'm not built to be. I'm lost in molding, shaping and playing 'God' with my life, instead of trusting that there's a much higher intelligence at work—inside of and all around me.

I play my humble role best, I make the greatest difference,
when "I" get out of my own way... and let go.

The biggest irony is that even Manifestors aren't as 'in charge' as they seem. Manifestors are the great initiators and doers of our world. Even though they're the people for whom the "JUST DO IT" Nike commercials and movies like The Secret actually apply, they still aren't in control.

My husband of 25 years, Kim, is a Manifestor. I feel I know something about Manifestors. It's interesting, because according to the research done by Human Design into the world population, only 8% of the entire population are actually designed to be Manifestors. What this essentially means is that there are relatively few people in this world who are built to manifest in the traditional sense of the word. These people can actually, or at least it can *look like* they can get an idea and then go out into the world and make that idea happen.

Indeed, Manifestors are here to go out and do something, to make an impact, based on something, (whether it be a want, an impulse, or a feeling) that originates from within them. They can initiate things; they can start a ball rolling that other people can then respond to or join.

Here's the thing. If you look at Manifestors more deeply, you'll see that even *they* aren't manifesting anything that truly originates from their minds. No ideas appear in the mind without first coming from and through the body, or Spirit, as some kind of a response to a complex environment.

The whole concept of the mind knowing anything 'first,' of being some autonomous, rational source of power and authority that functions independently of the body, of emotions, is an illusion—a concept that's been equally challenged by spiritual as well as scientific thinkers.

My husband Kim has the kind of Design that would drive him CRAZY if he tried to manifest every great idea that entered his head. (He actually spent the bulk of his life trying to do that, and it *did* drive him crazy, and me too.) Most of the time, Kim has no clue about what he's meant to manifest, until after a long LONG period of time. What he ends up manifesting rarely makes sense to his logical mind. With his particular Design, his manifestations usually come from a deeply emotional place. He's never in charge of the timing. It just happens when it's ready to happen, but then, watch out world, here he comes!

Not all Manifestors, of course, are slow percolators like Kim. (Later in the Workbook/Course, you'll learn about something called Authority, which will shed light on another essential element of who you are, and how you're meant to know what's right for you.) There **are** some people, not many, who can at least **seem** to have that kind of control and power to just go out there and make things happen... even quickly. They can have an experience of knowing what they want first, and then going out and doing it.

WHAT ABOUT THE REST OF US NON-MANIFESTORS?
(92% of the human population!)

The rest of us, whether we are Generators, Projectors or Reflectors aren't built to drum up a dream, pursue it and make it happen in a linear way. We're not meant to just know what we want off the top of our heads. The majority of us are actually designed to respond first and then act—although the specific **way** we respond and act can differ a great deal depending on what Type we are, where our Authority is, and how we are uniquely designed.

A while back, I was watching the Daily Show (a comedic news show in the U.S.). John Stuart, the host at the time, was interviewing an author who wrote a book that explored the question, "Why are human beings so bad at predicting what will make them happy?" Though unfortunately I can't remember the book's title, I do remember being deeply struck by the question.

If you really think about it, how many of us think we know what's going to make us happy,
and then, even if we manage to 'manifest' it,
we don't end up happy at all, or at least, not for long?

HUMAN DESIGN IS A LOT LIKE PRACTICAL BUDDHISM

(at least for some)

Similar to many of the profound Eastern teachings that have gained popularity in the West over the years, Human Design points to the potent connection between the nature of the mind, the act of Desire, and the experience of Suffering. Even though Human Design prescribes different spiritual practices to different people, the experiment of living as one's unique self, of honoring one's Strategy and Authority, are indeed practices. While each person's practice will differ on the surface, at core, everyone is learning the same essential lesson: to watch the mind, to dis-identify with its contents, to hold it lightly enough to resist getting caught in a never-ending cycle of wanting what the mind wants, achieving (or not achieving) what the mind desires, and being temporarily happy (or unhappy)... then wanting the next thing that the mind wants, achieving (or not achieving) that next thing, and still being temporarily happy (or unhappy).

In a very real way, you could say that Human Design is like a "New Zen," especially for the Generators of the world (who make up about 70% of the population), in that it's here to help so many of us get out of that viscous desire-driven cycle. It does so in two ways.

One: It discerns between two kinds of success:

1) The kind that comes from getting what you want, or at least what your mind—which unfortunately, more often than not represents your conditioning—has convinced you that you want. This kind rarely brings about true satisfaction or long-lasting fulfillment. And...

2) The kind of success that comes from getting the life that you're meant to have.

*Getting the life you're meant to have doesn't necessarily mean
that everything is fine and dandy,
or that you're happy all the time, or that everything works out just perfectly.*

I'm sure you've had experiences that weren't necessarily comfortable or obviously successful, but you knew and felt at some very deep level that those experiences were good for you. That you did the right thing, because you were able to milk the experience for all it was worth, or you learned something of value, or you were really authentic and 'yourself' in the process. You would never have had it any other way. Maybe it was a relationship, a job or an experience, or just a period in your life when you experienced a loss, or moved through a Dark Night of the Soul. Still, there was something about those feelings or experiences that felt right, that were right... for you. No blame. No shame. No regrets.

This is what we're talking about in Human Design.

So, the goal here is not about perfect success according to the eyes of the culture, your coach, parents, siblings, teachers, coaches, friends, or even spiritual Guru. It's the kind that actually leaves you feeling deeply satisfied, fulfilled, at peace, full of trust, happy to be who you are, with your good days and your bad days, your happy moments and your not-so-happy moments. It's the kind of success that doesn't just look great on the outside. It doesn't feel like slavery on the inside either. If Generators can feel like anything, they can really feel like slaves! They're such hard workers by nature, who have trouble knowing when enough is enough, and can end up feeling like super-slaves! They can be very successful slaves, but slaves none the less. (I know plenty of Manifestors, Projectors and Reflectors that feel like slaves too!)

Two: The other thing that HUMAN DESIGN does is put you in touch with that part of you that you can trust to make healthy decisions. Your Authority.

It also shows you, in a very concrete way, **how** to honor your Authority. Human Design doesn't just say, "Let go of the mind, meditate and be still, and then you'll know what decisions to make." Given how long it can take us humans to reach (and maintain!) a state of mental non-attachment and peace, this isn't always a practical goal.

Human Design acknowledges that the Monkey Mind isn't just going to go away. It's not going to stop its thinking, planning or scheming, just because we tell it to. This may not be such a bad thing after all. In the end, we actually really need our minds to witness, measure and discern, to accumulate and ultimately share wisdom.

*Ultimately our minds are meant to be wonderful **outer authorities**;*
they are what allow us to become such gifted teachers for other people.

It's just that our minds are not supposed to run our own show. All Human Design really does is take that decision-making power away from the mind, and restore it to its proper place, to our own Authority—wherever that happens to be for each of us. It shows us a very concrete, practical way to work with our unique Authority.

This way, as we move towards 'meditative enlightenment' (if that's what floats our boat), we can still manage to navigate through the everyday of our lives with integrity, relative ease and a good dose of self-love.

TIME TO DIVE DEEPER INTO YOUR TYPE

(IN HUMAN DESIGN LINGO)

PURE and MANIFESTING Generators

*If you are a full-fledged member of the
Pure Generator Flower Family,
then you are
a Blossoming Buddha Being!*

**By BUDDHA BEING, I mean that you are
here to surrender, and to trust that your
wonderful life will come to you,
and bring on your blossom!**

*If you are a full-fledged member of the
Manifesting Generator Flower Family,
then you are
a Blossoming Buddha-Warrior!*

**By BUDDHA WARRIOR, I mean that you
are here to surrender first…
and manifest second!**

Regardless of the specific kind of Generator you are, you are blessed with a fertile body, absolutely filled with creativity, just waiting to be put into action so that it can have its big influence.

You came to this world with a warm, welcoming, enveloping aura, taking everything and everyone in around you.

Your true power is your energy. And your energy is designed to be put to work! To get used up.

Finding the right work in life is essential to your satisfaction.

Your body is meant to FIND the right work, by waiting to respond. This means that you are most likely to find work, relationships and a life you find deeply fulfilling, once you learn to wait to respond to what and who life brings you.

You Can Respond to Anything!

You're designed to be available to life itself, and to respond to ANYTHING.

The universe is literally speaking to you all of the time, providing you with an infinite amount of invitations to light your belly up and make you come alive!

Once you've 'responded' genuinely to something, you're designed to use your creative intelligence and power to build and perfect those things that matter most to you. To master something, step by step, using the full force of your life-giving energy.

A "MANIFESTING GENERATOR" DOTH NOT MAKE A MANIFESTOR
(Don't be fooled by the name!)

Whether this has been your experience or not, you have tremendous staying power and persistence—especially once you've responded to something positively and authentically.

Here's the thing:

You can't be the creative force on the planet you're meant to be, at least not in a way that makes you happy, as long as you're plundering towards things, trying to be a Manifestor Flower.

This is the hardest thing for Manifesting Generators to accept. As you can hear, the word 'Manifestor' is in your name. This means that you actually have the power and capacity to manifest—to move extremely quickly and efficiently into action.

When your parents, or teachers, or the world wants you to be a Manifestor, you can actually perform.

Most Manifesting Generating Flowers have spent their entire lives acting like and feeling like Manifestors, albeit frustrated ones!

You see, you CAN make things happen. In a very real way, you feel at home in the manifesting world.

In traditional Human Design circles, Manifesting Generator Flowers like you are often referred to as Bulls in a China Shop (or bulldogs in a garden of orchids!), because they're so often plunging ahead into life, with so much busy-ness and productivity, that they miss things. They skip steps, and then have to go back to pick up the missing pieces.

Sometimes they make a big mess of their lives without even realizing it. They get the education; they set up the business; they do the project; they make the trip; they write the book—all before they've given themselves a chance to feel whether what they're manifesting is actually going to fulfill them or not.

In the meantime, all sorts of opportunities pass them by, opportunities that would have made them much happier, even more productive and efficient in the long run. These Manifesting Generator Flowers don't notice any of this because they're WAY too busy letting their minds make their decisions for them. They end up tragically trapped in their successes, or failing with a big old bang.

Your Mind Doesn't Go to Bed with People!

One of the most important things to remember is that your mind is a wonderful thing! Especially for others!

Your mind can be deeply inspiring and helpful to people. I'm using my mind right now, for example, in service of you and your worthy life. I no longer rely on my mind to make big decisions about my own life. No, Nilly! I used to, and it was a bit of a nightmare.

I invite you to consider the possibility that your mind is not meant for making your decisions in life.

Let me tell you why. It simply doesn't know enough about who you are and what's good for you. It doesn't even have direct access to your energy.

Ra Uru Hu, the man who brought Human Design into the world, liked to say, "Your mind has all kinds of ideas about what and who'll be good for you, but it's not your mind who goes to bed with people!"

When we begin to dive deeper into the Blossoming Bodygraph, you'll learn about the various Centers. For now, just know that only 4 of the Centers in the Bodygraph are considered to be motors—or places in your body where the energy and fuel for life comes from.

Here's the interesting thing. None of these motors are directly connected to the mind. In fact, the only Center that the mind has direct access to is the Throat.

That means that the mind has the potential to communicate its thoughts, ideas, insights, questions and hypothetical answers with words, through the Throat. It has no direct access to the motors—the parts of a body that can actually add energy to a thought or an idea.

Just think about it. A mind, on its own, at the very most, can speak. On its own, it cannot act. It needs the body's blessing for that.

That's why our minds have had to get so darned good at manipulating our own (and each other's!) bodies to fulfill our mental agendas!

Your Car Won't Go without its Motor
(or at least not for long, or happily)

Think of your whole body as a biological vehicle for a moment. Unless the mind is hooked up to a motor, its contents have no energy behind it. Its ideas have no direct access to fuel.

Similarly, a flower can't grow without the energy from the sun.

It just isn't possible to simply ACT on an IDEA... without the body's blessing.

Ideas are just ideas, to be enjoyed and played around with. They're not to be taken seriously, unless they have access to a body that can provide them with the energy required for that idea to become manifest.

You can't start your own motor, just because you want to!

Even though you and your body can do all sorts of things, once you've responded, you're not designed to initiate your life the way pure Manifesting Flowers do.

You're not meant to move towards things just because they seem like good ideas. You're not even designed to know who or what is good for you until you're actually there, until the opportunity has actually presented itself, and your body has had a chance to respond to it.

By respond, I mean to either get turned on by something ("Hey, yea, I can handle this,"), or not ("No, I don't have energy for this.").

If you're designed for anything, it's to feel deeply frustrated when you're pushing things too much or too hard. When you think you have to do something, or you **really should** do something, even when your body doesn't feel like it.

TAKE A MEAL

Someone says they're going to feed you a wonderful meal. They describe the 4-course meal to you, and it all sounds delicious to your mind. You may even recognize the names of the dishes, and approve of the list of ingredients.

You won't have a clue as to whether you're going to actually enjoy that food or not, or whether you're even in the mood for the meal, until you're actually sitting at the table and eating it.

It's a simple example, but it reflects a basic Generator Flower principle that applies to everything—to relationships, careers, calling, diet, etc.

The Bottom Line

You can pursue any career your mind thinks it wants…

You can take any education your mind thinks it wants…

You can join any religion or spiritual community your mind thinks it wants…

You can make any friends your mind thinks it wants…

You can decide to marry any person your mind thinks it wants…

You can market your business until the cows come home…

And… you won't know whether any of it is right for you; you won't know if you can commit to that thing with the full force of your creative being—until you're actually there, checking in with your body, for each unique situation, relationship or encounter. Until you're there, feeling and responding to each 'new bite' in your own body.

It All Comes Down to Your Intelligent Belly!
(Your Sacral Center)

Your consistently creative and highly intelligent belly is what makes you the Generator Flower—and the powerful life force—that you are. Your belly is Defined. (That means it's colored in Red, when you look at the Bodygraph. More to come later in the Workbook/Course.)

According to Human Design statistics, over 70% of people on the planet belong to the Generator Family. About half of those Generators are Pure Generators, and the other half Manifesting Generators.

There are a LOT of us lively flowers out here. (I'm a Manifesting Generator myself.) We are here to build and create.

This is why it's so important that we each come to know and appreciate ourselves. We want to fill this world up with our unique beauty, gifts and joy, instead of the deep frustration we feel when we're not living according to our true nature—when we're the slaves of our minds and the value systems of the people our minds so often represent.

YOUR BELLY & HOW IT WORKS

Think of your belly (Sacral Center) like a giant response machine. It can respond to anything. It can respond to a person, a question, a flower, a painting, a marketing task, paperwork, a dream, a piece of music, an invitation, an email. It can respond to a taste, a sound, a sight, a touch, a smell. It can respond to a job, an environment, a house, a career, the lover of your dreams.

Your belly is a giant resource—the seat of vitality itself, the seat of creativity and fertility. It holds an enormous power within you. Think of it as a literal generator in your belly—constantly buzzing, humming, waiting to be asked, waiting to be used, and to be used up to a point of satisfying exhaustion.

We Generator Flowers tend to be busy. We're wired for it. We're not always so comfortable being at rest— partly because once our inner engines shut down, it can be hard for us to re-boot on our own. (Remember, we can't just 'turn ourselves on' without pushing. We do best when we're turned on by something that comes from the outside.)

As tired as we can get, sometimes it just feels easier to keep that motor going.

This partially explains why receiving the invitation to "wait to respond" can make us a little (or a lot) anxious! Subconsciously, we're afraid if we stop, we won't be able to start again... at least not without a lot of pushing, mental manipulation and threats (which usually is met with inner resistance... eventually).

IT'S ALL ABOUT ENERGY

This is what you're about. Energy. This body-driven need to be put to work, to be put to good use. This availability to life—an availability that needs to be honored and channeled properly.

Few things can bring you deeper satisfaction than using your energy well. When you genuinely respond to something, it's not a mental thing at all. It's simply the motor in your belly getting turned on.

In the end, all that motor can ever really tell you is, "I can do this and more," or "I don't feel like doing this." (If it says nothing at all, that's a "nope." Or at least a "not yet.")

Whether your belly is making a decision for a moment or a lifetime, it's basically letting you know if something is going to use your power and energy correctly, or not.

An Interesting Bit About Sleep

Pure Generator Flowers tend to do best when they go to sleep when they're exhausted.

If you're a Generator, going to sleep too early, by the clock, or before you're tired may not always work for you.

While Pure Generator Flowers do best when they go to bed when they're exhausted, Manifesting Generator Flowers often benefit from going to bed before they're exhausted, and then making themselves exhausted on their way to sleep!

If you are a Manifesting Generator, exactly how you exhaust yourself is entirely up to you. Some like to read a book. Others watch TV. My daughter Maya, when she was about 3 years old, either jumped on the bed or sang loudly until she collapsed. What matters here is that you allow your energy to move to a place of completion. That way you can wake up with renewed power.

Think of your belly like a battery. It works best when it gets all used up, and then recharges.

Of course, just because you're built to use your energy completely doesn't mean that every act has to be an act of exhaustion! It does mean that you're going to give all of the energy that your belly can produce for that thing it said 'yes' to. When the act is done, you're going to feel satisfied.

It's going to be a deep satisfaction.

(There are no rules that apply to everyone when it comes to sleep. I recommend that you engage in a little sleep experiment with yourself, and see what happens! Especially if sleep is something you struggle with. You may learn something interesting!)

✳ Learn to Tell When You're Pushing the River

Whenever you're presented with something to respond to (i.e. a yes or no question, an opportunity, or a decision to make), your belly either surges with positive energy. Or it doesn't.

You may recognize this in your own life. The difference between saying 'yes' to someone or something, when you actually feel like you have your body with you? And, when your head makes a decision, because it seems like a good idea, then you have to muster up the energy to do that thing, or 'push the river.'

I remember sitting in class as a kid, (even as an adult!), and a question was asked by the teacher. So many times, before my hand even had a chance to go up, my body just came alive. My heart started to pound. I felt flushed in my cheeks. My stomach rumbled. Whenever that happened, I just knew that I was going to raise my hand and say something, even though half the time I felt really shy and had no idea what I actually wanted to say.

That's an example of how my belly has worked for me.
It's different for everyone.
How has it worked for you?

How do you know when your body is with you?

A First Response Isn't Always Enough for You Manifesting Generator Flowers!

Flowers like you often need more than Pure Generator Flowers to get to your true response. It's not enough for you to be presented with something—an opportunity, a question, an invitation, etc. You need more than a simple 'yes/no' question.

In fact, you won't actually know whether an activity is right for you, or what your genuine response to that activity is, until you're actually physically engaging in the activity itself.

> It follows that one of your biggest challenges in life is...
> ...to let go of the idea that you have to 'finish what you start.'

Especially at the beginning of your experiment, you may have to start many things that you ultimately don't follow through on.

Once you're engaged in the thing, and your body is in the act of doing, your belly might give you a big ol' surprising NO.

This can be especially difficult when you feel pressure from others, who are expecting you to keep feeling a 'yes' about something you've started. Only you can know when you know.

You have to give yourself permission, (especially in the beginning, before you get the hang of this process), to be a little messy. To start things, or lead people on, and then stop, re-center, re-group. Over time, you'll get better at not making promises based on an initial 'yes,' and at giving your belly a chance to find its answer once things have actually gotten started. (If you have Emotional Authority, which we'll get to later in this Workbook/Course, the process can get even more complex!)

It's all about energetic availability when it comes to making decisions in your life. That's ultimately all that matters. If your body isn't available, it either "ain't gonna happen," or it "ain't gonna be much fun."

What Happens if You Ignore Your Belly?

It's easy to ignore your Sacral Center. (Most of us Generators are experts at it!) You can totally bypass your body's 'say' and force yourself to do all kinds of things you actually don't have the energy for, things that don't truly nourish or satisfy you.

You may very well end up doing many things splendidly, and impressing a lot of people.

The more you push yourself to do—without the blessing of your body, the more you're going to start feeling like a slave (even if you're self-employed! Not kidding on that one!).

Trying to initiate your direction in life can be exhausting. You might end up quitting, or hating what you're doing. When there's a lack of patience and trust, you can end up sacrificing your power, and working with—or for—people who don't genuinely respect you.

You can have such a hard time giving up trying to run your life. You can be so afraid of losing what you have—even if what you have is frustrating, or feels empty.

It takes so much courage to drop what isn't working, to lift the veil of busy-ness, and to see and honor who you really are.

If you ignore your belly long enough, your Sacral Center can actually atrophy. Its generative, creative and persistent power can become de-generative, even destructive. Your strong Generator Flower Stem can go limp. It can get weak and soft.

YOUR BELLY HAS A VOICE!
(An intelligent one, not an intellectual one!)

We say 'soft' because aside from the Throat, the Sacral Center is the only other Center in your body that can actually speak.

Your belly speaks in the form of sub-vocal sounds and grunts.

It's particularly good at saying 'yes' or 'no' in response to a specific situation. Or, it can say nothing, which basically means 'I don't know.' (Again, your belly is extremely intelligent, but it's not an intellectual! It can only communicate whether it has energy for something or not. That's it. No rocket science here.)

Here are the classic Sacral Sounds:

"uh-huh" for YES (or "mmmhm," "yea," "mmmm," etc.)
"uh-uh" for NO (or "ugh," "uhn uhn," "ehhhh," "eew," "ick," etc.)

Of course, there are so many sounds that can come out of your belly, if you let them.

Next time you're listening to a friend share some feelings or a story, notice how many times you say "uh-huh" or respond with sounds instead of words. That's your Sacral voice talking. That's the voice in you, (more than any other voice, more than the words that come out of your mouth), that you can trust.

As crazy as it may seem, these strange guttural blurbs coming out of you, these animal-like sounds, these grunts, sighs and squeals that arise from your gut when you're least expecting it, are your holy messengers of truth. They're your body's way of telling you who and what is right for you. Your *Inner Wisdom Keeper* in action.

These sounds are here to be taken deeply seriously, and used consciously when you are faced with a decision in life.

Strange as it may seem, these sounds are actually more trustworthy than most words coming out of your mouth, no matter how articulate and sophisticated. Sacral sounds are more capable of steering you safely down your path, than your mind with all of its theories, concepts, and endless lists of pro's and con's.

Get Ready to Grunt!

Now of course, most of us are raised to talk and articulate ourselves like proper humans. "Use your words, dear!" As soon as we're old enough, and our tongues are coordinated enough to pronounce 'yes, please' and 'no, thank you,' we learn to repress our natural Sacral sounds, grunts, whines and woo-hooo's.

As we learn to speak with greater eloquence, our minds begin to take over. We get farther and farther away from our bodies, farther away from our gut, which for Generators like you and me, means farther away from who we actually are, and the voice within us that's able to guide and direct our energy.

Over time, our body gets to participate less and less as a co-decision-maker, and more and more like a mentally-dictated servant.

This is why people, when they first learn that they're Generators and that they are supposed to rely on their Sacral Center to get to their Truth, can feel really weird and awkward. Suddenly they're being asked to make room for all kinds of strange noises, coming from a place within them that they abandoned, rejected, discounted, or learned to feel embarrassed by, long ago.

Many of us don't only need to be reintroduced to that place in us.
We need to be given permission to let it speak!

As a Generator Flower, one of the most important things for you to experiment with is your Sacral voice, to start letting those crazy sounds out.

Notice how much they're actually coming out without your even realizing it. Start to delight when you encounter something delicious, and hear yourself saying, "m-hm," "ah," "M-hm," "uh," "ooo," and "Oh yea." Or when you catch a whiff of a stuffed garbage can, and you "EWE!!" It's time to start honoring your truthful, uncompromisingly honest belly. It is so worthy of your trust.

GIVE YOUR BELLY SOME AIR TIME!

One of the quickest ways for you to get in touch with your Sacral response, is to sit down with a friend you trust, (it has to be somebody that you trust, because the Sacral Center is known to be a horrible liar!), and to have your friend ask you all kinds of questions.

Let the questions range from the mundane, like "Do you like tuna fish?" or "Are you in the mood to eat out?" or "Do you want to go with me to see that movie?"…

…To the profound, "Do you believe in God?" or "Are you in love with your partner?" or "Do you even want to be in a relationship right now?"

Practice letting your Sacral respond with sounds.

It can be strange at first, and it can take time to get the hang of it. As you do, it gets easier… and more interesting.

The key is to stay open to surprise.

Be prepared to hear whatever your Sacral says.

If you're wanting to explore a difficult question, you might want your friend to preface the question with a, "Are you ready to know how you feel about _____?"

We're not always ready to hear our own truth, and it's important to respect that.

How Often You Don't Listen

One of the most important things for us Generators to get is how often we DON'T listen to our bellies., and how often we override our body's responses to life with our intellect and our words.

When someone asks you a 'yes' or 'no' question, try to take your wordy answers with a grain of salt. Check again, and see what your body has to say.

"YOU CAN'T START A CONVERSATION WITH A GRUNT"

This well-known Human Design joke is actually quite profound if you think about it. It's saying that the Sacral Center, that place in you that actually determines your ideal Strategy for life itself, JUST CAN'T INITIATE.

It can't start things.
It's not like the Throat that can actually initiate a conversation. The Sacral can't do that.
It has to come alive **as a response**.

This means that even as you go through this Workbook and come to know all kinds of wonderful things about your blossoming nature (i.e. your potential and gifts, your purpose in life, etc.), you still can't make or force any of that to happen. You can't just decide with your mind that you're going to go out there in the world and be a creative, productive member of society, or get some satisfying project up and running.

You still need to surrender to what comes your way. You still need to wait for opportunities and invitations to bring your body to life. You still have to trust your unique body to 'pick and choose' its responses.

Your Belly as a Bank Account!

For a moment, I'd like you to imagine that your Sacral Center is a bank account, and that the energy that resides in your belly is actual money—your hard-earned cash. (Ra Uru Hu used this metaphor, and I really have found it useful.)

You are the guardian of this account. You are the executor, the one who decides how the money (that remember, you've worked very hard to earn) gets spent.

Now imagine that someone comes up to you and asks you for something. Maybe they are asking for a favor. Or they want you to join them for lunch. Or they're inviting you to a party, or some kind of an event. Or they're offering you a job.

Whatever it is they're asking for in this scenario, you know that if you say 'yes,' it means you are committing your energy to this thing, whatever it is. You're actually going to have to pay them hard cool cash—taking it out of your bank account—in order to say 'yes.'

It can be very illuminating to play around with this metaphor, as strange (and capitalist) as it is, when thinking about your energy. Especially if you're a WE-oriented person!

I want you to get to a place where you actually 'get' how valuable and precious your energy is, and how easily you give it away, without even thinking of it.

The more you give your energy away "on automatic," the less of it will be available for those things that will truly bring you satisfaction.

When you don't just give it all away, you actually pull energy towards you. You build up a potent reservoir within you, a growing pool of resources. You actually grow your aura. The bigger your aura gets, the more likely you are to attract those things and people into your life that will ignite your true purpose. When they come, you'll have more than enough energy to whole-heartedly throw yourself into the experience, relationship or project. You can ultimately make a more positive contribution to the WE.

DON'T GIVE IT ALL AWAY

If you're constantly and indiscriminately giving your energy away, you can't as easily attract what you need to live a fulfilled life.

Even if you can still attract it, you won't have nearly as much energy to enjoy and milk the experience for all its worth.

At first, what I'm suggesting here can sound very selfish. In a way, it is. It has to be.

Ultimately, fulfillment is contagious. The better you get at honoring and using your energy well, the more of a positive impact you'll have on your surroundings. You'll have the full force of your energy to really go for what you're meant to do. You won't just be going around, feeling overwhelmed, under-appreciated and resentful.

It takes courage to demand respect from the world. That's what you're here for—to be respected. To enjoy being a powerful, creative person who uses your energy in a clean, satisfying way. You deserve to feel good at the end of each day.

For a We-oriented person, what I'm inviting you to experiment is not easy, and it's totally possible.

No one can do this for you. To say 'no' when you normally say 'yes' can be extremely uncomfortable... for you, and for all of the people who are used to you saying 'yes.'

SERIOUSLY, WOULD YOU PAY FOR THIS?

So… The next time you're trying to make a decision about what to do, ask yourself, "Is this something I'd be willing to pay for?"

Even if it's just a tiny thing—like talking to someone on the phone... if it's not something you'd pay for in that moment, practice saying 'no.' (Just because you can!) See what happens.

Notice what happens when you say 'no' to things, maybe lots of things, that your body isn't genuinely excited about. Notice what happens when you allow yourself to build up a lot of energy within you... that ultimately, you can throw into a good satisfying 'yes.'

I can't help but think about one of my favorite Country Western songs, introduced to me by that wonderful dentist I worked with years ago. It was by Deana Carter, and it was called, "And I Shaved My Legs for This?!" That's a great Generator line.

If It Ain't Easy, It Ain't Likely!

Another good rule of thumb, especially in the beginning!

Do an 'Opposite Experiment!'

Again, especially in the beginning of your experiment, it may be even MORE enlightening to notice just how often you say 'yes' when your body isn't into it.

How often do you keep calling someone, or trying to push something through, even if no one answers, or you keep getting met with resistance?

Even in this experiment, I recommend at least doing a Sacral check-in. Ask your body for its genuine answer.

Instead of insisting that you follow your Sacral's lead, that you say 'no' to all of the opportunities, people, and projects that aren't right for you, just try to notice what happens when you don't, when you say 'yes.'

Notice what thoughts go through your mind, how your mind convinces you to ignore your Sacral. Notice how the experience goes once you've entered into it. Notice if you feel frustration, or anger, or regret. Notice your energy level afterwards. Look for the backlash.

Have fun with it all. Be gentle with yourself. Remember, it's all an experiment. It's all learning.

WATCH YOUR MIND

During those times when you do manage to say 'no' to something your Sacral has rejected, notice what happens in you too. Notice how your mind talks to you.

- Is it busy giving you a guilt trip?

- Is it making you worry about missing out on something?

- Is it threatening you that you'll never get another opportunity?

If you can manage to eventually let the mental mess pass, notice how you feel. Notice your energy level. Your inspiration. Is there relief?

Growth Process for a Pure Generator Flower

Your growth process can look and feel quite different from that of a Manifesting Generator Flower.

Even when you're living a life in alignment with your belly's responses, you may still experience times when you feel stuck, or frustrated.

Some of that 'stuck-ness,' is actually normal and healthy for you.

There's a difference between the kind of frustration that comes when you hit your head against the wall, over and over again, trying to manifest or make something happen...

...and the kind I'm talking about here.

You can most definitely learn to tell the difference, thought it can take time.

As a Pure Generator Flower, you master things by going through a step by step process. You tend to grow in spurts.

There may be times in your life when you feel like you've hit a plateau, and fear that nothing new will ever happen. All of a sudden, (as long as you don't give up prematurely, which is a mistake that some Pure

Generators make, even those who enter into things properly!), with no apparent reason, everything can change.

You have a magnificent breakthrough.

Suddenly, you're alive again, taking what you're doing to an even higher level of mastery and skill. Either that, or changing what you're doing all together—making a quantum, evolutionary leap, and having a tremendous impact on the people around you, sharing your gifts with others in a way that leaves you feeling satisfied and received.

Sometimes you've just got to hang in there... especially when you're doing something that you've entered into through a genuine response. Just keep breathing, riding plateau periods like the temporary waves that they are, until metamorphosis takes place.

In the end, you'll come to recognize these periods as vital, natural parts of your life.

Transformative bumps in the road!

The Essence of the Generator Flower's Spirituality
Generators and Manifesting Generators are here to surrender to the NOW.

I shall leave you with a beautiful quote from Richard Rudd's article "The 4 Paths of Surrender":

"The awake Generator actually goes in the opposite direction from the Manifestor (albeit toward the same source). Whereas the awake Manifestor takes control of their own life, the awake Generator surrenders control. The surrender of response is the continual surrender to the next moment. This is the propaganda of 'nothing is up to me, it's all out of my hands.'

Spiritually speaking, this path is embodied in the Indian Vedic teachings known as 'Advaita,' but it can also be found in other teachings such as the Chinese Tao Te Ching, which centers on the concept of 'wu wei'—the art of doing nothing. Since it applies to over 70% of us, it is amusing how unpopular this kind of teaching really is. The Not-Self Generator much prefers the Manifestor propaganda that says: "No, I have a choice and I'm going to make a difference!"

THE ULTIMATE INVITATION FROM THIS POINT ON!

Let go of any idea or picture you have about what your life is supposed to look like. JUST LET IT GO! From here on out, your life gets to be a FABULOUS, OFTEN-SURPRISING ADVENTURE!

Projectors

YOU ARE A BEAUTIFUL PROJECTOR FLOWER!

As a member of the Projector Flower Family, you are not meant to go out and find your life.

You are meant to be FOUND by your life, and to be invited home. Once this has happened, you are here to share your wondrous gifts, to become a guiding light, and to be deeply fulfilled.

Here's the best part: You are meant to do all of this in a way that leaves you feeling relaxed and seen! NOT overworked or invisible, or like you're holding the entire world on your shoulders!

 Number one motto for Projectors: Work on the work you love doing, not on the work that needs to be done!

A lot of Projectors are born into this crazy manifestation-obsessed world of ours, and conditioned by their family or cultural environments to be 'doers'—to over-commit themselves. Flowers like you, ultimately, aren't here to do-do-do. You're actually here to guide the other 'doers,' and be seen for who you are.

What Projector Flowers Long for Most

Deep down, Projectors long for recognition, more than anything else. They want to be seen for who they are, so that they can bring their wonderful gifts to fruition.

Your Projector Gifts

If you belong to the Projector Flower Family, then you have so many wonderful gifts.

One of your greatest is the gift to SEE into others.

You are especially capable of understanding and guiding Generators, people who've got lots and lots of energy, and need to find a healthy place to put it! One of your true roles in life is to work with and manage the energy of others, in a way that brings out their most authentic and full expression, and in a way that serves our beautiful earth.

So, it makes sense that you have a special talent for recognizing the capabilities of people, and for helping them learn how to use their precious energy in efficient, constructive and collaborative ways.

THE RIGHT QUESTIONS

You also have the gift—under the right conditions—for knowing just the right questions to ask. *yes!*

Believe me; there are few things this world needs more than people who are wise enough to ask the right questions! (Think of how much havoc we've wreaked on our planet, just trying to answer irrelevant—even dangerous questions, like, "Whose God is the right one?" or "What's ugly about that dress?" or "How can we most efficiently kill those people over there?")

Actually, it's through your questioning, your agenda-free probing, that your awareness of the other comes into play. Your genuine, natural curiosity about people helps you guide them. You see their uniqueness, and that inevitably helps them express it!

A just-right question at a just-right time can open someone up to satori. It can shatter, awaken and transform them. (For you, the trick is two-fold: to ask when the question is truly desired, and to ask without attachment to the answer. The better your timing and the less attached you can be to the answer, the more powerful your guidance will be.)

YOU LOVE MIND CANDY!

As a Projector Flower, you also have a gift for taking in information, and for understanding systems.

It is said in Human Design circles, that more than any other Type, Projectors love mind candy!

And wow, can your alive and intelligent mind can be such a tool for service in this world. (As long as you don't make it the authority in your own life. For it is also said that there is nothing nuttier than a Projector on a mental decision-making trip!)

While members of the Generator Family come to this world longing to work and create, Projectors like you come to this world longing to LEARN!

This pure love of learning is one of your most wonderful qualities. Which is why it's so sad when this love isn't fully understood or celebrated by your environment—and when you're pushed to work, work, work, instead of learn, learn, learn (and relax and eat Bonbons as you go!)

Your Open, Receptive (and sometimes overworked!) Belly

One of the central aspects of your Blossoming Bodygraph that contributes to your being a Projector Flower is the condition of your Sacral Center—that big square, second up from the bottom.

Your Sacral Center is Open (or white). Think of it like an open, transparent window in your belly being.

We'll be exploring Openness more in depth later in this Workbook/Course, when we arrive at the Petal called "Observe the Flow of Your Energy." For now, all you need to know is that wherever you are Open, you are receptive and flexible. It is through the 'white' or transparent places in you that you actually take in and experience the other. It follows that through your Sacral Center, you receive a lot of the energy present in your environment.

For many reasons (both healthy and not), people tend to be extremely attracted to the Open places in their charts. These are the places we're meant to go to school.

Ultimately, what we learn about the aspects of life that are channeled through these places can lead us to our wisdom. Our Open Centers, Gates and Channels become grist for the wisdom mill, and very likely an essential part of our teaching repertoire.

But sometimes, we end up living our entire lives (and making all of our decisions) from these Open, easy-to-influence places in us. When we do this at the expense of who we truly are, we end up living conditioned lives, lives that aren't our own.

When you're alone, and you're not being impacted by the energies of anyone else—the stars included— your lovely Sacral Center takes a delicious nap. It rests and relaxes.

However, as soon as someone or something enters your space and lights up your Sacral Center, it comes to life. Your receptive belly doesn't just wake up. It springs out of bed! This is because your Sacral Center doesn't just 'take in' energy from the outside. It MAGNIFIES energy. It's like a powerful amplifier (as all Open Centers are).

Your belly isn't built for consistency or for handling the amount of energy it may be taking in, so it can get easily overwhelmed, and have you working way too hard to get rid of the discomfort you feel in your over-stimulated middle!

In the world of Human Design, an Open Sacral means that you weren't born to have consistent, reliable access to your own life force energy. Your body isn't meant to be always buzzing with energy. It's not hungry to use itself up to a point of exhaustion. It doesn't always speak to you with sounds that you can generally trust to be your truthful responses to life, or decision-making authority. (As is the case for Generator Flowers.)

At least when you're on your own, you can truly discharge and rest. You can unplug from the craziness of this world we live in... and enjoy simply being. You can actually space out!

Ahhhhhh....this is wonderful.

You're simply not meant to have the kind of staying power that a Generator Flower has. You're not built to keep going and going until you exhaust yourself. It's actually not healthy for you, and it's not likely to be much fun either.

You've come here to live an energetically balanced life, where you have plenty of time to rest and kick back. We want you making your contribution in the world in a way that doesn't burn you out, but instead, makes the most of the energy of the people around you.

You are not here to constantly be using your own energy to the point of exhaustion; you are here to understand energy and how it works, and with your intuitive gifts, to guide others in the most efficient and healthy use of their energy, for the sake of a better world.

In a way, on a mystical level, you could say you're here to allow energy to move through you, to allow Spirit, or whatever you want to call it, to do its work.

Important: The fact that you don't have reliable, consistent access to your energy doesn't mean you have no energy, or that you are not energetically available to life. You are. In fact, there are few things your body wants more than to share its gifts with others, and to reap the harvest of a life well-planted, and well-lived. When connected to others, ideally to the right others, you can have access to more than enough energy and power to guide and manage people through all sorts of meaningful, creative and inspiring processes.

At the same time, because of your Open (and not always consistent) Sacral Center, you also need others to recognize who you are and what gifts you bring. In a sense, you are the only flower that depends solely on others to fulfill your purpose in life. (Although of course, in the end, we all need each other!)

The Projector Leadership Paradox

You of the Projector Family are considered to be the 'new leaders of humanity.' In one way, you're at the top of the hierarchy, here to guide all of us human beings into the future.

Obama is a Projector. Nelson Mandela is a Projector. Whether or not you agree with their politics, the way they came into their leadership roles is reflective of a new way. Their power was given to them by the people. Rising up like waves in the ocean, grass roots movements lifted them up and carried them forward. They were handed energy to work with... and sought after because of who they were, not necessarily how crazily ambitious and action-oriented they were. (Not that they sat around and twiddled their thumbs!)

As we evolve as a species, we're going to need less and less of the top-down/master-slave kind of leader— like Hitler, a well-known Manifestor who was living out the *Shadow* aspect of his nature.

We're going to need more people like you, who understand and know how to work with energy. We're going to need people like you who can make the most of each person's unique potential, in service of the whole. (Just because Generator Flowers are blessed with a bundle consistent power and vitality within them, doesn't mean they have a clue as to how to use that power wisely!)

The Bottom Line

- Your true gifts emerge the moment you stop trying to live your life like a Generator.

- It's truly not healthy for you, or for our planet, when you take on too much work and don't give yourself enough time to withdraw and recharge.

- Our world needs you to feel relaxed and rejuvenated. We need your unique perspectives and prism—which are their clearest when you're not burned out.

There's no question that you're here to share your gifts with others. What IS in question is who you share those gifts with, and under what circumstances.

Again, and I can't stress this enough, your Sacral Center is Open. This means that whenever you're in the world, or brushing up against the public aura (which is almost always buzzing with Generator energy, since Generator Flowers make up 70% of the human population!), chances are very good that your Sacral Center is going to wake up… A LOT.

As I shared earlier, many Generators have no clue about how to use their energy properly. They're busy doing all kinds of things that either don't satisfy them, don't fulfill them, or that they're simply not suited for.

Here you are with this incredible gift for seeing people, their unique gifts, and how they can best manage their energy. Not just that, but you understand systems, and often know just what would be needed for a system to function with greater health and functionality.

You see what's needed on so many levels, and very likely feel a great deal of pressure to leap into all sorts of situations, so that you can save the day with your Projector gifts.

Add your deep longing to be seen to the picture, (and perhaps the fear that true recognition will never happen if you just sit around and wait for the miracle), and it's going to get even harder for you to restrain yourself (and avoid the pitfalls of rescuing and overwork).

You can easily end up throwing caution and selectivity to the wind, and jumping into all sorts of situations, making all sorts of commitments that leave you carrying everyone else's load but your own.

Not knowing when enough is enough, you can wind up throwing your resources down the drain, or exhausting yourself in an impossible effort to guide the wrong people through situations that aren't even interesting, relevant or healthy for you. Talk about getting lost in the WE!

The Big Secret
(THE RIGHT PEOPLE!)

The secret to leading a life that feels right in your Projector core, is to make sure that you are surrounded by and connected to the right people.

For you, it's so much less about quantity, and so much more about quality.

In other words, it's not about how many people you can have in your life, it's about the value of each being.

The right people are those who truly recognize you, who 'get' you, not just people who are impressed by some projection they have of you. If you spend too much of your time living with, loving or working with people who don't truly see you, you will suffer... and your gifts are likely to remain hidden.

Remember the great irony of your life. On the one hand, you have this incredible potential to guide others. On the other hand, you have an equally great potential to get totally lost in them.

This is why it's so incredibly important that you learn to surrender to your Strategy—or healthy growth path (as I'll soon describe to you), and that you learn how to surround yourself with the right people!

Believe me, there are few things worse than getting lost in the wrong people, in the wrong WE. No one has to be more vigilant about who they bring into their life than Projector Flowers like you. Generators can handle it. Manifestors can blow it off. Reflectors can let it slip right off. But not Projectors.

With this Open state of your Sacral Center, you can become quite dependent on the actual energy that people bring into your life.

Without even meaning to, you can slurp people up like a giant milkshake.

You Don't Need to Be Recognized by Everybody

You're designed in such a way that you may not always be or feel seen by everyone. You may even have to go through a lot of people in your life, before you find those who truly see you, and recognize you. This can be hard, and make you vulnerable to compromise.

"Well, they don't really get me, but they admire me and think I'll be good at this and that." Or, "They need me." Or, "They're counting on me." Or, "Maybe, if I hang around long enough, I can get them to see these other aspects of who I am, and finally get a chance to use my gifts when I'm around them."

Compromise, compromise, compromise.

Remember that even though someone thinks you're fantastic, it doesn't mean they truly know you, or are right for you. Someone might think you're amazing, but for all the wrong reasons. They may be on a big projection trip in relation to you, just as you may be on one in relation to them.

It can be challenging to discern the difference between plain old attention, and true recognition. When you get confused between the two, you can end up in relationships that either drain you or distract you from your wonderful life.

Your Strategy (or Healthy Growth Plan) as a PROJECTOR FLOWER

Your overriding Projector Strategy is not a moment-by-moment Strategy, like that of the Generator Flower Families. Your Strategy doesn't have to do with all of the tiny little decisions you make in life. (We'll get into that when we arrive at the "Support Your Life!" Petal, and begin to explore your unique Authority.)

Your Projector Flower Strategy is to be applied to the major decisions in your life.

It requires a great deal of patience and trust.

You weren't necessarily built to have an overnight path to success.

Given the complex (and crazy!) nature of us humans, it makes sense that learning how to understand and guide all of us into the future can take some time!

You come into your right leadership or guiding role by learning how people work and how they operate correctly. It's through this kind of systemically-oriented, interpersonal and energetically-attuned mastery process that you ultimately experience the success and fulfillment you long for.

Waiting for the Invitation

As a Projector Flower, you are here to wait for the invitation. In other words, you're not here to go wandering around with a plug, looking for 'people sockets' to plug yourself into.

You're here to wait for the right people with the right sockets to find you, and to invite you into their lives.

You see, you can only guide other people once you've been invited to guide them.

By real invitation, I mean from an actual person who is communicating directly to you.

The invitation doesn't have to be written down on fancy stationary, or delivered 'in person,' but it does have to be a direct request for *your* presence, work, friendship, even your words. Not just some mass email that's gone out to a bunch of people, but a question, an invitation, an open door that's meant for you in particular.

The formal invitations you are waiting for in life are basically only about 4 things:

- the invitation to love

- the invitation to career

- the invitation to bond with others

- and the invitation to a place to live

Some simple examples:

- "I like hanging out with you. Would you like to go out for coffee sometime?" (i.o.w. "Do you want to be my friend?")

- "You have the kind of knowledge and skills that are really needed. Would you like to teach a class at the school where I work?"

- "I've got a friend who's looking to rent out a great apartment you might like. Wanna come and check it out?"

- "I'm moving to Santa Fe. It's the funniest thing. Every time I go there, I think of you. I can really see you being happy there. Would you like to come check it out to see if it's a place you might want to call home?"

- "I think you have a real artistic gift. And I know an art school that would be just perfect for you. Would you like to visit it?

- "I'm going on an adventure, and I can't think of anyone I'd rather go with. Will you come with me?

- "The deeper our relationship gets, the more I know you, the more I can feel how much I love you. Will you marry or spend the rest of your life with me?"

What Do You Do While You're Waiting?

YOU DO WHAT YOU LOVE!

That's right.

Just do what you love.

The Projector Flower Strategy doesn't mean sitting around passively as life passes you by... until some sparkly human rides up on a rainbow unicorn and rescues you from your state of perpetual limpness.

Your job is to do what you love...

Learn, read, explore, take classes, dance, write, hike, take pictures, study, putz around aimlessly, swim, sing, enjoy a Workbook like this, get a massage, go for walks, go to a spa, make some art, work at a job that doesn't exhaust you and with colleagues you enjoy, etc. If it makes you come alive, if it fulfills you, if you like the people you're with, you're good to go. When your essence is humming, you're at your most delicious frequency.

I can't tell you how many Projector Flowers I know have received life-changing invitations while they were doing something they loved, with no expectation that an invitation was coming. Think of your naturalness as your greatest form of magnetism. It is your vibrational signature, your irresistible song to your people!

What Do You Do Once You've Received a Really Good Invitation?

WHATEVER THE HECK YOU WANT!

I'm serious.

This 'waiting business' is truly just about the entryway. It's your protection against getting involved in things and with people that aren't really a good fit for you. It's your protection against bitterness and burn out. It's only in relation to the four big things in life.

- Once you've been invited into a relationship (or a calling, or a true home), and you know it's the right one, you can become one of the most versatile beings around.

- **You can manifest, generate and reflect whatever you like. Like nobody's business. You become even more attractive to your right people!** *(Just make sure to cushion periods of major activity with coziness, self-care and rest!)*

What About the Rest of Your Decisions?

For the rest of your decisions (everything that isn't one of the BIG FOUR), you have your unique Authority—your inner truth compass—to rely on. We'll be exploring that when we get to the petal called, "Support Your Life!".

Your Projector Flower Aura

You have a powerful, magical and extremely trustworthy aura! It's true.

Your Projector Aura has a very specific frequency and a unique capacity to penetrate people. Without even realizing that you're doing it, you can hone in on people's essence, and see them for who they are.

Every time you look into someone, you have the chance to see an aspect of your own nature too. The more beings you look into, the more of yourself you can discover, like a multi-faceted diamond.

You belong to the most personal and relational Flower Family on this planet!

You are also deeply complex. (There are so many different kinds of Projector Flowers. Again, just because you're a member of a particular Flower Family, doesn't mean you're all alike!)

THE LAZER BEAM

It doesn't matter whether you are aware of this or not, or whether you feel like you have any control over this or not. When it comes to your Aura, you tend to zoom in on people—reading them (one at a time) like a laser beam.

When you're being true to yourself, and are connecting with 'your people,' this laser like Aura of yours is absolutely wonderful. It deepens relationships, enhances connectivity, and leaves everyone involved feeling 'gotten,' supported and aligned with who they are.

When you're not being true to yourself, or connecting with your right people, your Aura can be experienced as quite intense for others—even uncomfortable. I suppose this makes sense. Not everyone wants to be penetrated, to be probed or seen so deeply. Not everyone is ready for that.

Of course, while some people aren't ready for or wanting that level of contact, there are others who can't get enough of it!

Some people can actually become quite dependent on your attention. So addicted that it can be hard for them to let you go, even when that's what's truly needed. Or, they can feel envious or uncomfortably excluded when they see you giving your attention to someone else, even if that's the last thing you want them to feel.

While you can certainly learn to be especially sensitive to others in these situations, it's important that you accept that an element of this dynamic is purely, 'auric-ally' driven.

Your Aura is designed to zoom in on one being at a time, creating a bubble-like field around you and that person. You're not doing anything wrong or bad. You're just being yourself. Your Aura is just doing its honing thing.

WHAT ABOUT THOSE CONFUSING MESSAGES?

Some people may end up giving you very mixed messages. On the one hand, they want your attention. On the other hand, they don't want your probing. They don't really want you to see into them, or to make any demands on them.

If you don't give them your attention in the way they want it, on their terms, you can get the sense that they might take their energy away from you.

Of course, this is a subtle process. It's not like they think to themselves, or say out loud, "Hey, if you don't give me what I want, I'm going to take my energy away from you." It's not like that. It's more like they start to pull back, and you can feel it. You just can.

When people pull back their energy, it can feel very scary for a relational flower like you, with that Open Sacral Center of yours. It can feel like you've lost your juice, your spark, or like your life has fallen flat.

THE OTHER SIDE OF THE DEPENDENCY COIN

With this dynamic, you can end up becoming dependent on people too—especially the ones that light up your Sacral Center through your shared chemistry.

The problem with this kind of dependence is that it can make you willing to put up with all kinds of not-great dynamics (including overworking yourself)... just to keep people and their energy in your life.

When you find yourself compromising too much, especially in relationships where you're not really being seen and appreciated for who you are, you can end up feeling bitter about life as a whole... which can be very painful.

(Note: A certain amount of bitterness over the state of human affairs is both appropriate and understandable! When someone as wise as you looks out at what we humans are doing to each other and our planet, it's not going to feel that great... from a compassionate heart perspective! We don't want you feeling the kind of bitterness that comes from working too hard to please, support and help people who don't honor, appreciate or even see you. That's a whole different story. A bitterness you can definitely do without!)

Your laser beam Aura doubles as a STRAW! In other words, while your Aura is busy honing in on people, it's also taking them in. You literally ingest people's essence, and slurp up their energy. There's actually a really good reason for this!

Beneath the surface, your soul is always looking for your right people—those wonderful human beings who have the perfect keyholes to fit your brilliant crystal key. These are the people you came to this planet to see, care about and guide. These are the people who can reflect back to you all that you are.

*Your Aura was built to help you find your people,
so that you can live out your purpose. It's actually quite beautiful.*

It can also be intense, and not always delicious, especially if you haven't learned the healthy Art of Relational Selectivity!

A Little Discernment Tip!

Whenever you meet someone, ask yourself, "If this person were a meal, would I eat him or her?!"

I know. It may sound like a funny question, but it's truly profound, and can be so helpful!

Your job is to spend as much of your time with people you find tasty and delicious! People (both personal and professional) who are pleasurable and easy on your stomach.

Believe me; you don't want to get filled up with "people junk food." It might feel thrilling for a moment, but the aftertaste will be bad, and the long-term effects can be hard on the body and soul.

YOUR AURA IS MAGICAL
A NATURAL MAGNET & EFFECTIVE SCREENER ALL IN ONE!

Your Aura is PERFECT for your life. It's designed to attract the best people and invitations, and to keep the rest at bay. You've got to trust it, and let it do its thing.

More than any other Flower Type, you need to understand (and trust) the power of your Aura.

Think of it like a bio-energetic field that can be felt across a room, coded to a very distinct frequency.

Anyone who is not attuned to that specific frequency—unless you go out of your way to attract his or her attention!—just won't notice you.

Anyone who **is** attuned to your frequency simply cannot help but pick you out across a crowded room.

Your Aura is magical, and you can trust it.

When you allow it to do its thing, it will bring you who you need, and it will protect you from who and what you don't need.

If someone isn't naturally drawn into your Aura, they are probably not one of your people. It's that simple. (Either that, or the right timing for your connection hasn't come.)

Your main job is to sit back, relax and wait to see who notices you and steps forward. Remember, you were put on this planet not to go out and find your life, but to be found by your life. To be recognized and invited in. You don't have to jump up and down, or to shout, in order to be seen or heard by your people.

Learning to Tolerate the Discomfort of Saying 'No'

You know the pain of not being seen for who you are, so you can feel particularly tempted to accept invitations from people who notice you at all, even if they don't truly 'get' you.

Knowing how good it feels to receive an invitation, and worrying that another—or a better—one might never come, you can also be tempted to say 'yes' when you should be saying 'no.'

You might feel extra protective towards people who extend invitations your way because you understand the vulnerability one can feel when extending an invitation. Afraid to hurt peoples' feelings, or to discourage them from inviting you again another time, you can easily end up accepting more invitations than you should.

It's kind of ironic, because many Projector Flowers end up being the ones who are always extending the invitations!

Your job is to be like your Aura—an expert screener.

Your job is to learn how to tolerate the discomfort you feel when saying 'no thanks' to invitations that aren't right for you.

You may have to say 'no' to A LOT of invitations... at least more invitations than you'd like, before you get to the right ones. This is not only OK; it's necessary.

The Good News

The good news is that you are designed to get more recognition than many people! Especially when you're doing what you love, your right people can't help but notice you, and want to be around you.

This also means that you're designed to attract more invitations than most. One of the biggest invitations I want to extend to you is TO RELAX!!! You have to do so much less than you think for your magical life to unfold!

Even if you go through periods of what seems like Invitation Droughts, there's no need to worry.

Remember, when it comes to the big things in life, you actually don't need many invitations.

I mean, seriously. How many invitations do you need to marry? How many best friends do you need? How many places to live do you need? How many callings do you need?

Not many.

Once you've accepted a good invitation and entered into the situation in a self-honoring way, you don't need to wait again when it comes to that arena. You've gotten a free, lifetime pass into the amusement park. Have fun, and put your talents to work. (Without working too hard!)

Solitude is Medicine

If you are a Projector Flower, you need to be watered with plenty of alone time.

Given that Open Sacral Center of yours, your natural interest in others, and the fact that you're usually surrounded by energetic Generator Flowers, you need a break now and then.

You're designed to take in, amplify and act on the energy you receive from the people around you. A lot of the time, a chunk of that energy isn't even yours. You can drive yourself to a point of exhaustion before knowing what hit you.

It's extremely important to learn when ENOUGH is ENOUGH.

To make sure that you have regular periods of time where you get to unhook from the busy buzzing world around you. Setting time aside for re-centering, rejuvenating and re-orienting yourself is as important to you as eating and drinking.

Believe me; if you don't make self-care a major part of your practice, you'll end up working harder than most of the people you know, and either burning out or getting sick.

Sleep

Try going to sleep before you're tired. Give yourself time to unwind, to discharge all of the energy from the day.

Some Projector Flowers like to stretch out a little before getting into bed, doing some restorative relaxing poses. Some like to read, or to just look up at the ceiling. Some do a little journaling, or doodling, just to touch base with themselves.

Only you know what helps you make the transition from the activities of daily life, into the kind of surrender necessary for sleep. This is something you can experiment with. Most importantly, see if you can find ways to coax yourself into a relaxed state.

You need to acknowledge just how much of life's busy-ness you're actually taking in during the day. It's OK and natural if you need a little time to unwind.

The Key to Fulfillment
Non-Attachment & Agenda-Free Living

As I've mentioned before, whether you are being invited into a relationship, a career, or a place, you need to be very clear that you are being recognized for who you truly are, and by an energy that you are able to work with. Your potential and future depend on your attracting the kind of energy you're designed to guide.

This is why non-attachment is such a powerful practice for you! It's so important that you trust that you'll be seen by the right people... and not to take it personally when the wrong people don't see you.

It's so easy, especially for a sensitive person like you with so much to offer, to feel deeply hurt when you're not recognized or appreciated by someone. It's so easy to be hard on yourself, and to assume that there's something wrong with you.

If someone doesn't get you, it's never personal.
You must always remember this! There is absolutely nothing wrong with you.

Remember that you're like an extremely unique and brilliant crystal key. You are here to 'unlock' and enjoy a very particular group of people in this world. (It doesn't have to be a small group of people. It just has to be a particular group of people!)

The more you trust this, the more easily you'll be able to enjoy the process of checking out various people and environments, and seeing whether they're the right ones for you. The less energy you'll expend twisting yourself into a pretzel in order to get seen and recognized by people you don't even want to be with—if you're totally honest with yourself!

Really, you are so gifted at reading energies.

When you're really living at your spiritual zenith, you'll be practicing Agenda-free Living.

The less of an agenda you carry into any situation, the more easily you'll find and be found by your wondrous life!

The Essence of the Projector Flower's Spirituality
Projectors are here to Surrender to the Other.

Here's a beautiful quote from Richard Rudd's article "The 4 Paths of Surrender":

"Like the generator, the projector has a design to wait. But the awake projector cannot simply wait for the next moment to define them, they are actually defined by their relationships. Spiritually, this is symbolised by the path of Tantra, the union of two or more energies leading to transcendence (again, this is 'Tantra' in its purest form, rather than the modern western sexual interpretation). The secret of the projector's true path lies in the mastery of the undefined sacral, which always depends on the correct alignment of their own and someone else's energies. The spiritual propaganda of the projector path is all based on cooperation and love. This is the teaching that we are all one and that only by joining together can we attain transcendence. One can see how this is actually the most natural of all teachings, since projectors are the most natural teachers. It is the natural direction of humanity, and yet projectors cannot impose this way on others."

Summary of Your Healthy Growth Path

- Wait for the invitation in relation to the BIG FOUR, and while you're waiting, do what you love—both alone and with others.

- Once an invitation comes, sense whether you feel seen by the inviter, sense whether they seem to like the questions you just naturally ask.

- The next step is to follow your Authority (more information on this will come later in the course).

- If your Authority tells you 'no,' please don't take it personally.

- Just say, "Thanks, but no thanks!" Be grateful that you're not going to spend the next 10 years with the wrong people doing the wrong thing, and feeling very bitter about the whole business!

If your Authority says 'yes,' remember that it can take time for a relationship or situation to reveal its full potential to you. Even if a given situation doesn't work out in the long run, if you've entered into it properly, you'll likely come to see the value and beauty of the experience, and to apply that to your future endeavors.

Remember, we have so many lost souls in this world. It's such a beautiful thing to have people like you in the world, who are designed to tell us which way to go.

My dear Projector friend... Let go of all agendas... Beware of compromise...Most of all...

MANIFESTORS

So, you're a Manifestor, eh?

The Manifestor Flower Family comprises about 8% of the population. You are a member of a magnificent family.

You're one of the only Pure Doers in the world. In other words, you are here to start things, to initiate, to create... to get balls rolling, and then let others do the bulk of the work!

(Yup! Hard to believe—especially for those of you who're probably used to taking care of everyone, but true!)

Manifestors have been the monarchs or the high priests, ruling throughout history. This is because they have—because you have—a special and rare gift: **the ability to initiate action and have a very big impact on others.**

Manifestors can be independent... and free... in a way that others just can't, and have historically gained a lot of power. (Especially Manifestor men. I imagine Manifestor women—or people with qualities that have been associated with 'femininity'—have historically been quite oppressed.)

The Manifestors of today aren't like the Manifestors of the past. At least the role you're meant to play is in some ways different. Though you're certainly here to have a big impact, and to be empowered, you're not necessarily here to be a dominant force, or have a lot of power over other people... or to be stuck in one place with a heavy and relentless load of responsibilities. That's not what it's about for you this time around.

This time around, you're here to be FREE! You're here to be a glorious manifestation of Freedom, and to inspire Freedom in others.

Surrender

Whenever we're looking at any of the Types, we're looking at a kind of surrender. Generators are here to surrender to the NOW. Projectors are here to surrender to the OTHER. Reflectors are here to surrender to EXISTENCE itself.

Manifestors like you... are here to surrender to... FREEDOM!

One of the main things you're here to experience in this lifetime is *a deep sense of Peace*... which comes from your being free to do your thing, free to be YOU... without the people around you resisting, or controlling, or manipulating, or overwhelming, or violating you and your beautiful integrity.

Here's the thing...

You can't do any of this, you can't be the transformative and influential force on the planet you're meant to be, at least not in a way that makes you happy, as long as your mind is making your decisions for you. As long as you're waiting for things to happen, waiting to be initiated or given permission to act by someone 'out there.' Waiting for someone else to show you how to do something, to give you a template for life or work to safely follow, is not your way. This is where the "Manifestor" part comes in.

The BIG Irony

Most of us are conditioned to be whatever we're not.

Since most people on the planet aren't Manifestors, most of us are conditioned to be Manifestors. We're told "Just Do It." Think NIKE commercial. This idea of "Pull yourself up by your bootstraps and go make something of yourself" kind of implies that we all need to suck it up and just go out there and make it happen.

Especially in the West we are taught to be assertive, go out there and "Get 'em, Tiger!" Basically, "Go be a Manifestor!"

Most of us aren't really built to do that. Most of us are designed to come alive in response to life, to environments, to relationships, or to what people like **you** initiate. It's a very different process.

For a lot of us non-Manifestors, our Human Design experiment is all about letting go of that Western manifestation-obsessed conditioning, and learning how to live from a more responsive place.

We need to stop going out and pursuing or initiating things until we're blue in the face and burned out in the body.

THE EVEN BIGGER IRONY

You'd think, given the conditioning tendencies of the Western culture, that this world would be the perfect and most friendly place to grow up as a Manifestor.

Right? Not so.

Ironically, Manifestors are the only people around who are usually conditioned NOT to be Manifestors!

How unfair is that?!

It's like we live in this world of responsive beings who are taught to value the art of manifestation... but they're not Manifestors! They're not built to go around and make things happen in that way. Their auras, their ways of coming alive and becoming genuinely motivated are different.

Even though most of us Westerners think we should be Manifestors, and even though we totally idealize the process of manifestation, when it actually comes down to it, we have no idea how to see, support or handle people who are actually capable of pure manifestation. We have no clue!

When we're confronted with people like you, who were born to experience and express a profound level of personal freedom and independence in their lives, who were designed to have a big energetic impact... we can freak out. Usually we freak out unconsciously, because none of this is conscious. It's all happening beneath the surface.

THINK ABOUT IT

Most Manifestors like you are raised to be Generators. You're taught to wait for life to come to you, to wait for opportunities that you can respond to, instead of just going out there and initiating, just going out there and making something happen—no matter what anyone else is doing.

But you're not supposed to wait for life. You're supposed to go out there and make something happen. It doesn't matter whether that something is big or small, obvious or subtle, concrete or energetic.

You've come to this planet in order to start a fabulous ball rolling—a ball that has an impact, and ideally, a ball that'll inspire genuinely enthusiastic responses in other people (or beings), so that they can keep that ball merrily rolling along... while you take a little vacation!

This is an important point. If you get a ball rolling, it doesn't mean you've got to stick it out to the end, or accompany that ball to its ultimate destination. We actually don't want you to get stuck in the maintenance department forever (not unless you feel really free and happy doing that).

Generally speaking, Manifestors aren't here to maintain, maintain and maintain. They're here to give birth! To catalyze, to spark, to sprint... and then, to sip on a Piña Colada.

Being a Manifestor Child

Let's explore how it might feel to be a little Manifestor kid growing up in a world of responders who are trying to be Manifestors, but are actually terrified of that energy!

It's not a stretch to imagine how easy it could be for a Manifestor child to be misunderstood.

Think about it. You were born with this innate (not necessarily mental) 'knowing' of what you wanted to do... of what you were capable of. Going for it would have come extremely naturally to you.

What might *not* have come so naturally to you would be **to wait for permission** to do what you wanted to do.

Many of you, (especially those born into girl bodies) have had politeness, conscientiousness and selflessness drilled into you rather early on.

That said, before those 'good kid' conditioning forces really kicked in, I wouldn't be surprised if you were also one of those kids who—if you wanted to go outside and run through the forest—would just go out the door and head towards the forest! You wouldn't naturally think of asking for permission. You knew what you wanted. You knew what you were capable of. You couldn't see a problem.

Now maybe you never did that. Maybe it was never safe enough for you to engage your bold and brave nature in that way. If you are a Manifestor, however, that would have been your natural inclination... To you, it would be hard to see a problem with that inclination.

Unfortunately, it's likely that at least for a few of the people around you, there *was* a problem. These people were likely the ones who were in charge—whether they were your parents, teachers, older siblings, nannies, or caretakers. The likelihood that at least some of the 'authorities' of your youth experienced your natural strength, power and independence as a problem... well, THAT was very likely a problem for you.

Of course, I'm only speaking in generalities now about your Flower Family. Every Manifestor is unique. Your gifts are unique. Your sensitivities are unique, and your personal story is unique. As always, take what fits and leave the rest. I don't know what it was like to grow up as you, or what kind of a family and support system you were surrounded by.

My guess is that, whether or not your significant caretakers did the best job of raising you, they probably loved you, and genuinely tried to give you the kind of childhood they thought you needed and deserved. It's possible you were blessed with magnificent parents.

But even fabulous parents can have trouble understanding, raising and liberating Manifestor children.

The Parents (Caretakers) of Manifestors

Parents of Manifestors are often unsettled by their child's behaviors—by the fact that their Manifestor children don't seem to need them in the same way other kids need their parents.

It's also very possible that your parents or caretakers, not knowing how you operated, not knowing what a powerful and self-starting being you were, could have worried about you. If your parents had any insecurities, fears of the unknown, or fears of losing control, then they could have been quite threatened by you. I mean; a child who can't be controlled or tamed? In our world? That's a scary possibility, on many levels.

Depending on your own background, you could have been met by a whole continuum of responses to your natural inclination towards freedom.

A response could have been as innocent as, "Hey, that kid just goes out into the forest without asking permission. We've got to harness that kid. We've got to teach them how to survive in this world, how to stay safe. How to be a polite, good child, who is well-liked and won't get into any trouble."

Or, a response could have been quite oppressive (even if unconscious), like, "That kid is WAY too powerful. We need to tame this thing, to force it into obedience. If we don't, this kid might destroy, overpower, or outshine something or someone... even me!"

The extent to which your parents (caregivers) tried to control you would have depended on their own state of psychological and spiritual health. It would have depended on their own relationship to the power and courage that existed inside of them. It would have depended on their own temperament, and the chemistry between you.

Of course, it wouldn't have been all bad for you to learn how to get along in this world, how to be polite enough to be able to do your thing. I'll tell you in a bit just how important it is for someone with your kind of power to learn how to be polite.

In the end, you didn't come to this world to be controlled. You aren't here to be controlled now either.

You were put on this planet to experience freedom, to create your life and to make really cool things happen.

You were put on this planet to experience the PEACE that comes when you can pursue your heart's dreams and go on your creative adventures in the way that suits you best, without resistance from your environment.

ANGER (reactive or repressed)
It's a Theme...

In fact, nothing makes a Manifestor angrier—or feel more powerless—than being or feeling controlled, or blocked. Than feeling like their freedom to act and move and do as they wish is somehow being impinged upon.

In traditional Human Design circles, it is said that Manifestors, when they feel controlled, react with extreme amounts of anger and rebellion. Perhaps this was your experience growing up. Perhaps you had a temper, and it came out often.

For those of you who are females and Manifestors, most cultures don't look kindly upon girls who feel and express anger freely.

Whether or not you've preferred to avoid conflict, or have had the innate capacity for handling it, you probably didn't get to enjoy or embrace the art of confrontation all that much. (Or if you did, I wouldn't be surprised if you were made to feel guilty or 'bad' about that.)

(I'll be sharing more about the state of your Solar Plexus, your Emotional Center, during the next section of the Workbook. Whether you were designed to have an Open and receptive emotional system, or a Defined and consistent one, would have definitely impacted your relationship to your own anger, and to the anger of others.)

For now, what matters is that you have some compassion for yourself—whether you ended up expressing a lot of disapproved-of anger, and then feeling really guilty or ashamed because of that... or whether you repressed your anger, and turned it destructively inwards against yourself, and felt ashamed about that!

(An extra anger-related note: if you've managed to release some anger in your life, I want to say that this is actually a really good thing. If you haven't, I want to encourage you to open up and give yourself permission to feel and express it some more.

Of course, this doesn't mean it's not ultimately a part of your spiritual path to learn how to harness and channel that potent energy in ever-more life-enhancing ways. I'd just be relieved to know that your anger— your life force—has had at least some room for expression! Without that magical fuel, you're going to suffer. The world is going to miss out on what you're capable of!)

The Temptation to Give Up... or to Wait...

One thing that many Manifestors, especially girls or those brought up in hierarchical family or cultural systems, learn to do early on, is to suppress their power.

Even if on the outside, they're still kicking and screaming, deep down, they're saying to themselves, "It's just not worth it!" They're saying, "This world can't handle me. I'm just too much."

They give up on their Manifesting birthright, and they resign themselves to waiting. Waiting for their life to happen. Waiting for the approval of others. Waiting for the permission to be themselves to come. Which rarely comes.

Some Manifestors (who refuse to be suppressed) learn to live a double life.

Perhaps this has happened for you.

Maybe there's been something you've just had to do, even though the world was putting up loads of resistance. Maybe, if you knew you would never get the approval or encouragement you wanted, you just went ahead and did it. It was your little secret. Maybe you have had—or still have—a secret life. Or maybe you learned to keep your dreams and manifestation fantasies locked away in a diary. Or maybe, because your dreams were forced underground, they became distorted. And a healthy dream of freedom turned into a destructive form of recklessness, or self-loathing.

Reclaiming Your Inner Partner

C.G. Jung coined the terms "Animus" and "Anima" to refer to the masculine energies within women, and the feminine energies within men. Regardless of your body's assigned gender or how you identify, it can be useful to explore the possibility of an archetypal Inner Partner that exists inside of you. The role of such an Inner Partner is to help you become a whole being, able to honor your sensitivity, trust in your authority and celebrate your multi-faceted nature.

As a Manifestor, it is especially important that you get to know, embrace and cultivate a strong Inner Partner. This world needs you to fully embrace your whole self, so that what you initiate on this planet makes room for all of the beautiful, vulnerable, empowering, receptive, creative, dynamic, still and magnificent aspects of all beings.

You Are Designed to Make an Impact

As a Manifestor Flower, you are here to make an impact. You just are. You are here, simply by being yourself, to let others know that it is safe for them to be big and bold and free and unapologetically themselves.

It is very possible, that even if you tried very hard to repress your Manifestor self, you still ended up acting like a Manifestor ... without even realizing it!

Unconsciously, you could have just gone ahead and done your thing, not realizing that this might have been impacting the people around you.

In at least some areas of your life, you're probably still doing this.

One way to know if or when you're doing it is to simply look out and notice how others are responding to you.

If you feel like you're getting resistance from people, and their resistance confuses you, chances are you're doing it.

You're just moving ahead, doing your thing, without checking in to see how your actions or decisions are impacting the people around you. Without even realizing that your actions and decisions have the possibility of impacting people.

You may have absolutely no idea just how visible and influential you are.

Your Manifestor Strategy
The Art of Informing

One thing that Manifestor Flowers tend to do is get into a creative groove and not ask for help. They just go ahead and do their thing. They tend not to delegate. They "drive without honking."

This is where the Strategy—or the healthy growth path—of the Manifestor Flower comes in.

The trick is to learn how to honk... To honk is to INFORM, to fill people in on what you're up to.

I know it seems simple, and perhaps silly, but the more you learn how to do this, the more you'll be able to live your life with as little resistance as possible.

(Remember, the less resistance from the outer world you experience, the more FREEDOM and PEACE you get to experience! Ahhhhh....)

One interesting thing about the Manifestor Flower Strategy—something that makes it totally different from the strategies of the other flower families, is that it has to be learned!

The art of INFORMING doesn't come naturally. (Although I will say that I've noticed that women Manifestors tend to be better at this than men, likely because of the conditioning women receive to be good communicators, and to be more tuned into the needs of others.)

INFORMING DOES NOT MEAN ASKING FOR PERMISSION!

This is so important that I want to be sure I'm being clear here. **Learning how to inform others is not the same thing as asking for permission.**

All I'm encouraging you to do is to keep people posted—either once you've already made a decision, or while you're in the process of making a decision that might have an impact on someone.

Actually, learning how to ask for permission is super important for young Manifestors. When you as a Manifestor child learn how to ask for permission, what you're really learning is how to reduce resistance in your outer environment, so you can 'do your thing' as freely as possible. Asking for permission has the potential to buy you some freedom from the very parents (or people) who would otherwise try to control you.

When you as a child ask for permission, what you're really doing is learning how to put your parent (or teacher, or nanny, or big brother) at ease. You're showing them that they are respected, and that you can be trusted (even though deep down, you kind of know you don't really need anyone's permission anyway!)

When you're an adult, it's just about letting people know what you've decided you're going to do, once you've made your decision. Or like I said, keeping people posted on your process.

This applies to the seemingly smallest things, like saying "excuse me" when passing someone by in the grocery store, or when you're getting up to go to another room to do something, or when you notice that the garbage is full and you're taking it out, or that you're out of shampoo and are going to the store to pick some up.

This also applies to the bigger things, like letting your colleagues and friends know you've decided to leave the city where you're living, or that you've decided to go back to school, or to have a child, or…

A SIMPLE EXAMPLE

My husband Kim is a Manifestor Flower, from Denmark, so he's received his own unique kind of conditioning.

He—also like you—is much more than simply a "Manifestor." (Our designs are full of complexities, and Type is just one aspect!)

Still, I'd like to share a little snippet from our life, just to give you an example of how learning this healthy growth pattern, this Strategy of informing, can be so helpful for a Manifestor Flower in the context of a relationship.

(Also, notice that what Kim used to do isn't that atypical for men—who in many patriarchal cultures are more conditioned to act like somewhat-oblivious Manifestors than women are.)

Before either of us knew anything about Human Design, we used to get into these seemingly ridiculous, but very annoying situations. We'd be hanging out together, and then he'd get up, walk out the door and go into his office and work. Without a word.

At first, I'd be fine, thinking maybe he went to get something and would come back. As more time passed, I'd start to wonder. Was he going to come back? What was he doing? How long would it take? Should I start doing something else, or just wait for him? The more time passed, the more frustrated I found myself getting. By the time we reconnected, I'd be furious, and he'd be completely confused and feel totally unfairly accused.

Very likely, if he just told me where he was going and why, I'd be totally fine with it. He didn't even think to tell me; it just didn't occur to him. He did what he did, and that's the Manifestor's downfall.

That's why they have to learn how to inform.

Manifestors Truly Make an Impact

Whether or not you do the kind of thing that Kim used to do doesn't matter.

What you really have to understand is that (even if you don't think that you do, even if you feel invisible, even if you've been conditioned to think that you don't matter), you actually have a very big impact on people.

You just do.
It matters whether you're in the room or not. You matter.
A lot!

So a huge part of your learning process, or experiment, is first and foremost acknowledging that you make a difference. You're actually designed to have an influence.

There's nothing you can do about this, and that's a very good thing.

Hiding isn't really an option for you, even if you have yourself convinced that it is.

Another part of your experiment is to slow down enough to notice who you're having an impact on at any given moment, and how you're impacting them.

It's Not Just About Informing
It's About GATHERING!

From following my husband Kim's blossoming process (and the growth of my clients who belong to the Manifestor Flower Family), I've also learned that as important as informing is, GATHERING information is equally important!

Remember, you're here to initiate things, to have an impact on others. Informing people who are likely to be affected by what you're doing is a way of showing them respect.

It's also your way of prepping them, so that they're not shocked by your actions! What you end up doing in the world, the mark you make, may be provocative and bold, or surprising.

What you create may even make some people feel (healthfully) uncomfortable... or stretched.

That can be a very good thing. Something that we want!

What we don't want is you shocking the people that you need to support you in your manifestation!

When your support system is shocked, or too much in the dark, it won't be able to support you. In fact, it will resist you.

Remember, what you want more than anything else is freedom to do your thing, without being blocked at every corner.

You inform to reduce resistance, to make sure that the door that you're going to walk through is actually open. ('Cause you're going to walk through it regardless! It'll just feel a heck of a lot better if it's open.)

You LISTEN to reduce resistance. You do your research. You let the people—who will be most impacted by whatever your heart wants to do—speak.

 ## Helpful Questions to Ask Yourself

- Who are the people I'm about to influence?

- What are their needs, their fears, their concerns?

- Where are they open?

- Where are they shutting down in my presence?

- Do they seem to want my impact, my inspiration, my initiation? Or are they resisting me?

- Are these really the people I want to be working with?

- Is this really the environment, the community, I feel most inspired to impact?

It is so important that you give yourself plenty of time to do your research, to listen listen listen... before you act.

Every time you connect with someone, every time you enter a new environment, you are gathering information.

You are making sure that you're informed. You are finding out if this is a place for you to make a difference.

The more informed you are, the better you'll be at informing.

Again, this isn't about getting permission or approval. It's about being smart, reducing resistance inside and out. It's about paving a golden, welcoming path for your lovely self, so that you not only have a wonderful impact, but so that you can experience a deep sense of peace.

A Bit of Human Design Controversy

This may be controversial, from a pure Human Design perspective, but sometimes I think Manifestor Flowers and Projector Flowers have a lot more in common than one might think.

In a way, even though Manifestors can initiate, they need to be *energetically welcomed* first... which at least on a subtle level, can feel a whole lot like being recognized and invited in.

I've watched so many Manifestors suffer because they've been trying to initiate people and projects (with the best of intentions), without an energetic invitation.

It's like they're beating their well-meaning heads and sensitive creative hearts against the wall.

That's the other main reason why gathering information and listening on a deeply intuitive level can be so important for you.

You want to be able to tune into the people around you, to see if they actually are capable of saying 'yes' to what you're bringing.

Just like a Projector isn't designed to be seen or recognized by everyone, or to do everything, you're not necessarily designed to initiate everyone, or to start everything.

That's where the deep listening comes in... both within and without.

Again. This "informing" business isn't necessarily a Strategy that's going to come naturally to you. It's one you have to learn. For some Manifesting Flowers, it's actually really hard to learn. It may be especially challenging for you if your first instinct is to just go and do something, and to do it on your own, without asking for any help. As counter-intuitive as informing might feel, this strategy is one that can save you so much headache.

It's really powerful to experiment with this...

For many Manifestors who have learned to hold back their power, simply learning to discern between informing and asking for permission is HUGE.

How to stand strong in what you're doing, while still including others in the process...

This is a spiritual practice of self-assertion, of transparency, of respect for yourself and others at the same time.

Your Open Sacral Center

Another thing you have in common with the non-Generator Flowers is the Open state of your Sacral Center.

This means that even though you're here to make a difference, and you've got energy to really go for it, you are also here to have a deeply relaxing life, and to do what you truly love—which is sometimes to kick back and do nothing.

When you can resist the impulse to overload yourself with work, when you know when it's time to take a break, recharge and let someone else do the maintenance jobs, you can truly become an expert in (and witness to) the very nature of energy itself—its patterns, its movements, its ebbs and flows.

Another part of your process is to learn how to regularly 'unhook' from the world, to make sure that you always take time to nurture and re-set your body. The more you do that, the better you'll get not just at reading and tracking the energy of others, but knowing how to initiate that energy, and when it's time to inspire action in people. You'll also gather the energy and courage it often requires to go against the mainstream, to break through "business as usual," and bring something new into the world!

You're here to work in bursts, and to initiate the workers of the world (i.e. Generator Flowers) who are designed to sustain a consistent level of energy over time.

It's best to rest and relax during the natural pauses instead of fretting over whether a new period of productivity will come, because it will!

One of the biggest lessons for people with Open Sacrals—and We-oriented people who are constantly 'on duty'—is limit-setting.

You can't always depend on your own energy to show up whenever you want it to, so you must learn how to say 'no,' take breaks, and set boundaries. You must learn to read your body and emotions really well. The best time to take action is when you feel recharged, peaceful, at ease, and in touch with a genuine rush of energy pulling you in a direction. When you have that experience, don't wait. Get into that flow. Trust it. The Universe will happily join your team so you don't have to do the rest all by yourself.

As you become deeply attuned to the ebbs and flow of your own energy, and as you learn to respect your own boundaries and engage in those activities that excite you most, you can be wonderfully supportive to people who struggle with healthy limit-setting.

Your Manifesting Flower Aura

When official Human Design analysts talk about the Manifestor Aura, they describe it as closed, even repelling.

While this may be true in some cases, I don't necessarily see it that way.

Some of the juiciest and most attractive flowers I know belong to the Manifesting Family. I wouldn't be married to one if that weren't the case!

I prefer to say that your beautiful, intelligent, wisely selective Aura has been perfectly designed to support and protect your love of freedom.

In no way does that mean that you can't have wonderful, loving, long-lasting and intimate relationships. Or that you're can't let anyone in. Of course, you can!

In some ways, Manifestor Flowers need people in their lives as much—if not more—than most.

Your impactful Life Purpose requires that you have enthusiastic life collaborators. These people will welcome your impact. They will ultimately provide you with much of the energy you need to manifest what you're here to manifest in this world, and keep it going.

At the same time, Manifestor Flowers do seem to have a unique ability to select (though not always consciously) 'who gets in there' and who stays at a distance.

As a Manifestor, you may not have the kind of natural, easy way of connecting to other people and their auras, as others might.

The experience of being bound to someone, or super attached, may not come as easily to you as it might to a Generator Flower, whose Aura is open and enveloping, or to a Projector, whose Aura is deep and penetrating. Your Aura isn't built to be easily penetrated. (Thank the Lord!)

It's possible that there are more people actually wanting to reach out and connect with you than you realize. It's also possible that as much as they'd love to 'get in there' with you, they don't know how. They may not be able to sense whether you need them or not, whether you care about them or not, whether you respect them or not, whether you want their involvement or not.

This may be because they can't easily feel into you, like they can feel into other people.

The Essence of the Manifestor Flower's Spirituality
Manifestors are here to surrender to Freedom.

And now, a beautiful quote from Richard Rudd's article "The 4 Paths of Surrender":

"The more deeply a manifestor rests in their true nature, the more powerful their urge to be free becomes. By design, manifestors are archetypes of pure freedom, even though within the maya, this is an illusion. For a manifestor, freedom comes before everything, even before love. The propaganda of manifestors brings us the concept of freewill. This is the 'You create your own Reality' propaganda. This is 'we are the planet of choice'. Spiritually speaking, this is symbolised by the path of Yoga—a proactive path towards awakening (this is 'Yoga' as a teaching rather than the western body-centred discipline). When a manifestor comes to Human Design, they actually appear to make their awakening happen. Given the power of their conditioning, this may not be as easy as it sounds."

YOU MIGHT NEED TO WORK A BIT HARDER TO PUT (SOME) PEOPLE AT EASE

Remember, there are only 8% of Manifestors on the planet. While that's a lot of people, it's not a huge percentage of the population.

People aren't always used to encountering people like you. Your independent Aura, your whole way of being, can throw them off at first. You might seem less predictable to them, because you're not always looking for approval or agreement, or a "relational go ahead" to do what you want to do.

Watching you 'just do what you do' can make some people—who aren't able to live that way—feel insecure.

Even though you of course need people in your life, you may not necessarily need them in the way they're accustomed to being needed.

Privacy, for example, is so important to you—just as being self-reliant and self-empowered is. You can do many things without relying on others, and that's wonderful.

Remember, you're just being yourself here, and there's nothing to change about this. It's an aspect of your nature that needs to be embraced.

It's just good to become aware of, so that you can gain understanding and compassion for the people in your life—if they occasionally feel insecure, or unsure of how to reach you.

Even more importantly, you can gain compassion for yourself when it comes to relationship—if you don't always know how to let people in, or if it takes a bit of time.

Loving relationships are such wonderful places for you to learn and develop. So much joy and peace are to be found there.

Love requires that you open the door and let someone in.

A healthy relationship for you also requires that your intimate friends and partners respect and understand your deep need for freedom.

The perfect balance of INTIMACY and FREEDOM is just what your soul longs for the most!

REFLECTORS

You Are a Rare & Wondrous Gem!

Your blossoming process is designed to be quite different from most people's. If there have been times in your life when it's felt hard to 'find your place' in the garden, or to avoid getting lost in the WE, then there are good reasons for that.

There are also many more reasons to rejoice... because you are a deeply open, receptive and creative being blessed with profoundly unusual gifts and a potential for SO MUCH wisdom.

My biggest invitation to you, at the get go, is to enter this exploratory journey with an open and curious mind. Please don't worry if you don't feel like you've got logical answers to all of your questions right away. Just take this moment as a marker, as the beginning of a journey. Trust that over time, whatever you need to know, you'll know. Whatever you need to experience, you'll experience. For you more than anyone, life is meant to be a journey, not a destination.

How You Know You're a Reflector

It is the unusual state of the Centers in your Blossoming Bodygraph that reveal your Type. You are a Reflector because ALL of your Centers are Open (white), flexible and receptive. They're like wide open windows through which you take in the world around you.

These Open Centers represent the places in life that you're designed to go to school, to learn, and to gather so much wisdom. The fact that all of them are Open says that LIFE ITSELF is your sacred school-ground.

The majority of people have at least two Defined Centers in their Bodygraph.

We call a Center 'Defined' when it is 'colored in.' The energy (or awareness or characteristics) associated with a Defined Center is designed to operate in a relatively consistent manner. When an aspect of your nature is consistent, it becomes a place that can be relied on or returned to during times of pressure or chaos. It becomes a natural reference point.

But you see, you don't have this kind of consistent, reliable 'Definition.'

All of your Centers are OPEN... which means they're continually receiving, listening, and taking in all that's around you—the questions, the thoughts, the feelings, the pressures, the fears, the frustrations, the stress, etc. They're always, at some level, under the influence.

How Unusual You Are

For every 100 people you meet, only one or two of those people belong to the Reflector Flower Family. On the one hand, you are extremely rare. On the other, you're not alone! (Given the fact that our world population is over 7 billion, there are millions of Reflectors like you.)

That said, it's still important to understand that you are designed to blossom and grow very differently than most people in the world, especially when it comes to making decisions that are healthy for you.

You are very sensitive and open to your environment, so you can experience a lot of confusion when trying to figure out who and what is best for you. You can easily get way too busy up in that receptive mind of yours, spending way too much of your time trying to make sense of everything, trying to find something— anything—to hold onto.

But 'holding on' isn't what your life is about.

In a way, we could say that you're here to take everything in, without identifying with any of it.

It's actually when you identify with what comes in that you run into trouble. During those vulnerable moments when you forget that you're not here to own and attach, but instead, to reflect and release.

When You Reflect

When you reflect, you don't reflect one Center and its characteristics. You reflect the whole 'body' of people, the whole 'body' of your environment.

When, for example, child Reflectors go to a highly dysfunctional school, and they aren't receiving the kind of love and support they need to be true to themselves, they can end up acting out in ways that make it seem like THEY are the problem.

When that's not the case at all. They're just feeling the undercurrent of dysfunction in their environment; they're feeling the rebellion stirring beneath the surface in the other children. They're acting it out. Maybe even getting punished for it, but the 'rebellion' is not really theirs.

These Reflector children become unconsciously caught in an unfortunate collective current, and end up channeling the energy like an amplified mirror of what's not right.

The truth is that your ability to reflect the whole of your relational and physical environments is one of your greatest strengths. When you understand it, and hold it as a strength, you can experience such relief, and begin to see your entire life (especially the more difficult aspects) in a whole other, much more empowering light.

For you, simply understanding that you're designed to hold up a mirror to the world, that you're unusually and mystically gifted, that you have a limitless capacity for wisdom, that you're not supposed to be like everyone else, that your path is meant to crystallize over time, (which is why slooooowing down and relaxing is so important for you when it comes to making decisions) ... can be so helpful.

The Moon is Your Friend, Guide and Role Model

According to Human Design, the majority of the people on the planet (98%-ish) take their energy from the sun, and from each other.

You're designed to take your life force from the totality of existence, not just from individuals.

You are designed to be driven by the Moon, in fact. Not by the Sun and Earth like so many others.

You have a deep and special connection with the Moon, in fact. We could even say that you are here to represent the Moon, to ground her powers and light here on Earth. You are here to bring the gift of non-attached reflective light to the rest of us. Also like the Moon, you are as powerful and resilient as you are delicate and vulnerable.

One of the great keys to your living a happy life, is to maintain a sense of wonder, of awe.

You Belong at the Heart of Life

If we were to think of the other Types (or Flower Families) as points of a triangle, you'd be smack dab in the middle of that triangle... reflecting its essence.

That's your place... to be in the middle. To be at the heart of a community. To be in a place where you can learn from everyone around you. To be someone who models what it is to live a life that isn't driven by morality or judgment, but by a deep appreciation for diversity.

If you were a member of a Soccer team, you'd be the goalkeeper. To play your role, you don't need to move around the field like everyone else. You don't have to obey all of the same rules as everyone else. In fact, your team needs you to be willing to operate under a different set of rules.

It's not just that you CAN do things that the other players can't (like using your hands), you MUST. Otherwise your team (humanity, the Garden!) is sure to lose.

A SWEET STORY ABOUT A LITTLE REFLECTOR BOY

A while back I heard a sweet story about a young Reflector, told by his mother. The family had been invited to a teacher-organized event for kids. During the event, a game of Musical Chairs took place. All of the kids were lined up around the circle of chairs. This little Reflector sat off in the corner, watching the whole thing unfold. The teacher went over to him and asked where he'd like to sit, behind which chair, and he said, "in the middle."

While the music played, and all of the other kids played the game and circled their way around the chairs, he sat smack dab in the middle of the circle, watching the whole thing and happy as a clam.

This is a real-life, and oh-so-classic Reflector image.

You are like this little child. You are here to be in the middle of it all, to take it all in, and to reflect it all back. At the same time, you're not here to be playing the game in the same way everyone else is.

In fact, you're not here to play games at all. You're here to feel into them, witness them, penetrate into the essence of them... and help the players actually understand what they're doing, and whether the game is worth playing in the first place! (Lord knows we humans play more than our share of not-so-healthy games!)

GET THOSE REFLECTOR KIDS OUT OF THE HOUSE!

If you know or care for a Reflector child, see if (in addition to giving them lots of alone and relaxation time!), you can get them out of the house. Give them access to the world and the community. Let them get absorbed in it all. Know that as they learn how to feel their world, they'll be better and better able to recognize who they are.

Your Central Inquiry... and Purpose

Although you're a deeply wise observer of life, and quite gifted when it comes to reading people, you're not here to devote your life to understanding and guiding others, like a Projector.

You're not here to figure out who you are, like a Generator.

Or to figure out how to make the biggest impact, like a Manifestor.

The big central question for you is, "What or who am I today?"

For you, every day is different. Every day is a new experience, and not just a new experience of your surroundings, but of yourself.

It's not like you're here to find one role to play out in this life. It's not like your purpose is to be a super personally-driven over-achiever.

You are here to see where we're all going, and where we're coming from. To be the eyes of the world. To see the whole picture. The forest through the trees.

If anything, your flower is built to be a guardian of humanity—to act like a sacred sign post, letting the people around you know whether they're headed in the right direction, or not.

You can think of yourself like a potent radar screen, or a spotlight—able to reflect everything around you with perfect equanimity.

You have a gift for taking in everything around you, and then noticing when something unusual appears... something exciting, different... surprising!

As Close to the Divine that We Humans Get!

Ra Uru Hu, the originator of Human Design, was quite an amazing man. He also happened to be a potent Manifestor, and a real character—blessed with a good dose of humor and sarcasm (i.e. he used to call himself a "Depressed Buddhist").

When asked to describe the ideal Design, he used to say, "a Design that's TOTALLY Open!" No activations at all. No Open Centers. No hanging gates. Just pure white, pure Openness. He said, being totally Open was like being "one with the Gods."

He also joked that if "the Gods" had a bad meal, this person would get gas! Now of course, you're not that Open, and you're anything but a blank slate.

But there's something profound about his little joke, especially for someone like you.

You see, you *are* more Open than most people on the planet.

In a way, you are more connected to what Ra calls 'the Gods'—or the ALL, or Oneness, or the GREAT Garden.

How you're doing—at some level—is always going to be reflecting of how we're all doing. Like that gloriously sensitive, beautiful Canary bird—who thrives best in a thriving environment, and doesn't do nearly so well when in a toxic coal mine.

This can be a wonderful thing for you to hold in your awareness, when you think about yourself... and your life, and what's going on inside of that life.

With this knowledge, you don't have to take every little state you find yourself in so personally.

You can begin to use your current state as a potent way of reading your environment's weather, and of sensing how humanity is doing as a whole.

Born to Be Conditioned (in a good way!)

Most people on the planet are designed to have aspects of our nature that are always 'turned on'—always transmitting something out into the world. Our big challenge is to come to grips with who we are, and to learn how to live our lives without giving in to the power of conditioning.

As a Reflector, you were born to be conditioned, and in a very real way.

You weren't born with a fixed imprint, or with a fixed life force that gives you a fixed notion of where or what you should be. Not at all.

You were born to take in the world... to be influenced...
To reflect back to the rest of us what you've sampled.

You're here to be the ultimate judge of whether the community, the organization, the group, the family, the planet ... is healthy, or not.

You have the potential to see everything that is really happening in a way that no one else can. You have an opportunity for a mystical life that most people on the planet may never experience.

THIS DOESN'T MEAN YOU ARE SELF- or STRUCTURE-LESS!

This doesn't mean that you have no self! You do! You have a self. You can be yourself. You can feel like and act as yourself. You can learn how to trust yourself, and how to live in integrity with yourself.

The only real difference here is that your "self" is designed to reveal itself through a cyclical pattern, through a movement... a journey.

You have an inherent structure, but it's a moving one. That's your nature... to be moving, cycling, and spiraling through life.

Your Reflector Flower Aura

Let's take a moment to look at the REFLECTOR Aura.

From a Human Design perspective, your Aura is a personal electromagnetic signature that tells every living thing around you what you're all about. (It is said that your Aura extends up to 3 meters around the entire circumference of your body.)

Another way to think about your Aura is the 'vibe' that you give off. When someone meets you, they get a 'read' on you through your Aura. Similarly, when you meet someone, you get a 'read' on them through their Aura.

The Reflector Aura is an amazing thing.

Some call it a 'skimming' Aura... because it skims the surface of everyone and everything it encounters. It takes in the energy at the surface, continually tasting and reading others.

Some call it a TEFLON aura, because even though it's taking people in, nothing really sticks.

All Types, or Flower Families, have a kind of Aura, and all Auras are designed perfectly for the Type.

Since Projectors need others to live out their Life Purpose, they have particularly attractive and penetrating Auras that help them hone in on their 'right people.'

Since Generators need to live from a place of RESPONSE, they have open and enveloping Auras that bring lots of people and opportunities into their lives, so that they have plenty to respond to.

Since Manifestors need to be free to live independent and impactful lives, they have freedom-protecting Auras that let people in selectively so that they can do their own thing, without too much interference, and have their biggest impact.

YOUR AURA IS PARADOXICAL

On the one hand, your Aura is designed to allow you to take absolutely everything and everyone in, just absorbing everything around you. It even magnifies all that's around you, so that you can see it more clearly.

On the other hand, (when it's working properly), it protects you from taking things in too deeply. Your Aura contains intrinsic safeguards that protect you from over-identifying with incoming energies, and from being continuously overwhelmed by the emotions and pressures of the world.

As I mentioned at the beginning of the Workbook/Course, Ammaji, the hugging guru, can be so open to the people she interacts with, just taking it all in, and still remain protected. This is the potential of your Aura.

THE ART OF SAMPLING

Like Ammaji, your Aura allows you to 'sample' another person, without taking them in too deeply.

You do this, just naturally, without thinking about it.

One reason you do this (albeit unconscious) is to sense whether a person is ready to wake up and full-heartedly express their uniqueness in the world, or whether they're not ready to wake up.

Think of flat stones in a lake, and how they can bounce across a lake when thrown a particular way.

In this metaphor, the water is the Reflector. The stone is the rest of us human beings.

At times, people may feel when they're around you like they can't totally 'get in there,' that they somehow slide off.

The truth is you are taking them in, absorbing them... just in a very different way than they're accustomed to be 'taken in.'

THE DANGER OF FLOODING

There are few things more important for you than getting plenty of time on your own.

If you're deprived of solitude, of "human influence-free time," you can feel like you're getting completely filled up with everyone and everything around you.

It can feel like you're being so totally conditioned that there's nothing left of you.

Think of it like a dresser drawer stuffed with clothes. At some point, if you keep stuffing, there's no room left—not even for a pair of underwear!

If you reach this point, you can go numb.

You can't feel anything. You can't do anything. You can't decide anything. The Reflector has left the building!

The good news is that it actually doesn't take much for you to empty out and re-ground again.

If you just separate for a while, if you just take a little space, your Teflon Aura will recover its slippery nature...

Allowing you...

To let it all go.

To empty out.

To release all of life's stickiness... (i.e. everyone else's feelings and thoughts and desires and wants and expectations and values... they'll all just slip happily off.)

You will return to Center.

Being in the World, but Not of It

It's so important that you don't try to make things stick, or get hard on yourself if you can't stick to something, or with someone, in the way society is often telling us we should all be able to—and want to—do.

It's so important that you can learn to celebrate this incredible ability you have to sample everything, to READ everything, but not swallow it whole... to be in the world, but not of it.

You need to give yourself ample opportunities to just step back and away from all of the dramas of the world... and not add anything.

Your life isn't about accumulating.

It's not about hunting and gathering identities, or accomplishments, or people, or anything.

It's about reflecting... and awakening and liberating...

It's about being an example of someone who has nothing to prove, nothing to defend...

You have such an amazing potential to wake up every day, completely open to the surprises the day has in store for you.

You have the potential to remain delightfully non-attached to things being a certain way... and to live free of agendas.

You can enjoy people for what they are, and become deeply selective about who you let in, and where you spend your time.

You can learn how to live with your Openness and sensitivities without necessarily feeling like there's anything you have to DO about it all.

You can learn how to just open up and allow energy to flow through you... even the emotional climate of a room, without identifying with it.

You are the key to a global consciousness... to a WE AWARENESS. Your job is simply to be open to what's passing through.

Like a radar, you can detect that magnificent blip on the screen, that something or someone who is different, or unusual, or surprisingly awake!

Your job is to recognize and shine a brilliant (Moon!) light on that one thing that's going to take all of us to the next level in our evolution.

To Be You, As a Child...

Think about what it must have been like for you as a child. Again, you were born with this paradoxical aura. On the one hand, you were designed to take absolutely everything and everyone in, just absorbing everything around you.

On the other hand, you didn't really take anyone in, at least not in the way the majority of your siblings and parents and cousins and friends probably did.

People could just slide off of you like stones skipping over the surface of the water.

This could have been particularly painful when you were little, especially if your parents, or significant caretakers, weren't able to intuitively understand your unique nature.

Your parents could have been deeply hurt or confused by you, because you didn't seem able to receive them in the way other children seemed to receive their parents.

They could have taken it very personally, that their child wasn't seeming to take them so personally!

It's also possible that you could have related to your mother and father more like archetypes of motherhood and fatherhood, than "Mom and Dad."

If you got the sense that this wasn't OK, you could have learned very early on to try to be someone you weren't, that you should relate differently to others and the world.

If you had this feeling, that you had to be and act like someone other than yourself just to be loved, just to keep the people in your life comfortable enough to nurture you, this could have left you with a very deep feeling of disappointment.

Your Reflector Flower Strategy
Your Healthy (Cyclical and Slow!) Growth Path

One of the most important things for you to understand, as a Reflector, is that you need TIME to process things…You need time to make decisions.

The most important decisions you will ever need to make are:

- Where you live

- Who you live with

- Where you work

- Who you work with

Your Strategy is all about waiting out what we call a LUNAR CYCLE. With anything important, any big decision like the ones listed above, the big invitation here is to give yourself PLENTY of time, no matter how that might feel to you, no matter what kind of a rush the world seems to be in, or your mind seems to be in.

For you, it's about giving yourself at least a month, a full lunar cycle, to get clear.

This may sound challenging and risky! I wouldn't be surprised if most of your life, you've been tempted to act spontaneously and quickly.

So many good things can come to you, if you allow yourself to wait…

Waiting Out the Moon Cycle

Once you've been presented with an opportunity, you need time. Lots of time—28/29 days at the least.
Remember, you are a Moon Flower Being!
You reflect the lunar cycle.

The moon moves very quickly. Every 29.5 days, it goes through all of the 64 gates in the Blossoming Bodygraph.

For you, there is a regular cycle of conditioning or influence that comes from the Moon, a particular pattern that has been set for you in your life.

Even though you're super Open (with all of your Centers undefined), there is an incredible consistency in your process.

As the Moon moves through the gates each month, a pattern emerges, and this pattern is repeated, month after month.

You can actually totally rely on this consistent pattern. This pattern is your Authority, as opposed to a particular place in your body (as is the case with most other Types).

It is through this repeating cycle that you can find yourself. That you can find your Truth.

THE MAGICAL GESTATION PROCESS

The very moment in time that you come in contact with an opportunity, or a big decision to make, marks the beginning of a journey.

As soon as this unique and potent moment in time occurs, you must wait.

This doesn't mean you do nothing as you wait!

Think of waiting like gestating.

Just because a woman is pregnant doesn't mean nothing is happening inside of her!

So much can happen during a month, both externally and internally.

Internally, you can trust that transformation is happening in the 'dark,' that clarity is slowly but surely finding its form.

Externally, there's so much you can do. You can try out different environments. You can talk to all kinds of people.

You can explore, sample and take in various possibilities within the arena of the decision you're making, without pressuring yourself to know anything for sure until you're good and ready.

GATHERING CLARITY OVER TIME

You are designed to GATHER clarity over time. Not to get a spontaneous knowing.

Not to feel something out emotionally as you move through your wave.

Not to do what your Will tells you to do, but to collect information from an open, curious place.

When you're making a decision, your perspective is built to change over time. It's actually supposed to keep changing.

While that change is taking place, your job is to hold a neutral, inquisitive and un-invested stance.

A Magnificent Mosaic

Think of your decision-making process like a flying together, a falling into place. One day you're seeing a situation from one perspective. The next day, from another. The next day from yet another.

Your clarity-finding process is like a magnificent mosaic... with each piece revealing itself, one by one.

Until eventually, all of the pieces fall into place, and you have an embodied sense of what's right for you.

As you can imagine, this way of finding your truth is anything but rational, logical or linear. It can certainly feel disconcerting, disorienting and scattered at times (especially if you don't understand how it works!).

If you're patient and trusting enough.... all of a sudden, you'll find that you've made it through the fog.

There you are, perfectly able to see the whole picture, in all of its splendid detail, knowing exactly who and what's right for you.

A METAMORPHOSIS

You can also think about your decision-making process as moving from life as a caterpillar to a butterfly.

You need time to dissolve into the chrysalis.

You need to surrender to a period of what may feel A LOT like chaos and confusion... so that all of the cells of your new life, your new reality, can reorganize themselves... and be transmuted into a new form.

When you emerge from your decision-making cocoon, you are brand new. Your life is regenerated.

It's Always Worth the Wait!

If you give into the pressure of our society, (which is all about quick action and instant gratification), you run the risk of making decisions pre-maturely.

When you make a decision before you're ready, it's like making a decision with only a few pieces of the puzzle in place.

It's not that this will be disastrous. No need to have any fear pictures here. (In the end, there are no mistakes. Only glorious learning opportunities!)

It's just that you're likely to feel more fulfilled—and less disappointed—if you don't rush into things when you're feeling pressured.

THE ART OF ACTIVE WAITING

I can imagine what you may be thinking.

"WHAT?! I'm supposed to wait at least a month before I make any big decisions? Are you ABSOLUTELY OUT OF YOUR MIND?! By the time I'm ready to say 'yes' to anything, the opportunity will be gone!"

If you are thinking this, then know that you're not the only Reflector who's ever had these thoughts!

I'm personally a believer in the experimental aspect of Human Design.

In the end, you're the only one who's going to know what works for you.

All I can do here is extend an invitation to try something out for a while—perhaps in relation to things that don't feel quite so risky at first. See what happens. (And remember, we're not talking about waiting a month to find out if you're meant to have lunch! We're talking about the bigger decisions in life.)

As with any experiment, you won't know if something is going to be helpful unless you try.

Worst case scenario: You learn how to cultivate the ability to breathe through the discomfort that can come with waiting.

Lord knows, as a human being living in a crazy world, knowing how to breathe through the discomfort of ANYTHING can come in handy.

While you're waiting…

DO A PRESSURE CHECK

Check your motivations.

- Are you afraid of missing out if you wait? Are you afraid someone might lose interest?

- Are you afraid someone might get angry?

- Are you afraid you won't be able to support yourself financially?

- Are you afraid you might lose your reputation?

- Are you afraid no other opportunity will come?

You get the idea.

Remind yourself... when it comes to the BIG THINGS in life... If something or someone is truly right for you, it (they) will wait for you to get clear.

DO A DEPENDENCY CHECK

Some Reflectors become quite dependent on people who introduce them to something that they love, or inspire a direction in their life that really resonates.

For you, learning how to graciously receive these kinds of life-changing gifts from others, without necessarily demanding that you hold onto these people no matter what, is important.

Of course, some gift-bringing people will belong in your life for a long long time.

Others are more like angels, here 'stop by' to point you in a direction, or to connect you with an aspect of yourself, or a passion, or a wonderful opportunity... and then go on their merry way.

DO A DISCERNMENT CHECK
WHAT AM I TRULY?
WHAT or WHO AM I JUST REFLECTING?

It can take time for you, and practice, to get to know the difference between the 'you' who is reflecting the people and environments around you (or the stars' movements in the sky), and the true 'you.'

Chances are, the aspects of you—feelings, thoughts or expressions—that seem to shift and change a lot, are reflections of the outer.

The aspects of you that are more consistent over time, that keep cycling back through, no matter where you are or who you're with, no matter what stage of your life you find yourself in, are more connected to your true nature.

Over time, you will come to be more and more familiar with yourself. Your personal style will shine through. You'll find your own way of dressing, your most fun and inspiring relationships, your favorite places, your most exciting passions, and your strongest values and beliefs...

All of this will lead to you finding your most fulfilling work in the world.

The Luxury (and Necessity!) of Solitude

It's super important you get time alone, in your own aura... time to shake off the world, to shake off the conditioning that you're exposed to on a daily basis.

Like a Projector, you need plenty of time to relax. Go to bed before you're super-exhausted.

When you're considering bringing someone closer in, notice how they interact with others. Notice what they bring out in others, in the environment they're in.

Chances are, if someone is manipulative, destructive or out of integrity anywhere, they'll bring those characteristics out in you—if you let them in too close.

Do what you can to make sure you're not always filled up by Auras of others. Go on a retreat whenever you can!

What to Do While You're Waiting for Your Clarity?
(...for your Truth to 'Flow into place'?)

The very first thing you can do while you're waiting is...

SEEK OUT AND TALK TO THE RIGHT PEOPLE!

Few things are more important in your life than having trustworthy advisors and friends—good listeners who really get you...

... and who can let you speak, so that you can hear your own truth emerge over time.

Make sure that your 'people'—your listeners—can be neutral and compassionate.

In other words, we don't want you talking to people who are super invested, opinionated, or unable to understand that your perspective is SUPPOSED to change over time.

We want your people to understand that you might talk to them one day about a given situation and be all excited about it, and another day and be all rational about it, and another day and be not interested in it at all...

That's just a natural and healthy part of your process.

We don't want your listeners looking for inconsistencies, or pointing out what you said last time, or getting frustrated and impatient with you for seemingly 'flip-flopping.'

We want them to be holding the vision of your spiraling and 'sampling' your way towards the truth. We want them to appreciate the way your magnificent clarity mosaic 'flies together' over time.

We also want your people to trust that you're actually getting somewhere, even when you're not quite sure that's happening yourself!

KEEP TALKING!

Don't just talk to your people about a given situation once.
Talk about it AGAIN.

KEEP TALKING and revisiting the situation throughout the month.

Remember, your clarity crystallizes as you listen to your shifting and changing thoughts, feelings and intuitive hits over time. Listen for the tone in your voice. If over time, you continue to hear a happiness, strength or conviction in your voice when you talk about something, that's a good sign.

You Need People to Live Out Your Purpose

Even though you will always need time to yourself, you can only play out your role in life if you join the world and become a part of your environment.

Reflectors like you aren't meant to live in caves, even if there are times you might prefer it!

You have the gift of knowing where we're all headed, and where we need to be going as a collective. You can't get yourself there, or get all of us there, on your own. You need workers around you, creative people who love what they do, in order to make the most of your innate sense of our shared healthy direction. You need people around you who can press the gas pedal, and people who know how to handle the energy required by the journey. You need the right collaborators, and the right environment.

Become an Expert RIGHT-ENVIRONMENT Finder!

Environment is everything for you... for so many reasons. The right environment will take you to your right people, and your right people will lead you to your right environments.

One of your most central (and fun) tasks is to find lots of places that make you come alive (i.e. places to shop, places to live, places to have tea or coffee, places to vacation, places to have deep conversations with friends, places to hike, etc.).

Remember, you're going to reflect and mirror everything and everyone that surrounds you.

Just like it is with people, if your surroundings don't feel good or right, then you're not going to feel right.

The opposite is true as well. If the environment you're in feels good, you're likely to feel good.

THE SURPRISING BENEFITS OF A STABLE ENVIRONMENT

Generally speaking, Reflectors like you tend to do well in stable environments, where people—most of the time—play by the rules. When you're in environments that are stable, you are free to scan the environments and the people in them. You can get to know your community or organization over a long period of time—month after month, Moon cycle after Moon cycle.

The better you know your community, the better able you'll be to serve it—whether it's through spotting those individuals who have great potential within it, or whether it's through guiding the community into its next, more healthy and vibrant evolutionary state.

Even though you are extremely rare and unique, you don't necessarily have to live or work in an environment that is chock full of 'freaks' (or alternative Types)!

We actually need you and your Reflector gifts in what we could call 'normal' environments.

In fact, we need Reflectors like you EVERYWHERE!

We need you spread across the globe, so you can liberate wonderful people that have been hidden in the masses, so that they can then set even more people free.

Getting into the Nitty Gritty Details
(An Option)

Along with waiting out the Moon Cycle, talking things out with people you trust, and practicing your environmental sensitivity muscles, there's something else you can do as a Reflector... if you feel called to do it.

It's to really delve deep into the details of your Design, and get a serious grasp of this Human Design system.

Some Reflectors find it very helpful to spend time and get very specific support in learning how their unique Designs are impacted by the Moon, the movement of the stars and neutrinos. By watching and feeling what happens inside of them as each Gate in their Design lights up, one day at a time, they begin to grasp their lives, and the pattern of their lives, without being overwhelmed or enslaved by the conditioning world.

A very simple description of what's happening when your Design 'lights up': as you can see in your Blossoming Bodygraph, all of your Centers are 'white' or Open. Your Bodygraph isn't all white! You've got lots going on. Coming out of most of your Centers are what we call Gates. Either they're Red (unconscious), Black (conscious), or striped (both). All of these colored-in Gates are aspects of your unique and multi-faceted Nature. They come alive at different times during the month, depending on what's going on in the stars, who you're with and where you are.

For Centers to become Defined, they need a bridge, or a Channel. A whole Channel is comprised of two opposing Gates that come together. You could say, all of your Gates are waiting to be met by their opposite Gate, so that they can come alive and find expression. As you move from day to day, different Channels are formed inside of your Design. Bridges between Centers are created, causing the Centers and their respective Channels to 'light up,' to come to life. Whenever this happens, you get a new flavor of life, a new perspective on a situation. Over time, your perspective gets increasingly deep, rich and clear.

Please know that not all Reflectors feel they need to get into this level of detail. You'll know if this kind of study is right for you if you continue to feel excited about this level of learning, and passionately pulled towards it.

Just know that learning to track the Moon's cycle, and the passage of time's particular impact on your own Design can be a bit technical, and can definitely have you spending a lot of time up in the Open Head and Ajna Centers of yours. This can be helpful for a period of time. Eventually, Human Design should have a relieving effect on your mind... and your practice should leave you feeling more relaxed, trusting and not feeling like you have to figure everything out all the time!

WHAT MATTERS MOST

Perhaps what matters most, is that each day during a 29-day period, a different aspect of yourself comes to life so that you can feel it... in relation to a particular decision.

Each day, an awakening aspect of yourself, will have its own flavor.

Even if you're not tracking anything, even if you have no clue where you are in your cycle from a technical perspective, you can still get to know these different aspects of yourself, these different perspectives, as you allow yourself to talk about a given situation or decision that you're trying to make... over a period of time.

Even though the journey you take inside will be very multi-faceted and complex, there will be a pattern to it. One part of you will be lighting up after another, until all parts have lit up, and you've gathered together the 'big picture.'

If you let yourself talk about a particular situation throughout the cycle, you'll start to notice that each day, you'll get a different 'hit,' a different piece of the big puzzle. When the Moon and the transit field defines you emotionally (colors in your Solar Plexus), you'll get some clarity around an emotional aspect of the puzzle. When your Spleen becomes Defined or colored in by the transit, you'll find yourself getting a really strong intuitive hit. When your mind is Defined, you'll find yourself gaining greater intellectual insight into the situation, and be able to talk about it from the mental level.

If you'd like to monitor the daily transits, so you can see what energies you're likely to be impacted by and reflecting on a particular day, you should be able to find that information at JovianArchive.com. Last I checked there was some free software available.

One day you may feel particularly independent like a Manifestor. The next day, you may have the energy of a Generator. The next day, you may have the penetrating and guiding wisdom of a Projector. (If you get familiar enough with your cycle, you can even anticipate how you're likely to feel at certain times, and how to make the most of your intrinsic flow. You might, for example, plan to relax on your Projector days, and be more productive on your Manifesting Generator days!)

Each state you experience will provide you with an aspect of the truth… though none of it is WHO YOU ARE. Mindfulness is thus very important to keep as a practice during any decision-making journey.

One interesting thing that many Reflectors find, if they don't wait out the Moon cycle, is that they can act impulsively when their Throat comes under Definition… because the Throat is all about expression and communication. You can come under a lot of pressure to act on something, potentially before its time.

You don't have to learn to track all of this stuff. As long as you're giving yourself plenty of time, you'll be fine. No rush. No pressure.

You can simply rest in the knowledge that every time you make it through another Moon cycle with awareness, you become wiser, and clearer about who, what and WHERE is right for you.

BACK TO YOUR CHILDHOOD

Another thing that could have happened when you were little, is that you could have been pressured too much to act and make decisions spontaneously, which most kids are.

In the ideal world, any time your parents (or caregivers) had an idea for you and your life, and presented it to you, they would give you (at least) a few days to physically interact with that idea, place or person. Then they'd give you an entire month to feel it out.

Not only that, but they wouldn't present a bunch of other possibilities during that month. They'd understand that you do best—and learn to master life—when you can process one major thing at a time.

What parent—especially in our culture—does that? What parent understands that?

If you were hurried too much as a kid, or expected to 'just know' what was right for you. If your capacity to tap into the larger archetypal patterns kept you from getting bogged down in the small stuff of life, you could have easily lost your way, or gotten lost in the WE.

This is not in the way you're actually meant to absorb, metabolize and reflect the WE, but instead, in a way that left you feeling overwhelmed, or acting out, or reflecting an unhealthy 'WE.'

Disappointment

Every Type, or Flower Family, has a particular feeling that tends to arise when it is not living as authentically as it could.

- Generators tend to feel frustrated when they're pushing too hard, and not letting life come to them and 'turn them on.'

- Manifestors tend to feel angry when they're feeling controlled, trapped, or unable to have the impact they desire and know that they're capable of.

- Projectors tend to feel bitter when those around them can't—or won't—see or recognize them for who they are, and their gifts go unnoticed and under-utilized.

- Reflectors like you can end up feeling deeply disappointed in life, and in those around you.

Even though you're actually designed to be and shine at the hub of the community, you can end up feeling left out... while ironically feeling overwhelmed or filled up with everyone else's feelings, needs, desires, agendas, pain, stress and anxiety. If you're not careful, you can end up mistakenly thinking all of it is your own.

Some Reflectors worry that it's not safe to be themselves. They can be confused about whether they even have a self. They can wish that their identity felt more 'fixed and reliable,' and that they always had lots of energy and drive to do things. Some Reflectors fear being invisible.

Sometimes, when these fears and worries get the better of Reflectors, they attach themselves to different people, just to give them a solid sense of identity. But if the people aren't the right people, and they end up in environments that don't really nourish them, they can end up digesting and reflecting a WE that they'd be better off without.

DISAPPOINTMENT & PRESSURE

As you know, all of your Centers are what we call OPEN. Even though your 'Teflon' aura is built to protect you from taking the world in too deeply for too long, you're still going to be under all kinds of pressure—to be spontaneous, to get attention, to initiate, to not rock the boat, to prove yourself, to be certain about things, to hold on to the wrong people, to try to answer questions and figure out who you are and what you're supposed to do with your life, etc.

The more you get lost in any of these pressures, the more disappointed you're likely to feel.

You can also end up feeling uncomfortable with instability—which can translate into discomfort with those who 'break the rules' or the mold, or people who shake things up in unpredictable ways.

Especially as a kid, it could have been particularly upsetting for you when the rules were broken. If this was the case, it wasn't necessarily personal. You just happened to be born with an ability to tap into the underlying rhythms of life, to the structures and patterns that form the backbone of our world and human interactions. Just instinctively, you knew (know) how things are 'supposed to be.' When things aren't how they're supposed to be, it could have really thrown you for a loop.

Without realizing it, you could end up playing the role of police person—always making sure that everyone around you is toeing the line, or not making waves, or staying within the current cultural or religious paradigms.

To live this way, for too long, is not what you're ultimately here for. You're not here to be a reinforcing figurehead for the status quo.

Your True Self & Beautiful Gifts

You are here to get exceedingly comfortable with your fluid nature, to be a flowing, changing, rhythmic Moon being.

You are here to learn how to reflect your own truth, instead of all of the pain and mishegas of others.

You are here to be one of the wisest people on the planet.

You are here to find those rare and wondrous people who are ready to wake up and live a true authentic life!

You are here to literally translate the celestial realm into the human realm, and to reflect back to all of us how we're doing in this crazy human dance.

Two Paradoxes to Dance With

Remember, when swimming in paradoxical waters, there is no need to rely on rationality or logic. Just allow yourself to absorb the paradox as-is, and allow it to swish around inside of you until it finds a lovely, spacious place to paradoxically dwell.

PARADOX ONE

As a Reflector, you simply MUST participate in this world. Someone as gifted as you is so needed in communities—not just to reflect the health or ill-health of the community, but to lead it in the right direction, to lift out the people who have the potential to be liberated human beings. You are here to reflect, guide and teach your surroundings through your deep love of humanity.

On the other hand, you also need time to withdraw. You need times of solitude in order to protect yourself from overstimulation, to make sure you don't get way too 'filled up' by the world and the people in it—with all of their thoughts and feelings and pressures and frustrations and intentions and fears.

One of your greatest life tasks is to walk a very fine line, as I've mentioned before, between "being in the world," yet "not of it," to model something spiritually essential for the rest of us.

PARADOX TWO

As a Reflector, you're not necessarily designed to have the same kind of personal life or identity that the rest of us do.

And yet, you are most definitely a person, with a personal life, a relational life, and a personality that is all your own.

Another one of your greatest life tasks is to be totally true to yourself, even though you're not meant to cling to that 'self.' You are here to find ways to transcend all of the world's projections, to push past them, to find what's there at your spacious core.

Surprise & Delight
Your High North!

Even though there will always be a part of you that likes or at least feels more comfortable with predictability... when you're really living according to your true nature, you're here to absolutely LOVE and embrace the unexpected.

You have the potential to be deeply surprised by life, and to totally delight in that process.

What you really want, deep deep down, is to be surprised, is to find something, or someone, that has the courage to leap out of the expected box and become a free spirit.

No one can be as gifted as you at spotting people or situations that aren't like any other people or situations.

If anyone has the potential to break through the prison of mainstream conditioning and truly be themselves, you're going to be the first one to notice!

You can also spot situations or environments that have the potential to inspire true mutation, real change, for the whole species. It's a true gift you have...

... to see the rose budding out of the landfill
... the artist who's truly doing something different
... the ones whose courageous shamanic nature can lead us all to freedom.

YOUR DOUBLE-EDGED GIFT

You have this dual gift: one, to see patterns, and two is to notice when the patterns are being broken, or when they have the potential to be broken.

You can spot pattern-breakers.
You can spot people who have the capacity to wake up in a world where it seems everyone else is asleep... or crazy, or like drones.

It's not just to spot them, but to wake them up to THEIR potential, so they can wake more people up.

You're the one who awakens the awakeners!

YOUR AMAZING POTENTIAL TO EMBRACE THE "WE" ASPECT OF YOUR "ME"!

Your destiny is to sample the ALL...

To be completely open to the WE...

To dive into the mystery...

To be a guardian of humanity...

To do this job well, you must embody a certain kind of impartiality... or non-attachment.

Ironically, just as hard as it can be to prioritize yourself and not get lost in the WE through self-sacrifice, it can also be hard for a WE-oriented soul like you to honor your uniquely WE-oriented nature in this super attached, individuation-obsessed world of ours.

It's not easy to be impartial, and in some ways impersonal, when the rest of the world is pulling for the personal. When everyone around you wants you to be a good person, a good lover, a good spouse, a good parent, a good artist, a manifested business person, etc.

Please don't get me wrong. I'm not saying that you can't be your own very unique person, with your own qualities, talents, feelings, desires and goals. (Some of the most externally 'successful,' accomplished and creative people I know are Reflectors.)

It's just that all of that 'personal stuff' isn't ultimately what your path as a Reflector is about.

The point of your life isn't to accomplish or identify or achieve or prove yourself in a super worldly, concrete way.

The point isn't for you to drive yourself to exhaustion, trying to show the world what and who you are by doing, doing and doing some more.

The point, for you, is to transcend all of that, so that you can help the rest of us break out of our conditioned trance of over-identification. You can then help liberate us from our deep and totally hopeless attempts at achieving happiness by striving after external validation.

Somewhere deep down, you're likely to know this about yourself.

You're likely to feel that you're somehow connected to something much greater than what most of us can comprehend.

That we're One with everyone and everything, and that there's nothing, no other realization or experience, that could ever matter more than that.

There's no other aspect of your ME that is as worthy of your fierce protection, love and loyalty, as that.

THERE'S SO MUCH LESS TO WORRY ABOUT THAN YOU MAY THINK!

When you can truly embrace and embody this knowing, then the things you tend to worry about, or tend to be hard on yourself for, just won't have that much power over you.

It won't bother you if people seem to know their spot and you don't seem to know yours, or if it looks like others are getting what they want, and you're not getting what you want... because you'll know that you and 'those others' are just parts of the same whole.

You'll start to experience the people around you like hands helping a foot.

Everything else, all the rest, all experiences of separation or differentiation and ego proving, on some very real level, will be seen as what they truly are, just an illusion.

You'll be resting in this knowing, and in this way of being in the world... You will, in this way, be honoring your ME... and its unusual WE-WISDOM.

PATIENCE, FAITH & TRUST

Patience and faith are so important for you. You are here to trust the universe.

You are here to let go of the search for identity and love, and to simply allow life, love and direction to be shown to you.

As hard as it can be for you to understand this, it's not your job to know who you are, or to decide with your mind where you're supposed to go, or with whom you're meant to be.

By surrendering to the guidance that life naturally brings you, and by getting out of your own way, you have the potential to experience life as the most magical, synchronistic, love-filled journey.

The Essence of the Reflector Flower's Spirituality
Reflectors are here to surrender to their own Existence.

I shall leave you with a beautiful quote from Richard Rudd's article "The 4 Paths of Surrender":

"The awake reflector is a living archetype of transcendence. Their very being testifies that there is no individual self. This is symbolised by the spiritual teachings of negation - that all form is emptiness for example, as Buddha taught (one wonders about his design). The myth of Buddha is a wonderful archetype of the reflector—sitting beneath a tree for seven years until the deconditioning reveals the truth that there is no one sitting under the tree after all. For such a relatively small part of the population, the propaganda of this path is enormous. The reflector's propaganda is the propaganda of enlightenment! They represent the extreme. For a reflector, the repetition of the truth 'this isn't me' directly resonates. Every time the reflector looks in the mirror and identifies with what they see, they stop being a clear mirror for others."

Here to Help You Deepen Your Experiment

The following sections are here to help you deepen your experiment, and really start the 'practical' Human Design experiment. I may repeat essential bits of information here, to drive home their importance when it comes to your authentic blossoming practice.

Invitations for Generators

START PRACTICING RIGHT THIS MOMENT!

Start listening to your belly, even when you're going over this list of possible experiments! Remember, you may genuinely respond to some of these experiments, and not others. You may respond to the experiments in a completely different order than how they're presented here. You may not feel like trying any of this out now, but you may suddenly have the energy to do it all next week. Or next year! You can already begin trusting that brilliant belly of yours to guide you.

GIVE YOURSELF RADICAL BELLY TIME!

Set aside periods of time where you can practice REALLY honoring your body and its energy. Within these periods of time, be radical about it. Only do what your body responds to, even if it responds to nothing during that entire period of time.

You might start with short periods of time (20 minutes, 1 hour, etc.), and work your way up to longer periods of time (a full day, a week... a lifetime!)

In the beginning of your experiment, it's best to wait for things to appear to you in form, so that you can respond, and actually know you're responding. By 'form,' I mean something coming to you in the form of a direct question, a person extending an invitation, a letter in the mail, a phone call, a Facebook post, a specific song that comes on the radio, etc.

Over time, as you come to know the difference between a genuine response and manipulated one, you can respond without being 'approached' at all. It'll feel more like your body is simply moving on its own volition. Or like an internal tugging. Or a coming alive. Or an acting on your gut instinct. It's just that in the beginning, it's so easy for the mind to trick us into thinking that we're responding, when we're really not.

GET GOOD AT RECOGNIZING YOUR BODY'S WAY OF RESPONDING

"Response" feels different for each of us. Find out what it feels like for you. Is it a knowing, a feeling, a rush of energy or heat, a heart palpitation, a strange sense of calm coming over you? How do you know when your body is with you?

Write down what you learn about your own response system in your Blossoming Journal!

WATCH YOUR MIND!

Practice mindfulness in relation to your experiment. Ask yourself…
What are your mind's favorite ways to manipulate you into:

- not honoring your body

- not honoring your own timing

- overdoing

- saying 'yes' when you mean 'no'

- saying 'no' when you really mean 'yes'

What are the biggest fear pictures your mind shows you when it's trying to convince you to do, or not do something? What are its favorite threats to keep you 'safe' and in line?

PRACTICE WAITING FOR LIFE TO COME YOUR WAY

Practice waiting to be asked, approached, invited, called... even into conversations. Notice how often you feel tempted to initiate, pursue and make happen.

Practice not pushing in any way you can (i.e. if you're trying to reach someone and they don't answer the phone, stop trying, and wait until they call you, or until your body feels its next genuine desire to reach out.)

KEEP AN EYE OUT FOR GREEN AND RED LIGHTS!

GREEN **LIGHT:** Chances are you're trusting your body when you're feeling SATISFACTION.

RED **LIGHT:** Chances are you're pushing too hard if you feel a lot of FRUSTRATION.

WHEN YOU'RE NOT SURE...

If you're not sure whether you're responding to something from the outside, or trying to initiate something based on an idea in your head, just wait a bit longer... and see what happens.

Often, I find myself thinking that I should reach out to someone. I can feel that it's still operating as a 'should' in my mind, and I'm not quite sure if the energy is really there, and so, I wait. Often what happens is that they end up calling or reaching out to me. Either that, or I suddenly see a post of theirs on FB that I feel genuinely excited to respond to, or I read an article that totally reminds me of them and inspires me to reach out. When I do reach out, the whole process goes so much more smoothly and feels so much better.

I have this experience a lot in my business too. Lord knows, if you're an entrepreneur, there are always an abundance of things that you could, or feel like you SHOULD do. I might think, for example, that I need a certain kind of training. I might think that I should go to a networking event. If I let my mind be in charge of it all, I'd be going 24/7, doing things that most of the time leave me feeling over-stimulated, inadequate and like a total oddball.

Thanks to my understanding of my Design, I don't push myself to do any of that stuff anymore... unless it somehow finds its way into my field, usually through people I trust and respect.

I've gotten very good at knowing when I'm just feeling pressured, or afraid of 'not doing it right,' or fast enough, or successfully enough. I just don't act, until I'm genuinely excited.

ARE YOU BEING YOURSELF? ARE YOU FEELING RESPECTED?

Remember, one of your greatest gifts is your energy. It's SO IMPORTANT that you feel like you get to be yourself when you're doing something. You need to feel that you're being respected for the energy you're bringing into any situation... whether it's making someone dinner, or listening to someone when they're sad, or leading a team at work, or taking out the garbage, or simply responding to an email request.

If you're feeling taken for granted, disrespected, or conditionally accepted (and the conditions are that you abandon yourself, your truth or your values in some way), chances are pretty high that this is not a right use of your energy. (Or at least, it doesn't require too much of your energy!)

IF YOU'RE A **MANIFESTING GENERATOR**

Remember that you get a sense of your true response once your body has already ENGAGED in the thing in question. So, the first 'uh huh' may not be enough. It's when you get up to put that 'yes' into action that you'll really know if you've got the energy for it. You might especially enjoy creating the To-Do list process! (see below)

REMEMBER THE BANK ACCOUNT

When in doubt, remember to ask yourself, "Is this something I'd be willing to pay for?"

Even if it's just an invitation to go to a party.

If it's not something you'd happily pay for, practice saying "no." See what happens. See what happens when you say 'no' to things, maybe lots of things, that your body isn't so available for. This is the best way for you to build up a lot of energy to throw into a good satisfying 'yes.'

GO ON A MAJOR "SHOULD BINGE!"

Take a day to totally push yourself to do all sorts of things you really don't feel like doing, with people you don't feel like being with. Really push, initiate, pursue, keep pursuing, regardless of whether you feel a flow or received or resisted. Ignore your body's signals as much as you possibly can.

See what happens!

There is so much to be learned from this experiment. It's not always clear-cut. It can take a long time to get a feel for how your own response system works.

Some people—when they try to ignore their body's clear messages—end up having obviously horrible days and learn how important it is to trust their body's yes's and no's.

Others realize that they have no idea what their bodies are telling them, so they don't even know whether they're ignoring their bodies' messages or not. They learn that they need a lot more practice at simply understanding and communicating with their bodies.

Others have particularly confusing days—where some 'pushed-through' actions don't feel good at all, but others feel surprisingly good. (i.e. Someone really doesn't feel like going to a party, or a dance class, but once they're there, they have a great time.)

It can really take time to learn how to discern between resistance that comes from fear, and the genuine 'no'—or 'uhn uhn'—arising from the body.

Sometimes our bodies actually have energy to do something, but our minds have us convinced that doing it is dangerous or wrong. We experience an internal 'holding back' that could easily be confused with a lack of belly response.

When we decide to take a day where we push ourselves to do things we have resistance to, we can learn something about the source of the resistance. If we genuinely enjoy something we pushed through, chances are that there was a genuine response in there somewhere... and we may be dealing with an area of our life where our genuine energy has been habitually suppressed. This can lead to a very juicy inquiry... and further experimentation!

Similarly, sometimes our bodies seem driven to do something, but really, it's just an addictive pattern, driven by fear and/or survival coping strategies that have been operating in our lives for a long time. In these cases, the true response is overridden by the habitual behavior.

Patience and compassion and experimentation are key here.

LET YOURSELF LEAVE (Let "Oops!" be a legal word!)

Give yourself permission to stop doing something you've started, if you're not into it. Even if you sign up for a class and have paid for it... If you show up a few times, and you just aren't enjoying it, leave. If you go to a party, and you're not that into it, leave. Even if it feels forbidden, and scary.

This is especially (but not only) true for Manifesting Generators.

TRUST IN THE ABUNDANCE OF THE UNIVERSE!

It's important to remind yourself that the Universe is speaking to you all of the time, and that there will always be things, happenings, people and opportunities to respond to... even if you seem to be going through a drought period.

When you're waiting for something BIG to respond to (i.e. the next career, the new relationship, etc.), that's a really good time to start paying attention to the little things. (The call from a friend, the invitation to an exciting workshop, the popping up of a new favorite song, the first beautiful bud on your rose bush, etc.)

Let your body practice responding to the little things. As you do this, you'll be building your trust muscles—both your trust in your responsive belly, and your trust in an abundantly interesting Universe.

LET YOUR SOUNDS OUT

Some of the most important things for you to experiment with are your Sacral Sounds. Start letting them out. Start noticing how much they're actually coming out without your even realizing it.

Just pay attention the next time you're having a conversation with someone, and are listening to them talk. You'll begin to hear them. You'll hear yourself saying, "m-hm," or "ah," or "M-hm," or "uh," or "ooo," or "Oh yea." That's your Sacral voice.

You can look at (something awful) and find yourself saying, "uchh!" That's your Sacral talking too.

The Sacral is very, very truthful, uncompromisingly honest. Which is partly why you can trust it so much.

HAVE A SACRAL SESSION WITH A FRIEND YOU TRUST

As I described earlier in the Workbook/Course, one of the quickest ways for you to get in touch with your Sacral response, is to sit down with a friend you trust. (It has to be somebody that you trust, because the Sacral doesn't know how to lie!) Then have them ask you all kinds of questions—from the mundane, like "Do you like tuna fish?" or "Are you in the mood to eat out?" or "Do you want to go with me to see that movie?" To the profound, like, "Do you believe in God?" or "Are you in love with your partner?" or "Do you even want to be in a relationship right now?" or "Do you really want to go to Graduate School?" or "Are you happy where you're living?"

You can then let your Sacral respond, and stay open to surprise. Again, you have to be prepared to hear whatever your Sacral says. You might want your friend/support person to preface certain questions with a, "Are you ready for me to ask you a question about _____?" or "Do you want clarity regarding _____?" or "Do you NEED clarity regarding _____?"

We're not always ready to hear our own truth, and it's important to respect that.

TO-DO LISTS, SHOPPING & THE HAND-HUM TECHNIQUE

Make a To-Do list that includes fun, lazy, indulgent, playful, non-productive activities. Use what I call "The Hand-Hum Technique." Let your hand move its way over the list, and allow your Sacral voice to make sounds.

Start with the action that gets the yummiest hum, and then take it from there. Be open to your body's innate sequencing intelligence. You may find that your body first responds to a nap, then a snack, then a TV show, then another nap, then three pieces of chocolate.

All of a sudden, you'll feel genuine energy to pay the bills, or to write that article you've been totally procrastinating on.

Your body needs to know you trust it, in order to show you its trustworthiness!

This can take some time. This requires being willing to release your Mental Dictator from its usual duties for a while, and risk getting 'nothing done' for an uncomfortably long period of time.

But the rewards... when you finally are doing things in an order that honors your body, and when the force is truly with you... are TREMENDOUS!

(You may find that there are certain things, people and/or tasks on that list that NEVER evoke a genuine response. This may be an invitation to look deeper into the situation. There may be something you're pushing yourself to do, or a person you're pushing yourself to prioritize, that isn't right for your life... at least not now. As hard as this can be to acknowledge, there's so much freedom to be found in letting go.)

You can use the Hand-Hum Technique while shopping too. Just put your hands-on things, allow your belly to speak (softly if people are around and you're worried about embarrassing yourself), and only purchase those things that your belly genuinely responds to. You may walk out of the store with a jar of pickles, a bar of chocolate, a non-PC magazine and a toothbrush. Be open to the surprise, and have an adventure.

Remember, this is just a belly-trust exercise. It's a stage in your process of learning to trust yourself when it comes to the BIG THINGS.

The experiment only works if you let your belly have its way with you—even if your mind is kicking and screaming and thinks you're nuts!

PRACTICE DURING MEALS!

Every meal is an opportunity for you to practice listening to your belly. As you come to trust it more and more, your belly will let you know what it wants to eat, how much, and when it's done.

If you're with someone, have them ask you yes/no questions, like, "Do you want a salad?" or "Do you want your dressing on the side?" or "Are you in the mood for something warm?" or "Do you feel thirsty?"

If you have compulsive eating tendencies, or tend to be mentally strict about your diet, this practice can be both important... and challenging.

For those of you who tend to overeat, try to put more of an emphasis on becoming aware of what your body's genuine responses are, and what's happening, than on 'doing it right' or following all of its responses perfectly.

You may feel that your belly is no longer wanting food, that it's no longer responding to what's on your plate, but you keep on eating anyway. That's OK. At first, just noticing when the 'addictive' or compulsive drive kicks in can be deeply illuminating.

Notice how different it feels to be eating from that place of compulsion, than from genuine response.

Notice what's going on in your mind, or your emotional system... before you take that extra bite, during, and afterwards.

Do you notice an increased sense of numbness once you've overeaten; does your critical mind slow down; or does it amp up?

If you tend to be super strict with yourself, this may be a time to loosen up. For you, it may be more about learning to trust your body again than anything else. It may be about learning to trust that it knows what it needs to be safe and healthy—even if your mind isn't constantly whipping it into shape.

Again, only you know your story. If you have a background of compulsion, or an addictive reaction to certain foods, you may want to keep that in consideration. However, I have a feeling that there are some restrictions that would be safe to lift for a while, and see what happens.

Remember, this isn't about aiming for perfection. This is about coming to understand your body and how it works, your mind and how it works, and over time, to be living from a place of conscious authenticity, response and freedom, instead of unconscious pressure, reaction and restriction.

THERE SHOULD BE AN ELEMENT OF RISK

In this experiment, you are opening up to living your life from a different place than you're accustomed to. You're being asked to trust your body in a way that you haven't before.

You are going to be breaking some 'survival rules' from your growing up. While I want you to be gentle with yourself throughout, I also want you to take some risks. You can't really find out whether this stuff can transform your life, unless you let it transform your life!

IF YOU ARE A GENERATOR WITH EMOTIONAL AUTHORITY

If you have Emotional Authority, which we'll explore in Petal 5, your clarity-finding process will have an additional layer, which will likely require even more patience!

Your Sacral responses in the moment will be full of truth, but they won't necessarily provide you with your final answer. It can take time for your truth to fully be revealed.

An example of a layered response of an Emotionally Defined Generator:

First comes your Sacral 'hit' in the now (What is my first gut response?)

If you're a MANIFESTING GENERATOR, you must then energetically engage with your Sacral hit. (Only by beginning to move physically in the direction of your response can you really get a good sense of whether you've got the energy for it or not. "Do I really have energy to do this now, does it feel good when I start to engage my body in it?")

Finally, you wait to get a deep, clear emotional read on the response. ("Maybe this feels good right now, but does it still feel good tomorrow morning?" Your Solar Plexus/Emotional Authority is here to help you find out whether a momentary response has a solid shelf life. "Is this person/project going to be good for me in the long run? Is the timing right yet? Is this going to be good for all aspects of my life, for my kids/people/family/tribe?")

You will find, as you move through this Workbook/Course and experiment more and more with what you learn, that it is so important that you get to know your emotional rhythms. That you explore the typical thoughts and feelings that tend to attach themselves to your high and low ends of the wave.

- When are you most tempted to act impulsively?

- When are you most tempted to give up?

- What happens if you just ride it out a little longer?

(More will be explained when we get to Petal 5.)

For now…

Develop your 'play it by ear' and 'postponement before committing' muscles. Take more time than feels comfortable before deciding to dive into anything—a relationship, a joint venture, an experience... (even if you have a good intuitive 'hit' about the situation to begin with).

For you, buying yourself time and playing "hard to get" will be an important part of your experiment. More and more, as you develop the courage to trust in your own slow but deep decision-making process, you'll find that the right people and opportunities for you will ALWAYS wait until you are ready. (Often, by the time you're ready, the right ones will be even better offers than the first time around!)

Invitations for Projectors

IT'S ALL ABOUT THE PEOPLE!

Right now, at this very moment, I want to invite you to stop focusing on the content of your life, and to start focusing on the people in it! THERE IS NOTHING MORE IMPORTANT!

Remember, you could have the most impressive job in the world, and if you're not working with your people, you're going to be absolutely miserable. On the other hand, you could be cleaning a toilet with your best friend, and be totally blissed out.

The secret to leading a life that feels right in your Projector core, is to make sure that you are surrounded by and connected to the right people.

For you, it's so much less about quantity, and so much more about quality. In other words, it's not about how many people you can have in your life, it's about the value of each being.

The right people are those who truly recognize you, who 'get' you, not just people who are impressed by some projection they have of you.

If you spend too much of your time living with, loving or working with people who don't truly see you, you will suffer... and your gifts are likely to remain hidden.

Your experiment begins by simply adjusting your focus—from the 'what' to the WHO!

"TRUST" IS THE NAME OF THE LIFE GAME!

I invite you to create a sign that you can post somewhere, that reminds and inspires you to TRUST in life.

If you can trust in life, you're totally good to go. Your experiment is primarily an experiment in TRUST.

- Trust that it's all going to work out.

- Trust that the right people will find you.

- Trust that your right LIFE will find you.

Trust that your Aura will bring to you everything and everyone and every opportunity you could possibly need for your true gifts to emerge, and for you to feel deeply fulfilled.

TRUST TRUST TRUST. The rest is details!

NOTICE TRUE RECOGNITION AND PAY ATTENTION TO INVITATIONS

Approach this process as if it's a game. You're a crystal key waiting for the people you're designed to guide and 'unlock' to recognize you.

Please don't take it personally if someone doesn't see or choose you, even if your mind would love them to. (It's all about trusting that your people will find you. If someone doesn't notice you, they're not for you.)

Here are some good questions to ask yourself when you're with people (You can even make a little 'cheat sheet' to take with you when you could use the support!):

- Are they inviting me into their lives? Into the conversation? (Or am I uninteresting or invisible to them?)

- Do they see and appreciate me for who I am? Is it my gifts that they really want? (Or do they want me to be someone else? Do they want something from me that isn't all that exciting for me?)

- Do I come alive in their presence? (Or do I shrink?)

- Do I feel energized in a healthy way? (Or do I feel wired and burned out afterwards?)

- Do they want my guidance?

- Do they love the penetrating questions I ask? (Or do they resist me?)

- Are they yummy to me? (Or icky?)

- Can they respect and understand my 'no,' when I need to take a break, or to tweak my offering to them, or express my feelings? (Or do they get mad at me for not giving and being all that they expect?)

PRACTICE YOUR HEALTHY GROWTH PATH!

WAIT FOR THE INVITATION

Wait for the invitation when it comes to the 4 big things in life:

- to romantic love

- to bond with another

- to find a calling

- to find a place to live.

Once you've entered into one of these 4 life arenas properly, remember, you're free to do whatever you want! You can manifest, reflect and/or generate until the cows come home!

Waiting for the invitation is only about the portal, the entry way.

It's what makes sure that you don't end up working your butt off, in the wrong place, with people who don't get you, until you burn out.

IN THE MEAN TIME... Do what you love!!!!!

(I can't tell you how many miraculous stories I have of Projectors just going about their business, doing what they love, and being discovered by people who ultimately connected them to their life's purpose. It's totally crazy how often this happens!)

Honor your unique Authority (which you will learn more about when we get to Petal 5).

If your Authority tells you 'no,' please don't take it personally. Just say, "Thanks, but no thanks!"

Be grateful that you're not going to spend the next 10 years with the wrong people doing the wrong thing, and feeling very bitter about the whole business!

If your Authority says 'yes,' remember that it can take time for a relationship or situation to reveal its full potential to you. Even if a given situation doesn't work out in the long run, if you entered into it properly, you'll likely come to see the value and beauty of the experience, and apply that to your future endeavors.

GET REALLY GOOD AT RECOGNIZING A GOOD ENVIRONMENTAL FIT!

Practice entering an environment without working to be seen. See if you can just stand or sit there, quietly, and see who comes to you. Try not to initiate conversations, even if it's uncomfortable.

We want you to learn how to trust in your Aura to attract who you're meant to attract.

We also want to slowly make your life much EASIER, where you don't have to work so hard for every encounter, every interaction, every invitation. To get to this place, you have to build your waiting muscles...

Wherever you go (while in pursuit of doing what you love) ... Notice:

- Do I feel seen here?

- Do I feel comfortable, like I'm coming alive in this place?

- Are all parts of me welcome here?

PRACTICE WAITING FOR THE RIGHT MOMENT TO SHARE YOUR WISDOM, EXPERTISE & ADVICE

You have your most powerful impact when you are energetically invited in to share your gifts.

Even though you see so much, and could easily provide so many solutions to so many problems, make it part of your experiment to resist the temptation to offer your wisdom pearls prematurely.

Get really good at feeling when the doors are opened to you, and when your penetrating pearls of wisdom are seen, wanted and asked for.

If you're practically bursting with information that could be so useful to someone—who's ridiculously oblivious and simply not open to it, write everything you wish you could say to that person in your Blossoming Journal, or share your perspective with a friend you trust who can empathize with your frustration.

As hard as it might be (especially when it comes to family members, close friends and those who you're very involved with), keep breathing, and wait for your right moment.

If that right moment never comes, then this is clearly not one of your right people. There may be some grieving to do there. (This doesn't mean you cut the person out of your life entirely. It may mean that you let go of a long-time held wish that they could be different, and that one day, they'd be able to see and receive you differently.)

If you can't resist giving advice or providing constructive feedback, notice what happens. How do you feel after you've shared your pearls of wisdom to someone who isn't able to fully receive them?

(Special Note: There is a difference between offering advice and wisdom, and simply letting someone know how you feel. Sometimes the urge to offer advice is sourced in a deeper—and understandable—feeling of sadness and anger. Chances are, you will be better received if you are communicating from the deeper truth of your feelings and needs, than if you are trying to teach or educate the person.

Of course, there are some people who aren't even capable of hearing you share from a place of honest vulnerability. Again, this is an experiment. A chance for you to explore your relationships, and ultimately discover their potential and limitations.)

WATCH YOUR MIND WHILE YOU'RE
WAITING FOR RECOGNITION OR AN INVITATION

Notice how your mind pressures—or tortures—you. Notice how it tries to get you to twist yourself into a pretzel in order to be seen, heard and appreciated.

What are your mind's favorite ways to talk you into working too hard—in your professional life, in your relational life?

What are the biggest fears you have about not working so hard anymore?

CONTEMPLATE BITTERNESS

*Take some time to think about Bitterness, and write down some of your thoughts
in your Blossoming Journal.*

Here are some questions to stimulate your reflections:

- Is bitterness a feeling that you recognize?

- When have you felt it in the past?

- When have you felt it recently?

- What would you say are the kinds of experiences or relationships that leave you feeling most bitter?

- How do you tend to act, or relate to others, when you're feeling bitter?

- How do others tend to respond to you, when you're caught in a bitterness moment or cycle?

- Who are the people in your life who have helped you release bitterness and re-open your heart?

GET REALLY GOOD AT SAYING 'NO' TO THOSE NOT-SO-GREAT FITS

A big part of your experiment is learning that it is safe to say 'no' to bad fits (even if an invitation is tempting to your mind). If the person, group or organization doesn't see you for who you are, they are not for you!

Another big part of your experiment is learning not to take personally a bad fit. If a place or person doesn't seem to want you, remember... it's not personal. They're just not the people/place you're designed to guide or be intimately connected with.

GET REALLY COURAGEOUS WHEN A GOOD FIT COMES ALONG!

The other side of the coin, of course, is learning to say 'yes' to good fits—even when your mind doesn't quite grasp why, even if your 'yes' doesn't make logical sense.

If you feel essentially seen, if the relationship feels yummy for some strange reason, then accept the invitation and see what happens!

REMEMBER THE GOOD NEWS

Even if you go through periods of what seems like an INVITATION DROUGHT, there's no need to worry.

When it comes to the big things in life, you actually don't need many invitations.

Once you've accepted a good invitation and entered into the situation in a self-honoring way, you don't need to wait again when it comes to that arena. You got into the amusement park, and you got a lifetime pass. Have fun. Put your talents to work. (Without working too hard!)

ASK YOURSELF THIS QUESTION OFTEN
Am I doing (much) more than enough?

All signs point to "PROBABLY!"

You're designed to take in, amplify and act on the energy you receive from the people around you. A lot of the time, a chunk of that energy isn't even yours. You can drive yourself to a point of exhaustion before knowing what hit you.

It's extremely important to learn when ENOUGH is ENOUGH.

MAKE TIMES OF SOLITUDE A PRIORITY!

If you are a Projector Flower, you need to be watered with plenty of alone time.

You need to make sure that you have regular periods of time where you get to unhook from the busy buzzing world around you.

Setting time aside for re-centering, rejuvenating and re-orienting yourself is as important to you as eating and drinking.

Believe me; if you don't make self-care a major part of your practice, you'll end up working harder than most of the people you know, and either burning out or getting sick.

GO TO SLEEP BEFORE YOU'RE TIRED (another reminder from earlier)

Try going to sleep before you're tired. Give yourself time to unwind, to discharge all of the energy from the day.

Some Projector Flowers like to stretch out a little before getting into bed, doing some restorative relaxing poses. Some like to read, or to just look up at the ceiling. Some do a little journaling, or doodling, just to touch base with themselves. Some sleep better when they sleep alone.

Only you know what helps you make the transition from the activities of daily life, into the kind of surrender necessary for sleep.

This is something you can experiment with.

Most importantly, see if you can find ways to coax yourself into a relaxed state.

You need to acknowledge just how much of life's busy-ness you're actually taking in during the day.

It's OK and natural if you need a little time to unwind.

THE KEY TO FULFILLMENT

NON-ATTACHMENT & AGENDA-FREE LIVING

It's so easy, especially for a sensitive person like you with so much to offer, to feel deeply hurt when you're not recognized or appreciated by someone. It's also easy to be hard on yourself, and to assume that there's something wrong with you.

There's absolutely nothing wrong with you.

The less energy you'll expend trying to be someone other than who you are in order to get seen and recognized by people you don't even want to be with—if you're really honest with yourself!

When you're really living at your spiritual zenith, you'll be practicing AGENDA-FREE LIVING.

The less of an agenda you carry into any situation, the more easily you'll find and be found by your wondrous life!

INNER EXPLORATIONS FOR YOUR BLOSSOMING JOURNAL
(and for conversations with people you trust)

- Gather together a list of the people in your life right now who you feel seen and 'gotten' by.

(Contemplation: How do they see you? Do you find yourself prioritizing these relationships? If not, what might be holding you back from spending more time with them?)

- Gather together a list of those who you spend time with, but don't feel particularly seen by.

(Contemplation: In what ways don't you feel seen by them? What is it that keeps you connected to these people? What is it that they do give you? What keeps you from letting go of these relationships, or at least minimizing the amount of time and energy they take up in your life?)

- I invite you to do the same thing, but this time, looking back into the past.

(Contemplation: Who were the people in your life who truly saw/recognized you? How did you meet? Did they approach you? Did you approach them? Was there an invitation of some sort involved? What roles did they play in your life? What happened to the relationships? If they ended, how did they end? What did you come away with?)

(Contemplation: Who were the major people in your life that you never really felt seen by? How did they end up in your life? Were you born related to them? Did you invite them in? Did they initiate the relationship? Did you feel pressured in any way to maintain the relationship, even when it wasn't nourishing you? If so, how? What 'tactics' did your mind use to convince you that they were worth holding on to?)

- Think back to the times or experiences in your life when you felt most alive.

(Contemplation: What were you doing? Who were you with? What aspects of yourself were being ignited or used? How did those experiences get initiated? Did you make them happen? Did they arise out of a relationship? As a result of an invitation?)

- Think back to some of the main invitations you've received in your life.

(Contemplation: Which ones came from people who recognized you for who you were? Which ones came from people who didn't quite get you? Which ones did you accept? Which ones did you end up rejecting? How did the most significant 'invitationally-inspired' situations work out? Any insights there?)

- Think back on the times in your life where you got an idea and initiated it.

(Contemplation: When you took charge of making something happen on your own. How did those experiences work out? Which ones succeeded? What do you attribute the success to? Which ones didn't succeed? What do you attribute the lack of success to?)

- Think of times when waiting and being patient actually paid off!

- Make a list of what you love. Use your Passion Flower as inspiration.

Over time, and as you feel inspired, see whether you can expose yourself to the passions on the list. Practice 'Active Waiting.' Do what you love, then notice who notices you—or doesn't notice you—without taking it personally. If you feel recognized in a good way, stick around. If you don't, move on...

- Contemplate the difference between HOPE and TRUST.

(You might want to write out a short description of your fantasy life, two times. Once using the words, "I hope that..." The other time using the words, "I trust..." Notice how the different versions make you feel.)

- Practice consciously waiting to be asked before speaking.

(Contemplation: Notice the thoughts that arise in your mind while you wait, and the feelings arising in your emotional system. How does your mind try to convince you to speak, or not speak? How do you feel? What happens inside of you when you aren't feeling seen or received? What do you find yourself doing in order to be recognized more? When there's nothing you can do, what kind of thoughts do you have about yourself, others, life?)

Invitations for Manifestors

IT'S TIME TO EXPERIMENT!

(ONLY IF YOU FEEL LIKE IT...
YOU DON'T NEED ANYONE
TELLIN' YOU WHAT TO DO!)

(Authority will play a big role for you Manifestors, so additional layers to this process will be added when we get to Petal 5!)

REMEMBER TO HONK!
(and ask for help if you need it)

One thing that some Manifestor Flowers tend to do is get into a creative groove without letting people know what they're doing, delegating or asking for help.

They just go ahead and do their thing. They drive without honking.

One of your biggest experiments is simply learning how to honk. How to INFORM.

Not ask for permission!

This is about INFORMING people—once your decision has been made, or when you're in the process of making a decision, or when you're simply going through something that others are likely to feel, be impacted by or care about.

This goes from the smallest things, like saying excuse me when passing by someone in the market place, or when getting up to go to another room and start cleaning, or when getting ready to take your kids to an activity or playdate, or when you're out of kale and are deciding to go to the farmer's market.

From that kind of small thing, to letting your colleagues and friends know you've decided to leave your job of 23 years and start taking your artistic career seriously, or that you're considering asking your partner for a divorce, or that you're feeling down...

The more you learn how to do this, how to fill people in on what's going on with you, the more supported by—and less controlled/oppressed/overwhelmed by—the WE you're likely to feel.

This simple act of informing can really release you from a lot of external resistance, and give you the freedom you so deeply long for.

DON'T WORRY IF IT FEELS AWKWARD AT FIRST

Your Strategy of INFORMING isn't necessarily going to come naturally to you. Of all of the Strategies of all of the Flower Families, yours is the only one that must be learned. So, be gentle on yourself if you forget to tell people what you're doing, or what you're thinking or considering, or how you're feeling.

NOTICE YOUR MIND'S FAVORITE REASONS NOT TO INFORM PEOPLE

You're likely going to have a whole stockpile of reasons for not doing this. Here are just a few examples of what might go through your head, when you're considering informing others:

- "Oh, that's so unimportant. Why would anyone want or need to know that?"

- "If I tell them what I'm doing, they may try to stop me or slow me down."

- "If I tell them what I'm considering, they might have some opinion about it that I don't know if I can deal with. I don't want them to get upset."

- "I can't see why anyone would care about what I'm doing."

- "I don't want to bother anyone with this. They're probably busy with their own things."

- "Nothing may come of this anyway, so what's the point of letting anyone know? I'll let them know when it's done, if it happens."

- "I'm in such a groove, I don't want to stop or make things more complicated than they need to be."

- "I'd love to have help, but it's not worth all the trouble of asking, or having to teach people how to give me what I need, or feeling like I owe them something in return, or..."

- "If I keep this to myself, I won't run the risk of someone making me doubt or question myself."

- "No one will notice anyway."

- "I'm afraid they might notice! I don't know if I can handle the visibility."

NOTICE YOUR IMPACT

It's possible that the most important thing of all for you to understand is that you actually have a VERY BIG impact on people!

(This is true—sometimes especially true—when you don't think you make an impact, and when you often feel and tend to think about yourself as invisible and small.)

A huge part of your learning process, or experiment, is first and foremost, to acknowledge that you make an impact and designed to influence people. There's nothing you can do about it, or should ever want to do about it. Hiding isn't really an option for you, even if you've convinced yourself that it is.
Try just assuming that the people around you are going to be hyper-aware of you, no matter what.
Your big choice in life isn't whether to have an impact on others, but instead, what kind of an impact you want to have.

Do you want an unconscious and/or indirect impact? Do you want to hide in the corner, like a great giant who's pretending to be a mouse?

Or do you want to finally take ownership of the enormous light within you, and let it shine without apology?

It's your choice!

EXPLORATIONS FOR JOURNALING

WHAT SCARES YOU ABOUT SHINING?

Journal or talk to someone you trust about your relationship to visibility, to your own bigness. Even if on the surface, you seem comfortable in the limelight, are there parts of you that you hold back? Why?

EXPLORE YOUR RELATIONSHIP TO FREEDOM & CONTROL

Jot down insights, or talk to someone you trust about your relationship to Freedom and Control. Think about your intimate relationships. Think about your childhood.

- What have you learned about Freedom in your life? As a person? As a romantic partner? As the child of someone? As a professional? As a parent? As a grandparent?

- How much Freedom can you allow yourself?

- How have you managed to protect your Freedom? What have you sacrificed for your Freedom?

- In what ways have you been or felt controlled in your life? How might you still feel controlled?

- If you truly embraced your FREEDOM-loving nature, what might you do? What might you stop doing?

- What might you want to experience?

- Who might disapprove?

- What and who might you lose? What might you gain? What might you feel... and express?

- In which of your Flower Petals (i.e. Body, Love, Significant Other, Spirit, Success, Organization, Mission, etc.) are you most longing to feel free?

- WHAT ARE YOU WAITING FOR? Are you waiting for someone's permission? Someone's approval? A green light from the world?

EXPLORE YOUR RELATIONSHIP TO ANGER

Many We-Oriented Manifestors have been conditioned to be more nice, polite and compassionate than the rest of us, and sometimes women even more so. Feeling angry—which is only natural for a freedom-loving being whose power is being squelched—can feel very scary, and forbidden.

If this has been your experience, it may be time to really look at your relationship to anger.

- How would you describe your early childhood experience of anger? Your own anger? Your family members' anger? What did you learn about this emotion? Was it safe to feel, to express? Was it dangerous? Destructive? Something to be kept down, no matter what the expense?

- How did you learn to cope with anger when you were little? How did you come to see and relate to your own power?

- What makes you angry now, at this time of your life? What and who make you feel powerless? Cornered? Trapped? Controlled?

- What do you tend to do with your anger when it arises? Do you tend to lose control and lash out at others?

- Do you tend to lash out at yourself?

- Do you lash out at yourself for so long, with such an intensity, that you have no choice but to finally explode in a desperate act of self-defense?

- Are there any ways you might be living a 'double life' in order to avoid your own anger, or the anger of others? Are there aspects of you that you continue to hide, or repress?

- Do you tend to eat your anger? Drink your anger? 'Overwork' your anger?

- Do you tend to attract angry people into your life? Are you often the brunt of others' anger?

- In which ways can you support yourself in learning how to assert your needs and wants in more direct, self-honoring and healthy ways?

INFORMING AND GATHERING INFORMATION!

Remember, you're here to initiate things, to have an impact on others. The informing is your way of showing the people you're about to impact some respect. It's also your way of prepping them, so that they're not shocked by your actions... and you can move forward with greater ease and flow.

What you're here to manifest may be provocative. You're likely to initiate things that genuinely move and inspire people, that may even make them feel health-fully uncomfortable... as change often does.

However, we don't want you shocking the people you need to support you in your manifestation! When your support system is shocked, it will resist you.

What you want more than anything else is freedom to do your thing, without being blocked at every corner.

You inform to reduce resistance, to make sure that the door that you're going to walk through is actually open. (You're going to walk through it regardless—consciously or unconsciously! It'll just feel a hell of a lot better if it's open.)

The other side to informing is the LISTENING. You want to really listen to the people who are likely to be most impacted by whatever initiation your heart is wanting. You want to do your research.

 MORE QUESTIONS TO ASK YOURSELF

- Who are the people who I impact every day?

- Who are the people I'm likely to impact, if I initiate _____?

- What are their needs, their fears, their concerns?

- In what ways can I feel that they're open to me, and what I want to do?

- Are there any ways they are shutting down in my presence, or not responding to what I'm wanting to do?

- Do they seem to want my impact? Or are they resisting me?

- Are these really the people I want to be working with?

- Is this really the environment (the community, the organization, the field, etc.) I feel most inspired to impact?

This is so important... that you give yourself plenty of time to do your research, to listen listen listen... before you act.

Every time you connect with a friend, a colleague, a student, a client, a child of yours, a partner, a family member, an inspirational speaker, a pioneering role model, you are gathering information. You are making sure that you're informed. The more informed you are, the better you'll be at informing. Again, this isn't about getting permission or approval. It's about being smart. It's about reducing resistance inside and out. It's your way of making sure you're going to have the biggest, most effective, and empowering impact.

PATIENCE AND SURRENDER... EVEN FOR YOU!

Just because you're a Manifestor doesn't mean you always know what you're here to manifest. In fact, that's one of the biggest questions my Manifestor clients bring to me. "OK, so I'm a Manifestor," they say, "and I'm supposed to initiate something and have an impact on the world. What the h**!ck am I supposed to manifest?"

Of course, the answer is different for each person. So much depends on a person's nature, gifts, conditioning history, and the circumstances of their life.

Usually one thing is true—no matter who it is that's asking the question.

It can take time for Manifestors to get really clear about what they're here to manifest.

Even more than that, it can take time for them to know that they have the right to be here, and to be the powerful, free birds that they are.

Sometimes some deep inner work is required to pave the way, to get them to a place where they really feel an internal permission to have their impact.

CHANCES ARE YOU'RE ALREADY MANIFESTING
MORE THAN YOU KNOW!

Another thing I've noticed is that Manifestor Flowers are often manifesting A LOT, and they have absolutely no idea! They think that the process of manifestation has to look or feel a certain way.

Usually they think it has to be a very linear process, where they get a sense of what they want to do or create, and then they take a series of action steps, and plop, the manifestation is complete. But more often than that, they simply have a realization of what they want, and then it suddenly appears... as if from out of nowhere... in a slightly different form than they had envisioned. Or, people are simply initiated or inspired by their presence, or set in motion because of something they said, without even thinking about it.

Remember too, your power of manifestation works in both ways. You have the power to manifest wonderful things in this world, and beautiful relationships and experiences. You also have the power to manifest your fears (including the fear that you'll never be able to manifest what you want!). Embracing a self- and life-loving attitude for you is so important. (This doesn't mean your inner mind- and heart-scapes have to be perfect! Not at all. A more tender, positive inner life can go a long way for you. It's worth working those self-love muscles.)

ESPECIALLY FOR YOU WE-ORIENTED MANIFESTORS

For you, just learning to discern the difference between informing and asking for permission can be huge. You are here to learn how to stand strong in what you're doing, while still including others in the process... This is a spiritual practice of self-love, self-assertion, transparency, and respect for yourself and others at the same time.

NEEDS AND VULNERABILITY

As much as Manifestors can benefit from a deep exploration of anger, they can also benefit from a deep exploration of their sensitivity... their needs, feelings and vulnerability.

For some Manifestors, in order to really do what they're here to do, they must dare to let others help them. This means daring to let others know that they need them. It can also be a very scary thing since letting people in in the past may have been equated with being controlled, judged, manipulated or oppressed.

This is part of your journey too. To learn to be self-loving, to honor the ME, in a way that doesn't necessarily leave you feeling independent but isolated. You are here to learn to selectively let trustworthy people in, who can help you give birth to what you're here to manifest... which just may be a healthy, supportive, intimate relationship!

So, another one of your experiments is to let people in. To share how you're feeling. Let people know what you love about them. Ask for help. Share your fears about receiving help.

HONOR YOUR OPEN SACRAL CENTER

Please, beautiful Manifestor Flower. Make sure that you don't overdo it. There will be times when you have a lot of energy, and times when you need and deserve to take it easy. Don't let yourself get caught up in this crazy productivity-obsessed world. Give yourself breaks. Cushion in work periods with times of solitude and relaxation. Practice knowing when enough is enough, and saying 'no'! (Remember, you get to *get* things going. You don't have to keep everything going!)

Invitations for Reflectors

TAKE YOUR TIME...
Ahhhhh...
Deeeeeep breath...

EMBRACE & PRIORITIZE TIMES OF SOLITUDE

With your deep sensitivity, it's important that you find ways to be in your own space, outside of the crazy, buzzing energy of this 'Generator Flower' world.

Give yourself permission to leave large crowds or over-stimulating environments if it just feels too much. Give yourself plenty of time alone, where you can relax, allow your own Aura to fill up the space around you, and 'empty out' of all of the world's stress. Make a commitment to go on a retreat. You might want to begin with a short one, and work your way up to longer ones.

One day, when you're ready (if you haven't already done this before), I invite you to **take a whole month off and go somewhere where you don't know another soul**... even if the thought feels terrifying.

You can do this. It can be so healthy for you... to really let yourself let go of the world and find yourself, without all of the influence.

BEFRIEND THE MOON

Start cultivating (if you haven't already) a special relationship with the Moon. Go on Moon Walks. You can do some of your best thinking and feeling in the light of the Moon.

Start paying attention to the Moon's cycles. You might even want to start simple rituals that somehow incorporate the Moon's phases.

For example, you might want to plant seeds of intention during the New Moon, or do some letting go during a Full Moon, or whatever feels meaningful to you. What matters most is that you start feeling increasingly connected to and supported by the Moon.

EXPERIMENT WITH YOUR HEALTHY GROWTH PLAN

You may not be able to do this all of the time, and especially in the beginning, it may feel scary.

To the extent that you can, especially when it comes to the big things (i.e. where you live, who you live with, where you work, and who you work with), take plenty of time to make your decisions.

Ideally, give yourself—at least—29 days. Refuse to be rushed.

Try to only focus on one big decision at a time. If you have the chance to shelve something for a while, so that you can focus on something else, do it!

WATCH YOUR MIND

Notice how your mind tries to pressure you into moving quickly.

What does it tell you? (That you'll miss out? Lose an opportunity? That someone might feel hurt or upset with you? That you won't be able to survive financially? That if you don't do something, it won't get done, or it won't get done properly? That you won't be respected, or belong? That you'll never know who you are and why you're here?)

What fear pictures does your mind use to convince you to be spontaneous, or impulsive, or to hurry up?

See if you can breathe through the fear and discomfort, and buy yourself more time.

TALK TO PEOPLE & JOURNAL WHILE YOU'RE MAKING DECISIONS
EMBRACE YOUR FLUID NATURE AND PROCESS

Remember, clarity is designed to crystalize for you, over time.

The best way for you to allow the 'flying together' of your magnificent mosaic is to express yourself.

So, a big part of your experiment is simply allowing yourself to talk with good, reflective listeners.

Write down your thoughts, questions and feelings, as you move through a period of time.

Give yourself plenty of permission to change and shift your perspective about a given situation over a period of time. Remember, you're open and fluid. Even though you can certainly come to a place of clarity, you don't have to be absolutely mentally certain about anything... ever.

HONOR YOUR OPEN SACRAL CENTER

Make sure that you don't overdo it. There will be times when you have a lot of energy, and times when you need and deserve to take it easy.

Please don't let yourself get caught up in this crazy productivity-obsessed world. Give yourself breaks. Cushion in work periods with times of solitude and relaxation. Practice knowing when enough is enough!

COME TO SEE YOURSELF AS THE WISE BEING YOU ARE
Take some time to acknowledge and reflect upon your own wisdom in your Blossoming Journal:

- In what ways have you always been wise beyond your years?

- Who in your life can see and appreciate your wisdom?

- Who in your life may not be able to see this essential aspect of who you are?

- What would you say are the aspects of life that you understand the most deeply?

- How did you come to understand what you now understand?

- What were some of the most central, life-transformative experiences you had... that led you to know what you know?

GET REALLY GOOD AT RECOGNIZING A HEALTHY ENVIRONMENT FOR YOU

Even though you will always need time to yourself, given your rare and sensitive Reflector Flower nature, you can only play out your role in life if you join the world and become a part of your environment!

Remember, you're likely to reflect and mirror everything and everyone that is in your environment. If your surroundings don't feel good or right, then you're not going to feel good or right. The opposite is true as well. If the environment feels good, you're likely to thrive.

We want you in environments that bring out the best in you! A big part of your experiment may involve exploring different environments. Give yourself permission to spend a good chunk of time in different places (ideally a month, at least), so you can really feel into them... and their long-term impact on you.

Here are some qualities to look for in a healthy environment:

- You may do especially well in relatively stable environments, where people 'play by the rules' and things aren't too chaotic. These environments allow you to use your magical 'radar' and awaken the awakeners! (Even though you're a deeply sensitive, creative and unique soul, don't knock 'normal environments.' They may be the perfect place for your unusual gifts to be unleashed!)

- A healthy work environment for you is likely to be full of creative, energetic, competent and collaborative people who love what they do, and are open to your innate sense of direction.

- When you're in a healthy environment, you tend to come alive and play a central role. It's important that you feel like a full participant, that you can get nice and absorbed into the community, even if the role you play is quite different than the roles played by others.

PAY SPECIAL ATTENTION TO THE OPEN G/IDENTITY CENTER
(when we arrive at Petal 4)

EDUCATE YOUR PEOPLE; LET THEM KNOW WHAT YOU NEED

Make sure that the people in your life know that it's really helpful for you to have plenty of time when making decisions. Let them know that one way they can really support you is by not rushing you, and being neutral, supportive and flexible listeners.

MAKE SURE YOU'RE SURROUNDED BY THE RIGHT PEOPLE

I can't emphasize enough how important it is for you to have a consistent and supportive group of friends and loved ones.

The best people for you are people who can (most of the time!):

- Love you the way that you are, without trying to change you.

- Give you plenty of time and space to be on your own, whenever you need it.

- Let you take your time when making decisions. Good people for you don't apply pressure. They ease pressure! They are happy and willing to honor your long decision-making process.

- LISTEN! Your people are really good listeners. They happily allow you to speak, and compassionately reflect back to you what they're hearing, without imposing their own agendas. When you're with them, you feel like you can get a much clearer sense of how you feel and what you're dealing with. They're willing to hear you speak about the same questions or issues over time, so that you can experience your shifting perspectives, and ultimately arrive at more whole sense of what you want and need.

- Honor your environmentally sensitive nature. They accept that you're not going to feel comfortable or thrive just anywhere. If you're going out with them to a restaurant, for example, and you want to switch tables, or to go someplace else, they're happy to go along for the ride, without judging you. They also are really good at helping you recognize when an environment is a healthy one for you, and when it isn't. They know you well enough to be able to see what different environments bring out in you, and they want you to thrive!

- Let go of keeping tabs on **who needs who more** in the relationship. If they need you more, they're OK with that. They also don't apply pressure on you to need them more than you do, or in a different way than they seem to need you.

- Happily be mirrors for you. They realize that it is often through them that you find yourself, or see a truthful aspect of yourself.

- Understand that sometimes you find life disappointing. They can let you have your disappointments, without taking them personally. This allows you to feel what you feel, without having to be dragged into a whole unnecessary interpersonal drama!

- Understand and appreciate the special role you play for humanity! If you feel inspired to share about your Reflector nature, they're likely to be very interested in and supportive of it, even if Human Design isn't their thing.

EXPLORE YOUR RELATIONSHIP TO DISAPPOINTMENT
Take some time to journal or have a conversation about your relationship to disappointment.

- What would you say have been some of your most painful disappointments?

- Who has disappointed you the most?

- What do you do, how do you tend to act when you're feeling disappointment?

- How have the people around you responded to your when you've felt this way?

- Who in your life is particularly tuned into you when you're disappointed?

- Are you able to embrace this feeling? Or are you constantly trying to avoid this feeling? Are you terrified of disappointing others? How might this fear influence the choices you are making?

SURPRISES

Start noticing surprises when they occur.

- What tends to surprise you in people?

- In environments?

- What have some of your best surprises been?

- What have some of your most difficult surprises been?

- What kind of a surprise do you actually enjoy?

- What kind makes you feel scared and uncomfortable?

Please, don't take all of your suffering personally. Remember, at a very deep level, your inner state is going to be reflecting how we're ALL doing as a collective. This is not to minimize your pain, or make you feel like you don't have a personal story. Your pain is valid, and your story is as personal as anyone's. It does mean that part of your purpose, part of your service to this world, is to digest, metabolize and reflect the pain of humanity. While you may feel very deeply, I want you to give yourself permission not to identify with everything painful that moves through you.

Sometimes, it's just you doing a bit of work for the rest of us. If you can let it move through you, without clinging or over-identifying or thinking you have to personally work through and heal IT ALL, you'll find that it moves through much more easily.

Whatever personal pain is left can be much more manageable for you—a just-right proportion of personal material!

 UNCOVER YOUR UNIQUE TRUTH-FINDING PATTERN BY KEEPING A DAILY JOURNAL

If you feel inspired, I invite you to really use the Blossoming Reflector journal over the course of this Workbook/Course. Every day, just jot down a few words that capture the 'flavor' of that day.

It can be as simple as:

- Monday = emotional

- Tuesday = inspiring

- Wednesday = anxiety-ridden

- Thursday = productive, etc.

See if you find any patterns that repeat themselves, month after month!

For example, you might find that the second week of most months tend to be super emotional for you, and you get really tempted to act impulsively based on those emotions. Three days later, the emotion and impulsivity subsides and you get much clearer. You can make a little agreement with yourself to be particularly careful not to make any major decisions during that particularly emotionally charged time of your cycle.

IF YOU WANT TO "GET TECHNICAL"

If you find yourself wanting to learn about your Bodygraph from a super technical perspective, go for it! There are lots of resources out there, and Human Design analysts who specialize in helping Reflectors learn how to track the transits and their impact on their Design. I share some of Human Design resources at the end of the Course/Workbook.

Observe Your Energy Flow: Petal Three

Take a gander at your magnificent Blossoming Body!

OBSERVE THE FLOW!

When you look at your Blossoming Bodygraph, it's like looking at a blue print of your genetic make-up, your hard-wiring. In Integral Human Design circles, we consider your Bodygraph to be a physical map of your physical, spiritual and emotional imprinting. It is the embodiment of your story, your musical or life score, your personal, and in a way, our collective anthology, all encoded in a map. Another way to think of the Bodygraph is to think of it like a snapshot look at your "DNA," of your waking personality, a map of how energy flows within your body, and between you and your environment.

The Blossoming Bodygraph

Your Bodygraph contains NINE CENTERS, all connected by a network of Channels or Circuits. These nine Centers are based on the Hindu-Brahman tradition where they are known as Chakras—or hubs of subtle energy within the body. While you can find parallels between the way Human Design looks at these Centers and the way the Hindu tradition looks at them, there are some important differences.

The obvious one is that Human Design operates out of a 9-Centered system, as opposed to a 7-Centered system. Another important difference is that in Human Design, energy isn't seen as moving upwards only, from the Root to the Head (Crown). Instead, the energy moves in all directions, through the various lines (or Centers) connecting the various Centers—reflective of the Kabbalah's Tree of Life.

Some like to think of the Bodygraph as a *pressure sandwich*. Pressure comes down from the Head. The Head, acting as a mass storage and receptacle system, like the gray matter of the brain, is filled with a record of pretty much everything we've ever experienced (personal and archetypal), whether or not we remember these experiences, or even know we are having them when we do. This Head Center is there, pressuring us to make sense of our past, understand the future, and contemplate the big spiritual and philosophical questions in life. As it seems that only we humans do.

There's also the pressure coming from below, up from the Root Center. As opposed to the mental pressure coming from above, this is a very physical pressure. This incredibly powerful motor fuels all of our experiences. It fuels the energy in our bodies, which then travels upwards, pushing its way through the various Gates and Centers (**Black** roads and **Red** tunnels), in an effort to make it up to the Throat.

In a very real way, you could say that all of the energy moving through us is trying to make it to the Throat. In Human Design circles, it is often said, *"All roads lead to the Throat"*—since the Throat Center is essentially that place in our Bodygraphs, and in our lives, where metamorphosis, communication and manifestation take place.

You could say that all of the inspiration we receive, all of the questions and thoughts in our heads are trying to get to the Throat so that we can communicate what's on our mind. All of this fuel, all of our adrenalized feelings, intuitions and drives towards life, are rising up from the Root of our body, pushing their way up towards the Throat, so that they can actually manifest in the physical world.

What Your Bodygraph Can Show You

- It can show you the kind of life student you are designed to be, and how you are experienced by others—what kind of flower people see and smell and feel when they are around you. Your Bodygraph can reveal some of your most wonderful gifts, as well as the aspects of your nature that you can count on to be consistent and reliable.

- It can show you where you're meant to go to school in life, what and who you're most attracted to, and how you can turn negative conditioning into positive nurturance and deep wisdom. It can show you the areas in your life where you are wonderfully Open, flexible and receptive. It can reveal how the kind of garden in which you're planted can make a huge difference in how you feel, and what you express.

- It can illuminate the sacred relationship existing inside of you—your soulmates within. It can show you how surrendering to the relationship between your Mind and your Body (or your Soul and your Body) can catapult your Life Purpose into being.

- It can shed tremendous light on the potentials, challenges and chemistry in your relationships, and show you how to make the most of that chemistry. Ultimately, Human Design—when held within an integral world view—is all about cooperation. It's all about healthy relationships; it's about collaboration and creativity. The more we understand and *are* ourselves, the more we can understand and allow *others* to *be themselves*, the more we can find synergistic, organic ways to come together in service of the whole, and the more we can start offering up our gifts and co-creating the kinds of environments (or human gardens) that our world so desperately needs!

- It can reveal your deepest shadows, your highest service, and your most mystical potential. It can open the door to a greater mystery, a contemplative, transpersonal journey that will release your Genius, Radiance and Purpose. (I'm talking *Gene Keys* here. More of this to come!)

- It can show you HOW to break free of your inhibitions and release the unique form of creativity living inside of you.

BLACK and RED (Personality and Design)

In order to arrive at a complete Blossoming Bodygraph, two calculations are necessary. One is traditionally called the Personality calculation. Represented by all of the black lines in your Bodygraph, the Personality is derived by your actual time of birth, and reflects aspects of your being that you're likely to find in a traditional astrology chart.

The other calculation, which is unique to Human Design, is called the Design Calculation. Represented by all of the red lines in your Bodygraph, this is a prenatal calculation, made exactly 88 days or degrees of the sun, before the day of birth. Some say this is when the soul fully enters the body before we are born.

PERSONALITY (the Passenger—or Soul)

The Black in your Bodygraph points towards **what you already know about yourself**, what you find most easy to relate to. This conscious part of you reflects who and what you think you are.

For the more spiritually inclined, you think of the Personality as your Soul Identity—that part of you that is eternal, that at least in some form (or non-form), existed before you came into this body, and will exist after you leave it.

For the more 'earthly' inclined, you can think of your Personality as your mind, your witnessing capacity, the 'you' that goes to therapy to work on issues that you are all too aware of. This Personality is connected to—or finds its voice through—the neocortex of the brain, that part of you that can self-reflect.

It is your Personality that has so much trouble 'getting' that it's not only intimately connected to, but utterly dependent on the body. It tends to want to be in charge, and to think that it actually *is* in charge of your life, your body, and your personal growth process—even though it isn't.

One of the most central premises of Human Design is that the Personality is not intended to be in charge. Instead, it is designed to hang back and enjoy the 'ride of life' as a highly intelligent witness, or passenger.

DESIGN (the Vehicle—or Body)

The Red in your Bodygraph points to what you don't know about yourself, what you don't have access to. In Human Design, the Red is termed 'unconscious,' although the meaning is quite different than what we normally think of in psychological circles. Unlike the Freudian or Jungian 'unconscious,' the unconscious in Human Design is more akin to the body's mind, or your genetic hardwiring.

If your Personality is the passenger,
then your Design is the vehicle
taking your Personality for the ride of its life.

You could say your Design is that miraculous physical intelligence in your body that makes sure that your eyes blink, your heart pumps, and that you breathe while you sleep. Your Design also includes the very qualities, behaviors and habits that others are much more likely to notice in you than you are in yourself! It's what you do, the way that you do it, whether you know it or not. The Red represents your innocence— the genetically inherited aspects of you that can show up suddenly, and as a surprise.

Though you cannot control or intentionally access your Design, you can certainly come to know and recognize it over time—through your life's journey and the feedback you receive from other people. Ideally, you can learn to make decisions in a way that honors this invisible yet very real and beautiful part of you.

MAGNETIC MONOPOLE

(Feel free to take this literally or symbolically.)

If your Design is the vehicle and your Personality is the passenger, then the obvious question becomes: Who's driving?! In a sense, you could say that the driver is the marriage between the Personality and the Design. In Human Design, we call this strange, yet divine union the Magnetic Monopole.

Simply put, the Magnetic Monopole is like a powerful magnet sitting smack dab in the Center of your body. (More specifically, it sits right inside the Bodygraph's only diamond-shaped Center, the G-or Identity Center. More on this later.) This is the Center that is associated with your sense of love and direction.

This is not your ordinary magnet, in that it doesn't have both a positive and a negative pole. It doesn't both attract and repel. It only attracts. A magnetic MONO pole. One pole. Mechanically speaking, it literally pulls everything towards itself. For example, it pulls your Design (body) and Personality (soul) together. In doing so, it gives you the experience of being whole and unique. Through this holding together of your different parts, it also gives you the experience of being an independent entity, separate from everyone and everything else—which according to most mystical and an increasing number of scientific thinkers, is an illusion.

The Magnetic Monopole doesn't just pull your 'parts' together. It also pulls toward you the people and relationships you are meant to have. In that sense, you could say that it pulls you along in life, in the direction you're meant to go, with the people you're meant to be with. It's often talked about in Human Design circles as a cable car that is hooked up to an invisible grid.

The Magnetic Monopole is the driver, because only *it* knows where you're meant to go as a 'whole being.' Your conscious identity (i.e. your Personality, the Black part of your Bodygraph, your thinking mind) has only half of the story. Your unconscious body (i.e. your Design, the Red part of your Bodygraph, your genetic hardwiring) has the other half. Only the monopole has the whole story. That's why it must be in charge of the driving. In this way, you (or at least who you're accustomed to thinking you are) must ultimately surrender to a life much greater and perhaps quite different than you had 'in mind.'

YOU ARE SO MUCH MORE THAN
WHAT YOU THINK YOU ARE!

Human Design, in essence, celebrates that we are not just our Mind, but a deeply interconnected combination of body and mind (or body and soul). It gives us a very practical Strategy for living that takes our 'unconscious' potential, our body's intelligence, into consideration. It allows us to live our lives in ways that honor the marriage between what is conscious and unconscious in us, between those things we have at least some control over and the many **many** more things that we don't. In doing so, it helps us rejoice in and surrender to the incredible uniqueness that comes out of that marriage.

Human Design is an invitation to think of your body and mind as the ultimate soulmates!

Imagine a life where you truly felt that your body was exactly the one that 'you' were meant for, exactly the one that you needed to express all of who you are!

A MORE INTEGRAL LOOK AT THE BODYGRAPH

One thing we're learning (Bruce Lipton is a wonderful voice for this kind of information) is just how much our PERCEPTION controls and influences our biology. From a more traditional Human Design perspective, we might look at a Bodygraph and see a code, almost like we'd look at an item in a grocery store. Once you have a code, it doesn't change. You have no choice about who you are. You can either accept your nature, or you can spend your life fighting against the inevitable.

The new paradigm emerging in science is showing that even if you can't change the code, you can certainly impact its *frequency*, the vibration with which it expresses itself. (Richard Rudd's work with the *Gene Keys*, as well as Integral Human Design—an intricate, rich and transpersonal version of Human Design, co-developed with Werner and Laura Pitzal, all go very deeply into the essential role *frequency* plays in the embodiment and expression of our Designs.)

I'm no scientist, and I'm sure there are plenty of places where you can learn a lot more about this, but I've learned that our cell membranes actually have little switches, little receptors, that take in information from our environment. They're constantly interacting with our environment. The way we SEE and interact with our environment can actually determine how our code plays out.

Emotions, thoughts and attitudes that are driven by fear, anger, jealousy or frustration, actually have been proven to cause a contraction in our DNA. Similarly, what we tend to call 'positive' attitudes, intentions and emotions (like gratitude, love and compassion) can cause our DNA to relax and open.

While our cells are permanently coded, our conscious awareness and attitudes (whether we're being driven by fear and self-loathing, or whether we're being driven by love and self-acceptance) are what ultimately determine our perceptions, beliefs, behaviors, moods, temperaments, and ultimately our experiences.

When you explore your Blossoming Bodygraph, I want you to think about it as a map of a living, breathing, receptive, ever-evolving, mysterious and beautiful territory. Remember that your DNA is listening all of the time, responding to your attitudes more than you know.

THE NINE CENTERS

A SIMPLE WALK THROUGH THE NINE CENTERS

Now let's take a very simple walk through the 9 Centers, starting at the top and working our way down. Aside from representing psychological awareness, spiritual and physical functions, each of these 9 Centers houses biological functions and organs in the body. This is complex stuff, and there are many ways to learn more.

HEAD Center
(Biological associations: Pineal Gland)

The Head Center is the place where we experience mental pressure. It is where we receive ideas and inspiration, and where all of the questions we grapple with as human beings are sourced. Who are we? Where do we come from? Where are we going? Why are we here? The essence of this Center—of INSPIRATION—is the deepening and expansion of consciousness itself.

AJNA Center
(Biological associations: Anterior and Posterior Pituitary Glands)

The Ajna Center is what we usually refer to as the Mind. It's that place where we experience mental awareness, as well as our ability to conceptualize, analyze, rationalize, strategize, form opinions, ideas, beliefs, etc. You could say it's the home of the witness, the neocortex of the brain, that part of us that is able to self-reflect. It's not only the place where we store concrete data or think; it's also the place where we experience mental anxiety. It's the place through which our diverse conditioning sources fight for our attention and obedience, by filling our heads with lots of 'shoulds.'

For thousands of years, we human beings have been relying on this strategic awareness Center to make our decisions for us. Though Human Design points to a shifting away from the Ajna as the ultimate Authority, we would not have survived or thrived as a species, if this Center hadn't played such a central role in our evolution. THANK YOU, dear Ajna.

Ultimately, the MIND is here to help us attain a deeper understanding of life itself, and to cultivate self-reflective awareness.

THROAT Center
(Biological associations: Thyroid/ Parathyroid Glands, Metabolism)

The Throat, just beneath the Ajna, is connected to our capacity to communicate with words, as well as to manifest things in the outer world. According to Human Design, our purpose in life, what we're meant to do and create in this world, can be found in the Throat. Ultimately, the THROAT CENTER is here to support the clear emergence of our unique, and tangible contribution to the world.

G-Center/IDENTITY Center

(Biological associations: Liver and Blood)

The Yellow diamond just below the Throat Center is called the G- or Identity Center. This is the place where the "self" resides, where we get a sense of identity, direction in life, and where we experience love. This Center also houses something fascinating called the **Magnetic Monopole**, as I shared about earlier. It gives us the illusion that we are each separate, whole beings, even though at a spiritual and sub-atomic level, we are all deeply interconnected. Ultimately, the ESSENCE of IDENTITY is here to help us feel aligned with our deepest core being, as well as the world around us. When we are truly living out our identity, we enter a deep state of Oneness with everything.

HEART Center/EGO Center

(Biological associations: Stomach, Heart, Gall Bladder, Thymus Gland)

If you go just below and to the right of the G-Center, you'll see a little red triangle. This is the Heart Center (or Ego Center). In Human Design, this is quite different than what we usually think about when we think of our hearts. The Heart Center is one of the body's four motors, and it has everything to do with Will, values, commitment, loyalty, competition and courage. It also has to do with manifesting on the material plane, whether we're talking about money or all of the many services, contributions and support structures that are needed for families, communities and cultures to survive and thrive.

When we are genuinely connected to our Will, in a healthy way, we just naturally join others in a Spirit of cooperation, synergy and collaboration. Our Wills are designed to value and align in service of the whole, to make sure that everyone's basic human needs are being met.

SACRAL Center

(Biological associations: Ovaries, Testes)

Heading straight down from the G-Center, you'll find a big red square. This is the Sacral Center, another motor in the body. It's the place where our work force, life force and sexual energy are experienced. This Center has to do with power, fertility and creativity. It also has to do with availability, and the ability to sustain activity and work in life. The Sacral Center actually has a voice. More often than not, this voice speaks in sounds (i.e. hums, grunts, squeals, etc.) as opposed to words. Anyone whose Sacral Center is colored in is a **Generator.**

When we're connected to this powerful ENERGY source, we become in tune with the flow of life itself. It's like *the force is with us*! We are able to move in the world with our creative power intact.

SPLENIC Center
(Biological associations: Lymphatic System, Spleen, T-Cells)

To the Left of the Sacral Center is the Spleen. This is the seat of our immune system, our intuition, our primal survival fears, as well as our ability to be physically aware in the now. It's the oldest awareness Center that we have. In fact, all animals have it. You could call it the seat of our instinctual animal awareness. When our Splenic Centers are healthy, we experience true embodied presence. We just naturally experience and express our body's intelligence.

SOLAR PLEXUS/EMOTIONAL Center
(Biological associations: Kidneys, Prostate, Pancreas, Nervous System, Lungs)

To the Right of the Sacral is the other inward pointing triangle called the Solar Plexus, or the Emotional Center. This is where our emotions, our capacity for pain, pleasure and nervousness reside. This is the third of our three awareness Centers. According to Human Design, this Center is undergoing a powerful transformation, moving from being a blind motor to an awareness Center. (More on this later!)

Ultimately, the essence of EMOTION is to support us in feeling true serenity, and to embody empathy and compassion.

ROOT Center
(Biological associations: Adrenal Glands)

Finally, we have the Root Center at the very bottom. This is where we experience stress and adrenaline, the pressure to move, to change, to start things, to need, to desire, to have new experiences. It's where we get the fuel for life itself. The Root Center is all about the original IMPULSE. It's where we experience the momentum to grow. It's the driver of human evolution itself.

Your Petal Three Invitations

#1: Be Gentle with Your Lovely Self
(Embrace a DNA-enhancing attitude!)

If there's one attitude I want you to embrace more than anything, it's self-love, self-acceptance, self-appreciation, and that you be **gentle gentle gentle** with yourself!!!!!

That means not even taking the advice I'm giving you now, and using it to beat yourself up... by telling yourself that your attitude isn't positive enough!

I know that you could do that, because I've been there. I still visit that place on more than a few occasions.

Let's support each other in softening, loosening up, and relaxing and trusting that we're OK, just the way we are.

As is often the case, we're dealing with a paradox. On the one hand, we're talking about raising consciousness and embracing more positive attitudes. On the other hand, the entire concept of 'raising' consciousness creates a separation between us and where we think we should be.

Even dualistic terms like 'positive' and 'negative,' 'good' and 'bad,' keep us in that place of judgment, which is the very thing we're trying to avoid.

Even if I invite you to do some exploring or shifting around, so that you can experience more joy, fulfillment, peace and happy surprises, please don't AVOID anything that doesn't belong to those categories.

The true invitation here is to apply love and compassion to whatever's happening, to whatever you're feeling, to whatever you discover about yourself and your life through this process.

We're here to learn how much we can love ourselves when we're feeling jealous. How much love we can apply to our terror. How much love we can give to ourselves when we get lost comparing ourselves to everyone else.

It's in these moments, when we're applying love to the fear (not pushing it away), that those little receptors open and our DNA shifts its form to something far more relaxing and open and transmutable than we can imagine.

#2: Bring Your Centers to Life!

You can do this LIFE SIZE or miniature size with paints, art materials, or a pen and sheet of paper. You can do this together with someone (i.e. outline each other's bodies on big sheets of paper), or on your own. It's entirely up to you. There are no rules.

The main invitation here is to create an image of your own body and its 9 Centers. Make sure all of the Centers (or Chakras) are represented on the body. (Feel free to use the Human Design Bodygraph as inspiration, so you know where to put what, without getting too perfectionistic about anything.)

Try not to think too much about what you're doing. Just fill in each CENTER in a way that feels somehow aligned with your experience of these aspects of your body and life. Again, see if you can let your process be intuitive. Music can help you relax and enjoy the process, without too much mental intervention! Almost like a doodle.

If you're drawn to visual images, but you're not in the mood to draw, collage, paint or make something major, try doing something like I did. Make an outline of your body, mark the various Centers, and then place postcards (or pictures, or ripped up images from magazines, or objects you find around the house) on the body that for some reason feels right. Given my background in expressive arts therapy, I have a fun little post card collection. I picked just a few postcards for each Center. Without thinking much about what I was doing at all, I just picked them out and laid them out on the body outline that my husband helped me make.

Tend to the In-Between

Now spend a little time working with the space *in between* the Centers. Fill in the space in a way that feels reflective of how you experience your body. Add color or draw lines between the Centers that feel connected to you. Draw boundaries... or leave empty spaces... where you sense a lack of connection. There's no judgment here. We're only exploring.

(I'll share a bit from my own process on the following pages, for inspiration!)

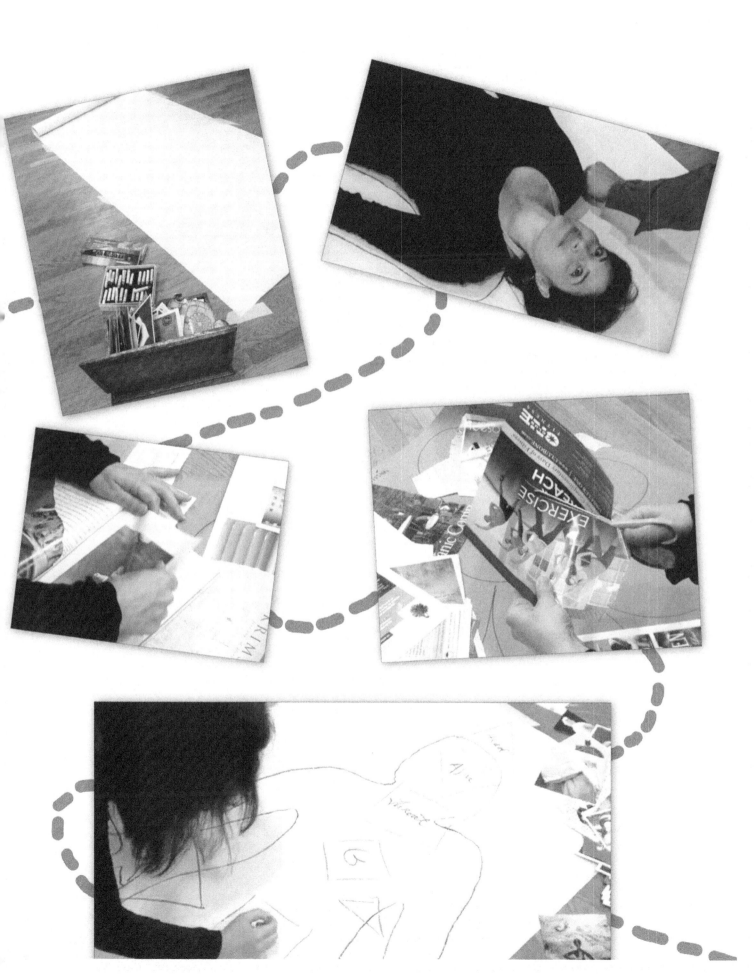

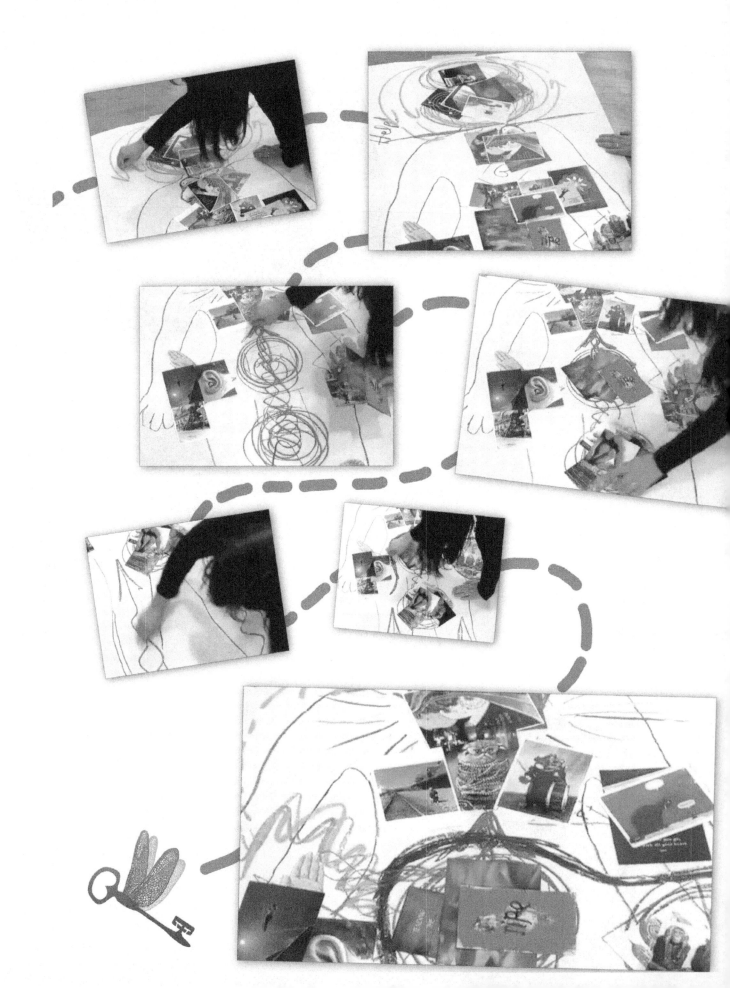

Here are some inspiring examples from the *Designed to Blossom* participants!

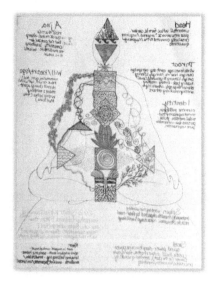 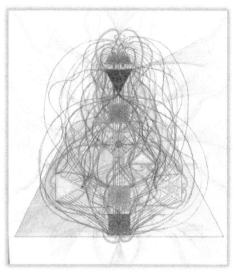 

Feel Free to Do it Your Own Way!

If you're not so visually oriented, there are so many other ways to do this. You can, for example, find a song that represents each Center for you, and make a CD, and listen to it! Or you can find a little movement for each Center, and dance the body out. Or you can write a poem that somehow captures the essence of how you feel in the various Centers... right now, or in general.

My sister, husband and parents once did this amazing thing for me, on one of my birthdays. They literally went through my whole life, coming up with memories, places, songs, events, issues I dealt with—and they placed them in the various Centers. I'll show you a picture here in case you feel inspired to do something like this. (Of course, you don't have to make it so detailed or organized!) I still can't believe they did that, especially my parents who thought Human Design was about the strangest thing in the world!

Whatever you do, make this process easy and interesting for yourself.
Remember to share about your process with someone you love and trust!
Even if you don't share about it, take a picture of it or find a way to document it, especially if it's something that'll ultimately be dismantled.

Most of all, have fun!

#3: A Bit of Contemplation

Once you have something to look at, some kind of body image, notice any thoughts, words or feelings that emerge in you. Are there certain Centers that are easier to fill up or illustrate than others? Easier to relate to than others? Are there Centers that you wish you felt more connected to, that you wish you knew better? That you wish weren't so conflict-filled?

 Jot down a few of your insights or questions that arise for you—either directly on the body before you, or inside of your Blossoming Journal.

If it feels right, please share your reflections with a friend or loved one. Let the conversation unfold, and be open to learning something new about yourself, and your relationship to your body and life.

Synthesize Your Parts: Petal Four

Enjoy the best of both worlds,
your innate gifts and your beautiful receptivity!

NATURE and NURTURE
(Yup; it's both!)

As we explored in our last Petal, one way to think of a Bodygraph is as a blue print of your genetic make-up, your hard-wiring. It's like a snapshot look at the "DNA" of your waking personality, a map of how energy flows within your body, and between you and your environment. The Bodygraph includes what you put out, what you transmit into the world, as well as what you take in.

DEFINITION

When we speak of Definition in Human Design, we're referring to your **Nature**. We are talking about what you are uniquely designed to be and do in life, your potential, your life force.

The colored in areas of your Bodygraph have so much to say about what kind of 'student' you are when it comes to the school of life. They indicate what is solid and reliable in you, what makes up those parts of your nature that are consistent and free from outer influence. They also reflect what you transmit into the world around you, simply by being you (as well as what you most likely take for granted!).

An example: Any time you have a Center that is colored in, it means you have a consistent way of processing the kind of energy represented by that Center. If you have a Defined Ajna Center, this means that you have a specific and consistent way of processing information. You have a consistent way of thinking.

OPENNESS

When we speak of Openness in Human Design, we are referring to the parts of you that are open to being **Nurtured**. Through the 'white' (or transparent) parts of your Bodygraph, you can see the specific areas in your life where you are Open and flexible, where you are built to take in the 'other' and the world around you.

> While your Definition speaks to the kind of student you are,
> your Openness shows you where you are meant to go to school in life.

While you can be deeply nurtured by others through your Openness, you can also be negatively conditioned. Knowing your Design does not only allow you to see how 'negative conditioning' operates in your life; it teaches you how to turn negative conditioning into positive nurturance—simply by learning how to make decisions in alignment with your Nature.

> *HUMAN DESIGN IS LIKE A CHIROPRACTIC ADJUSTMENT*
> *FOR THE BODY and SOUL*

Human Design doesn't ask us to 'get rid' of anything; for everything in us has a value and purpose. It does invite us to allow things to shift around a bit. Most importantly, it takes the Authority out of the Mind, which is usually busy trying to convince us to be who we're not, and delivers that Authority back to the very parts of us that we can count on to be consistent. In other words, it takes our decision-making out of our Openness, and returns it to our Definition. The more decisions we make from our Definition, the freer we are to enjoy and learn from our Openness, with a sense of healthy non-attachment.

Instead of losing ourselves, we find our inner *Wisdom Keeper*. Our Mind, instead of spending all of its precious energy trying to solve our own problems, based on an over-identification with everything we're soaking up from our environment, becomes this incredible place of deep intuitive and loving intelligence. No longer meddling in our own decision-making business, it is free to become the "Outer Authority" it's meant to be—to be able to teach, awaken and stimulate others with its unique form of brilliance.

> One of the most important things to understand is that we each are given EXACTLY the amount
> and kind of definition we need in order to make the most of our Openness!

THE BEAUTY & CHALLENGE
OF OPENNESS

(The nurturing... and de-railing... potential of our innate receptivity)

The white Centers in your Bodygraph are called Open Centers. Like highly sensitive 'energy-receiving hubs,' your Open Centers remain faithfully 'open' to the influence of the world around you. More often than not, they point to the people, energies and aspects of life that you find most attractive. Not just you, but your genes! You could say that your reproductively driven body is always looking to hook up with people who are **Defined** in the areas where you are not, in order to mix up and positively mutate the gene pool. (They don't say 'opposites attract' for no reason!)

As a child, it is through your **Open Centers** that you take in the thoughts, values and energies of your parents and culture, learning that your safety and potential for success lie in your being more like other people than yourself. Slowly, as you become 'conditioned' to think, feel and act like the people around you, you begin to dismiss your True Nature. You begin to make one decision after another, based on an Authority, a truth compass, that isn't even yours. You continue to attract people into your life that 'define' you in the same ways that the significant people in your early life did.

Your attraction isn't just about your genes looking for someone to make babies with, or your 'inner child' looking to repeat relational patterns from the past. *It is also about your soul looking for wisdom.* You are not 'fixed' in these Open Centers, so you can process the energies you experience through them in an abundance of ways. Your potential for experience, for understanding and mastery in these wonderful life arenas is literally limitless! (As long as you are not identifying with what comes in through your Openness, but instead, remaining an awake, curious witness…)

Please understand that this receptivity business is rarely a conscious process, for anyone involved. As a child, you simply take others in, from the day you are born—or conceived!—absorbing at a very deep level who 'the others' are, as if *who they are* is *who YOU are.* Similarly, your parents or teachers aren't necessarily trying to mold, force or push you away from your true Nature. Most of the time, they're just being who they are, transmitting their Nature without even thinking about it. Even if you have parents that are consciously trying to 'mold' you, chances are they're just sharing the values and beliefs they themselves have been conditioned to think will keep you safe and on a path towards success and safety. This is really not about blame. It's about liberating everyone through a path of understanding.

HOW YOUR OPEN CENTERS COMMUNICATE

The Open Centers speak to you through your mind, especially when you're facing a decision in your life. They try to get you to make decisions as the person you've been conditioned to be, not as your most natural self. Chances are, you've temporarily lost track of your flower nature if you're listening too much to these voices.

Your Openness speaks in 'shoulds.' You could also say the conditioning that comes through your Openness uses your mind to speak to and direct you. When you're hearing a lot of 'shoulds,' that's a pretty good sign it's your Openness talking.

- "You should be smarter.
- "You should lose weight."
- "You should be more successful."
- "You should sacrifice your needs for someone else."
- "You should be more productive."
- "You should go faster."
- "You should love someone else."

You get the idea. Any time your mind is trying to convince you to say, do, or decide something that goes against the grain of who you are, without the blessing of your Strategy and Authority, whether that means act too quickly, or not quickly enough, in relationship with people who aren't right for you, or careers that don't make you happy, chances are your mind is speaking on behalf of one or more of your Open Centers. It's speaking on behalf of those white Gates and Centers in your Design that have the potential to bridge your different parts. It's speaking from all of the places in you that are particularly vulnerable to conditioning, whether it be the old conditioning you carry from your past, or the current conditioning of the people in your present, or even the transits in the stars.

If you listen to your temporarily conditioning-possessed mind, if you give your Authority to those places that are Open, inconsistent and/or vulnerable in you, if you make your decisions from these places, and that's all I'm really talking about, you can risk not living out your true potential. Even worse, you can end up channeling all of the incredible power and potential that you do have, of your True Nature, in a direction that is not supportive of your life. You can wind up making decisions for all the wrong reasons.

 A Mini-Invitation

The next time you hear a 'should,' or feel a lot of pressure, or are in a major guilt trip, I invite you to imagine some blinking (and loving) red lights. They're there to remind you it's time to slow down and postpone any decision-making until you've reconnected with your Authority. The more you are able to take the Authority for your own decision-making process away from your mind, the better able your mind will be to provide those around you with its unique wisdom.

ARE YOUR OPEN CENTERS BLOOMING?
OR WILTING?
Let's take a look!

YOUR BLOSSOMING OPEN HEAD

Your Open HEAD Center is likely blossoming if you really enjoy basking and playing in the infinitely vast field of thought—exploring ideas, questions and inspiration, without having to identify with (or act on) any of it.

When you don't let the mental questions, doubts and confusion of others usurp your life, you actually free your mind to do what it's best at: playing, learning, discerning and sharing your particular brand of receptive brilliance with others.

When you're being true to who you are, you have the potential to get quite comfortable with the unknown, and to tolerate the discomfort, confusion and doubt that so often accompany a good mystery (like life itself!). You can model for others a deep trust in the organic, natural resolution of complex problems. You also have a special gift for spotting truly inspiring minds and relevant questions. The more inspired you allow yourself to be, and the more you trust what genuinely inspires you, the more inspiring you can be for others!

YOUR WILTING OPEN HEAD

Your Open Head may be wilting if you find yourself working way too hard trying to answer questions that (when it really comes down to it) don't actually matter.

Your Open Head is likely wilting when you're full of worries and anxieties that aren't even yours, but instead, belong to someone else. Your Open Head may be wilting if you find yourself prematurely rushing into action, just to put an end to a doubt or confusion you're experiencing.

Wisdom-Bringing Questions for your beautiful Open Head

●   Are you working way too hard trying to answer questions that (when it really comes down to it) don't actually matter?

●   Are your worries and anxieties really yours? Or might they belong to someone else?

●   Do you tend to prematurely rush into action, just to put an end to a doubt or confusion that you're experiencing?

●   Can other people get you to obsessively think about stuff that isn't even relevant to your own life, or genuinely inspiring?

●   Does it feel impossible sometimes to unwind mentally? Do you feel like you're always in a state of self-doubt and confusion?

●   Are there times when you can't get interested in anything at all?

YOUR BLOSSOMING OPEN AJNA

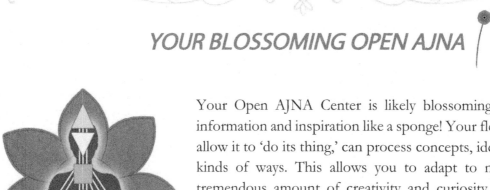

Your Open AJNA Center is likely blossoming if you can soak up information and inspiration like a sponge! Your flexible mind, when you allow it to 'do its thing,' can process concepts, ideas and thoughts in all kinds of ways. This allows you to adapt to new situations with a tremendous amount of creativity and curiosity. Weaving conceptual tapestries like nobody's business, the realm of your intellect can really become your playground, where anything is possible and thoughts are allowed to flow in and through the mind freely.

You're actually designed to be more fascinated by *wonder* than attached to being right. Your Open Mind is likely blossoming if you genuinely enjoy not knowing anything for sure, and if you don't need to engage in mental power struggles or rigidly hold onto beliefs or opinions. You have the gift of recognizing (and dancing with) a valuable concept when you meet one.

YOUR WILTING OPEN AJNA

Your Open Ajna may be wilting if you find yourself spending a whole lot of time trying to figure things (and people, including yourself!) out. Or if you expect yourself to be certain about things, and it's super important to you that you're perceived as intelligent. Your Open Ajna may be overworking if you sometimes judge yourself for not being able to control, harness or discipline your mind like others seem to be able to do.

Your Open Ajna may be wilting if you find yourself involved in mental power struggles, trying to convince people (or at least yourself) that your view point is the right one.

If you find yourself holding onto ideas, beliefs or concepts that don't actually serve you in your life anymore, it may be time to hold that Open Mind of yours a tad more lightly, and allow it to become that fluid, non-attached, curious sponge it's meant to be!

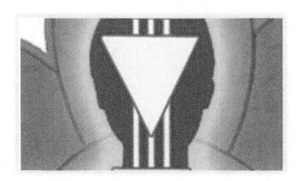

Wisdom-Bringing Questions for your beautiful Open Ajna

● Do you spend a whole lot of time trying to figure things out?

● Do you expect yourself to be certain about things?

● Is it important to you that you're perceived as intelligent?

● Do you sometimes judge yourself for not being able to control, harness or discipline your mind like others seem to be able to do?

● Do you at times find yourself involved in mental power struggles, trying to convince people (or at least yourself) that your view point is the right one?

● Are you holding onto ideas, beliefs or concepts that don't actually serve you in your life anymore?

YOUR BLOSSOMING OPEN THROAT

Your Open THROAT Center is likely blossoming if you have a flexible, sensitive communication system with a very wide range. You actually have the potential to be an incredibly gifted singer or speaker, with wonderful language skills.

If you manage to resist the pressure you can feel at times to fill up empty space, and instead simply witness what's going on around you, your 'truth-detecting' ears can hear what's not being spoken. When your Open Throat is operating at its best, you can also spot the people who can actually 'keep their word,' as opposed to those who are 'all talk and no action.'

You have the potential to truly trust your aura to speak for you, and to learn that simply by being present, you will be recognized and invited to share your gifts. More than anyone, you can truly luxuriate in silence. Instead of prematurely attempting to attract the attention of others through your words and actions, or rehearsing what you're going to say before you speak, you can learn how to relax and wait for the right moment to enter a conversation or a project. The more comfortable you get with this kind of waiting, the more you find that others naturally turn to you and invite you in, and that your words flow easily and eloquently.

In general, the more impeccable your timing, the more powerful your impact, and the more seen and appreciated you feel.

YOUR WILTING OPEN THROAT

Your Open Throat may be wilting if you often feel invisible, or try to attract attention through your talking. Or if you ever had the thought that if you could only talk more, or be more articulate, others would notice you and you'd be more successful. Or when you are with other people, and there's a silent pause, and you feel uncomfortable, or compelled to somehow fill that silence and initiate a conversation. Your Open Throat is probably getting the better of you when you find yourself speaking about things that don't really matter to you, and instead, giving voice to what's 'in the room,' to what others aren't saying. An overwhelmed Open Throat is going to get you rehearsing what you're going to say in your mind before you say it. It might also leave you feeling like you don't have much control over what does ultimately come out of your mouth!

If you spend a lot of time preoccupied about what you're here to manifest in life, you may need to hold that Open Throat of yours more lightly and lovingly!

Wisdom-Bringing Questions for your beautiful Open Throat

● Do you often feel invisible, or try to attract attention through your talking?

● Have you ever had the thought that if you could only talk more, or be more articulate, others would notice you and you'd be more successful?

● When you are with other people, and there's a silent pause, do you feel uncomfortable, or compelled to somehow fill that silence and initiate a conversation?

● Are you speaking about things that really matter to you?

● Or are you giving voice to what's 'in the room,' to what others aren't saying?

● Do you often feel like you have to rehearse what you're going to say in your mind before you say it? Do you sometimes feel like you don't have much control over what does ultimately come out of your mouth?

● Do you spend a lot of time preoccupied about what you're here to manifest in life?

YOUR BLOSSOMING OPEN G- IDENTITY CENTER

Your Open G/IDENTITY Center is likely blossoming if you genuinely trust the universe. You have the potential to totally let go of the search for identity and love, and to simply allow life, love and direction to be shown to you. As hard as it may have been for you to understand this in the past, you now know that it's not your job to know who you are, or to decide with your mind where you're supposed to go, or with whom you're meant to be. You know how to surrender to the guidance that life naturally brings you, and how to get out of your own way, and so you can experience life as a magical, synchronistic, love-filled journey.

If your Open G-Center is blossoming, you actually enjoy the fact that you are free to experience all kinds of identities, all kinds of love, all kinds of directions, and enjoy being with all kinds of people. You are a true diversity-lover with a unique ability to relate to and reflect back the identities of others, with genuine appreciation and without judgment. You know how to hold the whole *identity quest* lightly, and enjoy not being 'boxed in' as well as the often-surprising nature of your path.

With a blossoming Open G-Center, you are happy to embrace your sensitivity to your environment. You often find that when you're in the right place, you meet the right people. Similarly, you find that when you're with the right people, you're taken to the right place. Over the years, you've found lots of places that make you come alive, and look forward to finding more!

YOUR WILTING OPEN G- IDENTITY CENTER

Your Open G/IDENTITY Center may be wilting if you feel like you **need** to know who you are and where you're going in order to be happy. Or, if your mind is often obsessed with finding the perfect purpose for your life, or the 'just right' title for what you do. Or, if you're sure everything would totally fall into place if you could just find your one true soulmate.

Your Open G-Center may be getting the better of you if you often feel lost, and like you don't have an identity that you can truly rely on. Or, if you find yourself hopping from identity to identity, from relationship to relationship, in an effort to finally figure out who you are.

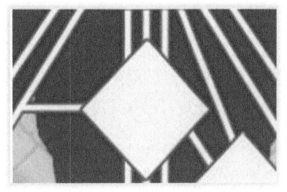

Wisdom-Bringing Questions for your beautiful Open G-Center

● Is it very important for you to know who you are and where you're going?

● Is your mind practically obsessed with finding the perfect purpose for your life, or the 'just right' title for what you do, or your true soulmate, with whom everything in your life will just fall into place?

● Do you find yourself hopping from identity to identity, from relationship to relationship, in an effort to find out who you are?

● Are you tempted to make choices, just because you think they will lead you to feel more solid as a person?

- Do you worry that if you don't *make your life happen*, if you don't set your own course or pursue the relationships you think you need, you'll never find your way or connect with the right people?

- Do you sometimes force yourself to go to or stay in a place you actually don't like, because you think being there will get you the love or solid sense of self you're looking for?

YOUR BLOSSOMING OPEN EGO/HEART

Your Open HEART/EGO Center is likely blossoming if you genuinely enjoy being in the world, but you don't get all caught up in it. You've realized by now—deep down—that you are worthy and lovable exactly as you are. You just don't get lost in unhealthy 'ego trips.' You know that you don't have to spend your life trying to prove, improve or change yourself, in order to earn anyone's love or respect. You've found, over the years, that the less you give into the competitive pressures of the world around you, the more you learn about the nature of competition itself. In fact, you are extremely skilled at not just surviving, but thriving and navigating through the material aspects of life with grace.

You often take special care not to place yourself under too much pressure by making all kinds of promises. You intuitively get that sometimes you have access to your will power, and other times you just don't. You avoid setting your life up in a way that puts you under constant pressure to 'come through,' regardless of your energy level in the moment. Instead, you enjoy keeping things open and fluid whenever you can, and you give yourself plenty of permission to play life by ear.

Maybe you did at one point, but you no longer spend your time pumping up your ego. Perhaps this is why you've become so good at spotting a healthy ego when you see one, as well as an ego that's out of control. With your blossoming Open Ego/Heart Center, you know just who can be trusted to keep their word, and who can't, and so you find that your personal and professional relationships are essentially healthy and mutual.

YOUR WILTING OPEN HEART

Your Open Heart/Ego Center may be wilting if you often feel like you need to prove yourself in order to feel valuable or worthy—both to yourself and to others. Your Open Ego/Heart may be under too much pressure if you find yourself making more promises than you are able to keep. Or, if you put yourself under a lot of pressure to keep the promises that you make, even when your body protests.

Chances are your Open Heart/Ego Center is wilting if you're always thinking about ways to improve yourself—your appearance, your physical stamina, your professional skills, your spiritual knowledge and enlightened state, etc. Or, if it is extremely important to you that others experience you as trustworthy, reliable or courageous.

If you tend to push yourself hard in life, trying to 'will' your way to success, chances are it's time to pay some attention to that Open Ego/Heart Center, and to relieve yourself of some unnecessary pressure!

Wisdom-Bringing Questions for your beautiful Open Ego/Heart Center

● Do you often feel like you need to prove yourself in order to feel valuable or worthy? To others? To yourself?

● Do you make more promises than you are able to keep?

● Do you put yourself under a lot of pressure to keep the promises that you make, even when your body protests?

● Are you always thinking about ways to improve yourself—your appearance, your physical stamina, your professional skills, your spiritual knowledge and enlightened state, etc.?

● Is it extremely important to you that others experience you as trustworthy, reliable or courageous?

● Do you push yourself hard in life, trying to 'will' your way to success?

YOUR BLOSSOMING OPEN SACRAL

Your Open SACRAL Center is likely blossoming if you have a deeply relaxing life and are doing what you truly love. You are naturally attracted to life itself. You've learned to resist the impulse to overload yourself with work, and you've become quite an expert in (and witness to) the very nature of energy itself—its patterns, its movements, its ebbs and flows.

With your blossoming Open Sacral Center, you've become quite good at regularly 'unhooking' from the world, and at nurturing and resting your body. This has made you super good at not just reading and tracking the energy of others, but guiding it.

By now you've learned that you're not here to do, do, do. You actually prefer to work in bursts, and to act as a guide or inspiration for other people who are actually built to chug-chug away like a Choo Choo train.

One of the most valuable lessons you've learned in life is limit-setting. You've learned how to say 'no,' to take breaks and to set boundaries. You don't expect yourself to have endless workhorse energy anymore. You've become too deeply attuned to the ebbs and flows of your own energy for that. You've learned to respect your own boundaries, and you have a special gift for supporting people who really struggle with healthy limit-setting.

WILTING OPEN SACRAL

Your Open Sacral may be wilting if you often find it difficult to know when 'enough is enough', and if—even when you're tired—you don't give yourself permission to stop and give your body the rest it needs.

If it's hard for you to 'unplug' from the world or the people in your life, or to let yourself go off on your own and just be, chances are your Open Sacral Center is overloaded. Another possible sign of Sacral Center overload is addiction—to work, sex, or whatever life arena that seems particularly exciting or juicy to you!

If you often find yourself saying 'yes' when you really should be saying 'no,' if you often feel like you're carrying more of the work load than anyone else, if you sometimes feel overwhelmed walking down an urban street, or shopping in a busy grocery store, if by the time night rolls around, you are so exhausted that you just collapse, or are so wired that you can't even fall asleep, there's a good chance that your sweet Sacral Center is calling out for your attention, and for a well-deserved break!

Wisdom-Bringing Questions for your beautiful Open Sacral

- Do you often find it difficult to know when 'enough is enough'?

- When you're tired, do you give yourself permission to stop and give your body the rest it needs?

- Is it hard for you to 'unplug' from the world or the people in your life, to let yourself go off on your own and just be?

- Are you addicted to work? To sex? To wherever you find excitement?

- Do you often find yourself saying 'yes' when you really should be saying 'no'?

- Do you often feel like you're carrying more of the work load than anyone else?

- Do you often feel overwhelmed walking down an urban street, or shopping in a busy grocery store?

- By the time night rolls around, are you so exhausted you just collapse, or are you so wired that you can't even fall asleep?

YOUR BLOSSOMING OPEN SOLAR PLEXUS

Your Open SOLAR PLEXUS is likely blossoming if you have a great deal of empathy. Simply by remaining open to the people you're with and the environments you're in, you experience and understand the entire continuum of feelings available to humanity.

With your Open Solar Plexus, your deep sensitivity allows you to take the emotional temperature of any situation, and to recognize who is emotionally healthy, and who isn't. When you're alone, you generally feel calm, and enjoy an emotionally quiet inner landscape.

You've learned over time how to witness the many feelings that move through your system. You don't make hasty emotional decisions. You are an honest, brave and authentic person. The people around you really look to you for inspiration, when it comes to the emotional realm. You are someone who knows how to healthfully respond to painful or difficult situations, instead of *avoiding* or *reacting*.

You no longer hide who you are and what you need. You know how to be in the world as yourself, how to have the confrontations that are healthy for you—even if this means upsetting someone you care about with your truth. At the same time, you know when to walk away from conflicts that don't belong to you, without feeling guilty.

YOUR WILTING OPEN SOLAR PLEXUS

Your Open Solar Plexus may be wilting if you are easily influenced by the way others feel. Or, if you tend to take other people's feelings very personally. Or, if you carry around an awful lot of guilt, shame (and even physical aches) in your belly.

There may be times when you feel like your own emotions are out of control, and that there's something wrong with you.

Other signs of an overstimulated Open Solar Plexus is working really hard to please others—to 'make nice,' and to avoid rocking the boat. Avoiding—or denying—your own truth, because you're afraid it might upset someone in your life, or lead to an uncomfortable confrontation, is another biggie. If you've spent more than your fair share of years on a therapist's couch (or have even been trained as a therapist or emotional healer), learning how to understand, work through and heal your own feelings, it may be time to give some loving attention to that Open Solar Plexus of yours.

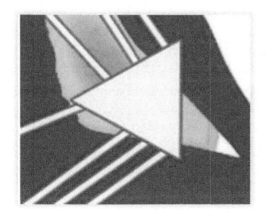

Wisdom-Bringing Questions for your beautiful Open Solar Plexus

- Are you easily influenced by the way others feel?

- Do you tend to take other people's feelings very personally?

- Do you carry around an awful lot of guilt and shame in your belly?

- Do you sometimes feel like your own emotions are out of control, and like there's something wrong with you?

- Do you often find yourself working hard to please others, to 'make nice,' in order to avoid rocking the boat?

- Do you sometimes avoid your own truth, because you're afraid it might upset someone in your life, or lead to an uncomfortable confrontation?

- Do you sometimes avoid doing something that might be good for you because you're afraid it won't work out, and leave you feeling unbearably disappointed?

- Do you use food to stuff down, control or regulate your feelings?

- Have you spent years on a therapist's couch (or being trained as one), learning how to understand, work with and heal through your feelings?

YOUR BLOSSOMING OPEN SPLEEN

Your Open SPLEEN is likely blossoming if you are and feel truly healthy—in your body, relationships and life. Over the years, you've learned how to listen to and trust your highly communicative body. You've become very good at sensing who and what is healthy for you, and who and what is not. You have a deep trust that your body is 'on your side,' providing you with the information you enjoy your aliveness and physicality. You've learned how to slow down, take your time, and resist the occasional urge you might feel to leap into (or out of!) a situation out of fear.

You've cultivated the ability to *be comfortable with physical discomfort*, partly because you know that all periods of discomfort eventually subside. With your blossoming Open Spleen, you ride any physically uncomfortable experience out, without giving into the temptation of the 'quick unhealthy fix.'

You know how to face your fears head on, instead of running away from them. Time and time again, you discover that your fears are true places of mastery.

You are known by the people in your life as someone who is really good at self-care. Not only that, but as someone who could easily be (or already is) a wonderful healer and self-care teacher. You enjoy gentle, subtle and alternative forms of medicine.

YOUR WILTING OPEN SPLEEN

Your Open Spleen may be wilting if you often make decisions out of fear. Or if you have an especially hard time letting go of relationships, jobs or situations that deep down, you know aren't good for you. Or if your mind is often busy trying to convince you to hold onto someone, some place, or some job, for all the wrong reasons. A sign of an overworked Open Spleen is an exaggerated willingness to do (or not do) just about anything—in order to be liked, to avoid feeling afraid, or to make money. If you tend to leap into things spontaneously or impulsively, just because it feels good in the moment, or you've struggled with co-dependent relationships, or substance abuse, or overeating, or some other addictions, your Open Spleen may be keeping you from living your authentic life. If you have a particularly high tolerance for unhealthy relationships, and you often struggle with feelings of inadequacy, then it may be time to share some of your loving attention with your Open Spleen.

Wisdom-Bringing Questions for your beautiful Open Spleen

● Do you often make decisions out of fear? Do you have a really hard time letting go of relationships, jobs or situations that deep down, you know aren't good for you?

● Is your mind often busy trying to convince you to hold onto someone, some place, or some job, for all the wrong reasons?

● Are you sometimes willing to do (or not do) just about anything to be liked, or to avoid feeling afraid?

● Do you tend to leap into things spontaneously or impulsively, just because it feels good in the moment?

● Have you struggled with co-dependent relationships? Substance abuse? Overeating? Other addictions?

● Do you have a particularly high tolerance for unhealthy relationships? Do you often struggle with feelings of inadequacy?

YOUR BLOSSOMING OPEN ROOT

Your Open ROOT Center is likely blossoming if you are living your life on your own terms. You simply understand that stress is a part of the world we live in, and that it's never going to go away. You've made a deep inner choice to stop allowing the pressures of the world to run (or ruin!) your life.

You've learned to take your time, to honor your own rhythms, and to make room for de-stressing activities, including a plethora of *non*-activities. You've become somewhat of an expert at taking in the pressures of the world, and then letting them flow right back out! Without acting on any of them.

With your blossoming Open Root, you also have become really good at discerning between positive pressure and the unhelpful kind. When a burst of 'positive pressure' comes along, you consciously and skillfully use that energy to your advantage, allowing tasks to be completed with incredible speed and efficiency.

Over the years, you have learned to cultivate—and ultimately facilitate in the world around you—the Art of Pacing.

YOUR WILTING OPEN ROOT

Your Open Root may be wilting if you **really** *don't enjoy* feeling stressed out! In fact, you hate it.
Or if you often feel like you're constantly living under a pressure cooker, and like the people and world around you are running your life. Or, if you're often hurrying up to get something done, so that you can finally rest.

There's a good chance your Open Root is overwhelmed if much of the time you find yourself making decisions under pressure, and starting **way** more things than you should.

If every time someone asks you to do something, you feel like you have to do it immediately.

Your Open Root is likely overloaded if you feel like you're living according to everyone else's schedule. If you find yourself driving fast, eating fast, doing everything fast, so that you can get to that next thing, so that you can finally be done with it all, it may be time to slow down and give that lovely Open Root of yours some care, attention, and a big ol' break!

Wisdom-Bringing Questions for your beautiful Open Root

● Do you *really really really not enjoy* feeling stressed out? Do you often feel like you're living under a pressure cooker? Like the world around you is running your life?

● Are you often hurrying up to get something done, so that you can finally rest?

● Do you make decisions under pressure, starting way more things than you should?

● If someone asks you to do something, do you feel like you have to do it now?

● Do you feel like you're living according to everyone else's schedule or rhythm than your own?

● Do you find yourself driving fast, eating fast, doing everything fast, so that you can get to that next thing?

THE IMPORTANCE OF EXPLORING
YOUR OPENNESS

I can't emphasize enough how important a deep and sincere exploration of your Openness can be. Unless you cultivate an awareness of your Openness and its impact on you, you can learn about the rest of your Design until the cows come home, and it isn't going to be much help.

While **so** much of your wisdom potential lies in these Open, receptive places in you, it will be quite challenging for you to access that wisdom until you fully understand just how skilled these Open Centers can be at sabotaging your life. Remember, these are the places in you where you're most vulnerable to the conditioning messages that keep telling you that you should be who you aren't. It is in these places that you're most likely to get pulled away from your truth, your Authority, your inner *Wisdom Keeper* who wants nothing more than to bring you fulfillment.

If you leave this Workbook/Course with anything, let it be a compassionate and lasting curiosity towards your Openness—a willingness, over time, to get to know each of your Open Centers, how they make you feel, how they speak to you, who in your early or present life they represent, and ultimately, how they get you to think that it's safer, smarter, or better for you to be someone that you're not.

Even if you don't have any Open Centers, and you aren't able to track your Openness in the same way that people with Open Centers can, you have *plenty* of Open places in your Design. All of us are much more Open and receptive than we are Defined.

Whenever you see a white place in your Design, whether it's a Center, Channel or a Gate, you are looking at something you're deeply attracted to. You're looking at those places in you where you are receptive and flexible, where you are open to change, where you are penetrable, inconsistent, where you actually take in, experience and reflect back the other (whether it be another person, an environment, or a universal transit).

Although these are places that you are designed to witness, play with and learn a great deal from, not to mention teach about, you are not necessarily naturally designed to easily handle the energies that they bring.

When someone walks up to you who is Defined where you're not, and you suddenly get filled up with these energies, (and remember, as soon as they come in, they get AMPLIFIED in you), you can end up working extremely hard—without even realizing it—either to manage and master the energies, to become an expert in them, or to get rid of the discomfort they bring, as quickly as possible.

When people learn about their Human Design for the first time, they can often be surprised to learn that they're open where they are, and Defined where they are. That totally happened to me. This is because we are so attracted to these Open places in us that we tend to live our entire lives in these arenas. We tend to think that those places are who we are, as opposed to places we're here to learn all about— and enjoy, play with and teach about—but not identify with.

ME BEFORE HUMAN DESIGN

If you were to ask me what kind of a person I was, before I knew anything about Human Design, I would confidently say that I was an extremely emotional person who spent the majority of her time (when she wasn't busy processing her feelings) thinking and trying to make sense of EVERYTHING, with a special emphasis on figuring out who she was and where she was going.

Basically, I'd be describing my four Open Centers—the Solar Plexus, Head, Ajna and G-Center. I was completely identified with these Centers and everything they represented. Learning about my Design was rather startling to me. Partly because much of my Definition is unconscious. (I have very little direct access to it.) Partly because I had devoted practically **my entire life** to the personal growth, self-discovery process. It was hard for me to imagine that after all of my efforts, I still knew so little about myself. Everything got turned upside down for me, which was both worrisome and intriguing. It took me some serious time to really grasp what it meant to live as my natural, unadulterated self.

As a deeply trained psychotherapist (and an experienced client!), I found it particularly challenging to understand the nature of the Solar Plexus, and how it operated in me, in others, and between us. When studying Human Design, I felt concerned that some people were being told that their feelings were real, and others (like me) were being told that their feelings weren't. It felt like some people were being given all of the emotional responsibility when it came to interpersonal conflicts, and others were being robbed of theirs. Now I know that none of that is true. We all have feelings. We all have responsibility for the emotional field that we co-inhabit. We just have different ways of experiencing emotionality, and different challenges.

It has taken me time to understand—not just intellectually, but in my own body, the energetic value of this knowledge, and how in the end, an awareness of the Solar Plexus has the potential to make me—all of us—even more conscious and responsible for our emotional lives.

I've had to do a lot of experimenting, and still do, where I go in and out of peoples' auras—or public spaces—in order to see what's coming from me, and what's coming from the outside, what are truly my own feelings, and what is just my particular brand of empathy, or my own highly sensitive reactions to and identifications with the feelings of others. I've found this tracking capacity extremely helpful in my own marriage with my husband, who is Defined emotionally, as well as in the relationship with my emotionally Defined daughter (and parents!).

My understanding is getting more nuanced over time. I'm getting delightfully less reactive, taking things less personally, and am much better at speaking my truth, and not running away from emotionally upsetting situations or confrontations. My husband Kim has also gotten much better at understanding and containing his own emotional process, taking his time in making decisions, and expressing himself in ways that don't freak me out so much that I end up reacting so strongly emotionally that he can't even feel his feelings, or his truth, anymore.

The Emotional Center is a BIG topic on a collective level. Supposedly our whole species is undergoing some big changes here—changes that hopefully will make us much more emotionally intelligent creatures! (Fingers triple-crossed on that one!)

For now, my main intention is to give you permission to take this information in, and to play around with it in your own way, at your own pace.

Watch your mind… Practice mindfulness in relation to this entire process. Notice your mind's favorite ways to manipulate you into not honoring your body, or not taking your time, or into overdoing, or staying in a place/relationship that isn't healthy for you. What are the biggest fear pictures it shows you?

(If you have Open Centers, as most of us do, start tracking the voices of your Open Centers. 'Ah, now it's that Open Head Center talking. I can feel the pressure to answer questions, that when I really think about it, aren't actually relevant to my life.' Or, 'Oh, now it's that Open G-Center. I'm feeling pressured to make this decision because I'm afraid if I don't, I won't have an identity or purpose that everyone can understand, or I might lose the love of someone I care about.' Or, 'Oh, there's that Open Root Center pushing me to do something now, when my body is exhausted... because I have this thought that if I can just get this over with, then I'll be able to rest, or because everyone around me is stressing me out, and I just want to get rid of the stress.')

Even if you don't have Open Centers, it doesn't matter. Just track those kinds of voices anyway. They're likely reflecting some of the Open Gates and Channels that are all over your Bodygraph. Either way, it's such a good practice to become really familiar with your mind's favorite manipulative, self-sabotaging—even though the intention is to be protective—tactics. You get the idea.

Feel free to say 'no' to or challenge what you're learning here too. It may not be true for you. Or you just might need your own way to relate to it. There are as many Human Design prisms as there are people learning and teaching Human Design.

That said, I wouldn't be here, offering this information to you, if over the course of my own experiment, and my work with countless clients over the years, I didn't find something profoundly valuable in this mysterious Human Design world. Part of my desire to share this knowledge with you is to expand the research pool. Ultimately, I'm hoping that together we can gain a broader sense of how Human Design applies, or doesn't, to different people.

I truly invite and encourage you to try to stay open to the possibility that who you've always thought you were, you may not be, and who you never thought you were, you actually are. At the very least, you'll be giving yourself an opportunity to uncover aspects of yourself that have long been buried, and free yourself of some identifications that haven't served you well.

ARE YOUR DEFINED CENTERS BLOOMING? OR WILTING?

We all experience conditioning!

When we speak of "Definition" in Human Design, we're referring to your **Nature**. We are talking about what you are uniquely designed to be and do in life, your potential, your life force. The colored in areas (Centers, Channels, Gates) of your Bodygraph have so much to say about what kind of 'student' you are when it comes to the school of life. They indicate what is solid and reliable in you, what makes up those parts of your nature that are consistent and free from outer influence. They also reflect what you transmit into the world around you, simply by being you (as well as what you most likely take for granted!).

(An example: Any time you have a Center that is colored in, it means you have a consistent or specialized way of processing the kind of energy represented by that Center. If you have a Defined or colored in Ajna Center, this means that you have a specific and specialized way of processing information. You have a consistent way of thinking.)

Remember, when we're working with Human Design, we're looking at a map. As the transpersonalists say, the map is not to be confused with the territory! When we look at areas of your Design that reflect your Definition, please remember that you're so much more than what can be captured here.

Also, even if our conditioning enters our bodies through our "Openness," this doesn't mean that we can't experience the impact of conditioning on our Definition, or Nature. In fact, I've found that many people experience a great deal of difficulties in relation to their True Nature because of their conditioning.

Many women I know who have Defined Ego Centers, for example, were deeply shamed for being too strong-willed when they were young. They received conditioning messages saying, "Good girls should be feminine, obedient and soft, not stubborn, strong-willed and unruly." Similarly, men are constantly bombarded by messages telling them that they should be tough, confident, unfeeling and unshakable. They face being teased, bullied and the victims of our unfortunately misogynistic culture if they show or nurture their sensitivity, or characteristics associated with being female.

Even though people have 'Defined Ego Centers,' they can experience the impact of deeply negative conditioning in relation to that Center. What sometimes happens is that the expression of that Center becomes distorted. It becomes either reactive or repressive, taking on a 'shadow' form.

Many women, for example, end up turning their strong Will against themselves, instead of using it as a path towards self-empowerment and service to the world. Either that, or they learn to use their Will in indirect ways, and are experienced as manipulative. Many men learn to override or repress more sensitive aspects of their personalities in favor of an exaggerated Ego, and end up emotionally crippled, relationally isolated, and helplessly caught playing out empty, often destructive narcissistic wounds.

When we look at Jungian psychology, and we talk about the *Shadow*, it can be helpful to remember that the *Shadow* isn't always a reflection of those human qualities that are obviously shunned by society, like anger, jealousy, vindictiveness, vulnerability, etc. The *Shadow* can just as well be our Light, our strength, our talent, our joy, our capacity for ecstasy. Our Nature.

What makes something a *Shadow* is not the quality itself, but the fact that that quality has been forbidden, cast out, forced to split off from our conscious identity.

I don't want us to get too rigid here. It's easy in Human Design circles to say, "Oh, I've got seven Open Centers, so I'm much more vulnerable to conditioning than someone with fewer." While there may be some truth to that, it's certainly not the whole story.

So many factors contribute to our experience of Openness and Definition.

Some people I know with many Open Centers have an incredible core strength that allows them to transmute their sensitivity into wisdom and clarity. Somehow, they're able to take a lot in without being flooded, or over-identifying with what's coming into their systems.

Some highly-Defined people I know—because of their specific backgrounds—experience enormous vulnerability in the few yet potent places where they are Open. The accumulated strength of their Definition becomes a horrible self-berating force to be reckoned with.

Just as I don't want you to become over-identified with or feel 'victimized' by your Openness, I don't want you to become over-identified with or victimized by your Nature. Remember, you were born with the absolutely perfect combination of Definition and Openness for your you to live out your unique purpose!

Please hold the descriptions below lightly. They are simply *possible* ways to understand and appreciate yourself, your gifts and tendencies.

Another thing I want you to keep in mind about the Bodygraph—this map—is that it isn't two dimensional. It's multi-dimensional. There is a whole range of frequencies with which an inner quality can come to life and be expressed—all the way from the most shadowy, to the most sublime.

It's all evolving. Nothing is written in stone.

HEAD

The Head Center is the place where we experience mental pressure. It is also where we receive ideas and inspiration, and where all of the questions we grapple with as human beings are sourced.

- Who are we?

- Where do we come from?

- Where are we going?

- Why are we here?

YOUR BLOOMING DEFINED HEAD CENTER

From an Integral perspective, it is the Head Center where the deepening and expansion of consciousness itself takes place.

When your Defined Head Center is truly blooming, you are likely honoring and using your mind's natural—and specialized!—gift for inspiration. The specific Gates activating your Head Center are going to illuminate your unique way of experiencing inspired intelligence. (While I don't cover this level of Design detail in this Workbook, I will be sharing resources at the end of our journey together, in case you'd like to delve deeper into the details.)

When your Defined Head Center is blooming, you don't only allow yourself to be deeply inspired by whatever themes interest you, but you easily and happily share the fruits of your intellectual explorations with other people (the right people!)—in a way that truly inspires them.

YOUR WILTING DEFINED HEAD CENTER

If your Defined Head Center is wilting, you might find that the people around you aren't quite as interested, inspired by or able to understand the themes that matter to you. This can be difficult, painful and lonely.

When you're under the influence of 'negative conditioning pressures,' you can end up taking your beautiful, unique intellectual gifts and repressing them.

If the people around you don't understand you, you can end up ignoring or dismissing your true interests. You can walk around feeling deeply misunderstood and hopeless about ever being met by people who truly appreciate and care about what you care about.

Other possible shadow expressions of your Defined Head Center could be:

- a tendency for tunnel vision

- a tendency to 'talk at' people, sharing your ideas and questions without necessarily checking in with them

- being so caught up in the activities of your mind that you lose touch with your environment

AJNA

The Ajna Center is what we usually refer to as the Mind. It's that place where we experience mental awareness, as well as our ability to conceptualize, analyze, rationalize, strategize, form opinions, ideas, beliefs, etc.

You could say the Ajna is the home of the witness, the neo-cortex of the brain, that part of us that is able to self-reflect, and to experience awareness itself. There is tremendous potential here.

The Ajna is not only the place where we store concrete data or think; it's also the place where we experience mental anxiety. It's the place through which our diverse conditioning sources fight for our attention and obedience, by filling our heads with lots of 'shoulds.'

(For thousands of years, we human beings have been relying on this strategic awareness Center to make our decisions for us. Though Human Design points to a shifting away from the Ajna as the ultimate Authority, we would not have survived or thrived as a species, if this Center hadn't played such a central role in our evolution.)

YOUR BLOOMING DEFINED AJNA CENTER

From an Integral perspective, it is the Ajna Center where our potential to develop self-reflective awareness sits.

When your Defined Ajna Center is truly blooming, you are likely honoring and enjoying your mind's natural—and specialized!—way of thinking. The specific Gates activating your Ajna Center are going to illuminate your unique cognitive style and way of processing information.

When your Defined Ajna Center is blooming, you don't only allow your mind to think the way it thinks, but you really love processing concepts that interest you, and you do it in a way that is comprehensive and satisfying.

YOUR WILTING DEFINED AJNA CENTER

If your Defined Ajna Center is wilting, you might find that the people around you don't quite relate to the way that you think, and this can be painful or lonely. You can feel easily misunderstood.

When you're under the influence of 'negative conditioning pressures,' you can end up taking your active mind and turning its gift for thinking against yourself… through self-judgment, self-doubting and over-analyzing.

Other possible shadow expressions of your Defined Ajna Center could be:

- difficulties looking at things from an alternative point of view

- stubbornly holding onto your perspective as the only correct one

- feeling uncomfortable or insecure when presented with themes and concepts that don't necessarily mesh with your own way of thinking.

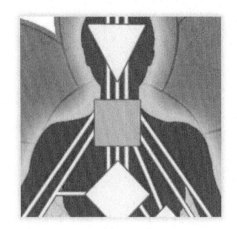

THROAT

The Throat Center is connected to our capacity to communicate with words, as well as to manifest things in the outer world. It is all about self-expression—whether through words or actions, and our essential need and desire to contribute something meaningful and tangible to the world.

YOUR BLOOMING DEFINED THROAT CENTER

From an Integral perspective, it is the Throat Center that houses the essence of Expression.

When your Defined Throat Center is truly blooming, you are likely honoring and enjoying your natural—and specialized!—way of expressing yourself in the world. You have a very special way of speaking and acting, and you trust in your ability and readiness to impact the world positively through your unique self-expression.

The specific Gates activating your Throat Center are going to illuminate your unique style of expression.

YOUR WILTING DEFINED THROAT CENTER

If your Defined Throat Center is wilting, you might find yourself sharing too much, or acting impulsively—in the presence of people who aren't necessarily open or ready to receive your expression. One of the big lessons for you in life is to know when it's time to practice restraint and to develop sensitivity to your environment.

When you're under the influence of 'negative conditioning pressures,' you can end up learning that in order to survive, or to avoid painful resistance or rejection, you have to suppress your natural self-expression.

Other possible shadow expressions of your Defined Throat Center could be:

- tendencies to carry a deep fear that you won't be received when you express yourself

- tendencies to go on and on without realizing it

- tendencies to interrupt.

G/IDENTITY

The G- or Identity Center is where the "self" resides, where we get a sense of identity, a direction in life, and where we experience love and an inner sense of alignment.

This Center also houses something fascinating called the Magnetic Monopole. (As shared earlier, the Magnetic Monopole is a magnetic-like force that only attracts, bringing all of our 'parts'—body, mind, Spirit—together, bringing the right people and experiences to us, as well as pulling us along our own unique path in life. It gives us the illusion that we are each separate, whole beings, even though at a spiritual and sub-atomic level, we are all deeply inter-connected.)

YOUR BLOOMING DEFINED G/IDENTITY CENTER

From an Integral perspective, it is the G-Center that is all about Identity and Alignment.

When your Defined G-Center is truly blooming, you are likely honoring and enjoying your strong and very particular identity as you move through the world. You have the potential to truly experience a clear inner orientation and sense of self. With this built-in compass, you can walk your own path in life, as well as inspire authentic paths for others. You also can really become a Love specialist!

The specific Gates activating your G-Center are going to illuminate your unique relationship to identity, direction and love.

YOUR WILTING DEFINED G/IDENTITY CENTER

When your Defined G-Center is wilting, you might find it difficult to switch course, or to change your direction, when life is asking for this kind of flexibility. The inner urges you feel to stick with your own habitual direction in life can be so strong at times, that you stop listening or seeing the signs. This can cause you to miss out on opportunities and experiences that could be healthy or beneficial for you.

When you're under the influence of 'negative conditioning pressures,' you can end up ignoring, holding back or restricting your own natural alignment, sense of direction, or way of loving. This is especially true when you can feel that others don't necessarily understand you or your unique way of moving through life.

Other possible shadow expressions of your Defined G-Center could be:

- carrying a deep fear that if you're true to yourself, you'll have to walk your path alone

- abandoning your inner alignment and your own life journey, and just doing what others expect or want you to do

- judging your natural approach to love.

EGO/HEART

As shared about earlier, in Human Design, the Heart/Ego Center is quite different than what we usually think about when we think of our hearts. The Heart Center is one of the body's four motors, and it has everything to do with Will, commitment, loyalty, competition and courage.

It also has to do with manifesting on the material plane, whether we're talking about money or all of the many services, contributions and support structures that are needed for families, communities and cultures to survive and thrive. It has to do with what we value.

YOUR BLOOMING DEFINED EGO/HEART CENTER

From an Integral perspective, the Ego/Heart Center is all about cooperation. It's about our human capacity to bring our individual wills together for the purpose of fulfilling our collective human and spiritual needs. When we can do this, we begin to taste what it means to live together in a peaceful, synergistic and sustainable way.

When your Defined Ego/Heart Center is truly blooming, you are built to use your Will in order to contribute to this wonderful world of ours in a very unique and specialized way. You know and trust this about yourself, you feel both ready and motivated to make your contribution, and you value what you do... just as you value the contributions of others.

The specific Gates activating your Ego/Heart Center are going to illuminate how your communal self relates to identity, direction and love (G-Center), how it manifests and expresses itself (Throat Center) within the context of *the tribe*, and how your emotional life (Solar Plexus) and intuitive instincts (Splenic Center) can be used in service of collaboration.

YOUR WILTING DEFINED EGO/HEART CENTER

When your Ego/Heart Center is wilting, you may have trouble recognizing, respecting and valuing other people's contributions.

When you're under the influence of 'negative conditioning pressures,' you can end up oppressing your own Will and feel deeply unrecognized for all that you do, like you're caught in an endless rat race or an unwanted competition (where you end up in the losing position), or hopelessly overworked and underpaid.

Other possible shadow expressions of your Defined Ego/Heart Center could be:

- tendencies to overemphasize the importance of your own priorities

- tendencies to exaggerate the size of your own contributions

- tendencies to experience intestinal and/or cardiovascular issues.

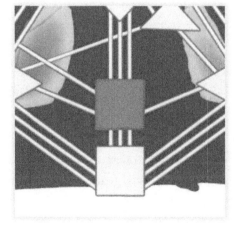

SACRAL

As shared earlier, the Sacral Center is one of the 4 motors in the body. It's all about ENERGY. This is the place where our work force, life force and sexual energy are experienced. This Center has to do with power, fertility and creativity. It also has to do with availability, and the ability to sustain activity and work in life.

The Sacral Center actually has a voice. More often than not, this voice speaks in sounds (i.e. hums, grunts, squeals, etc.) as opposed to words. Anyone whose Sacral Center is colored in is a Generator.

YOUR BLOOMING DEFINED SACRAL CENTER

From an Integral perspective, the Sacral Center is all about the natural flow of energy. When your Defined Sacral Center is truly blooming, your energy is designed to flow out into the world in a very specialized way.

The specific Gates activating your Sacral Center are going to illuminate your unique relationship to your energetic and creative life.

YOUR WILTING DEFINED SACRAL CENTER

When your Sacral Center is wilting, you may feel a great deal of frustration when you're pushing yourself to do things that aren't truly aligned with your nature, or that you just don't want to do, or feel like doing in the moment.

When you're under the influence of 'negative conditioning pressures,' you can end up using all of your precious life force energy in all the wrong places, doing all of the wrong things. You can end up working like a slave, doing menial work, and not engaging your body in ways that make the most of its natural aliveness and power.

Other possible shadow expressions of your Defined Sacral Center could be:

- burnout

- workaholism

- frustration

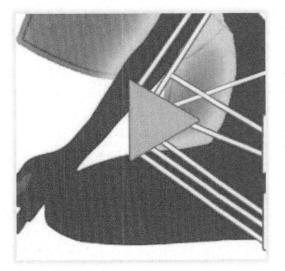

SPLEEN

As shared earlier, the Spleen is the seat of our immune system, our intuition, our primal survival fears, as well as our ability to be physically aware in the now. It's the oldest awareness Center that we have. In fact, all animals have it. You could call it the seat of our instinctual animal awareness.

YOUR BLOOMING DEFINED SPLENIC CENTER

From an Integral perspective, the Spleen is all about the Intuition. It's about our capacity as human beings to practice embodied presence, to be fully aligned with our body's intelligence. When your Defined Spleen is truly blooming, your intuitive perception is specialized. You have a very particular way of following your body's sensations, and trusting them to guide the way in which you intuitively interact with the world.

The specific Gates activating your Spleen are going to illuminate your unique relationship to your intuition and body.

When you really embrace your blooming Spleen, you find that you have tremendous clarity. Without overthinking, you surrender to your instincts and trust your body's intelligence. At lightning speed, you can use your intuitive gifts to determine who and what are healthy, safe and right for you.

YOUR WILTING DEFINED SPLENIC CENTER

When your Splenic Center is wilting, you may have a difficult time discerning between spontaneous intuition, natural alertness... and mental fear. It can be difficult to take action when you need to, and not bogged down by a logical and doubt-ridden mindset. You could end up second-guessing yourself when it's time to take a leap.

When you're under the influence of 'negative conditioning pressures,' you can take your strong body for granted and ignore your body's signals and need for regular health check-ups. You can become a very slow and sluggish decision-maker. You can end up feeling very alone when it comes to your own sense of timing.

Other possible shadow expressions of your Defined Splenic Center could be:

- impatience and agitation

- feeling 'hectic'

- a tendency to constantly overreact to stimuli

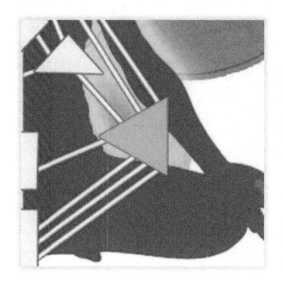

SOLAR PLEXUS

The Solar Plexus, or the Emotional Center, is where our emotions, our capacity for pain and pleasure and nervousness reside. According to Human Design, this Center is undergoing a powerful transformation, moving from being a blind motor to an awareness Center.

When you have a Defined Solar Plexus, you are designed to experience yourself and others through a particular filter of emotional awareness. You also have a specialized way of moving through your own emotions.

YOUR BLOOMING DEFINED SOLAR PLEXUS

From an Integral perspective, the Solar Plexus is all about the field of Emotion. When your Defined Solar Plexus is truly blooming, you both enjoy and respect the depth and breadth of your own emotional landscape.

The specific Gates activating your Solar Plexus are going to illuminate your particular way of experiencing your emotional life and wave.

When you really embrace your blooming Solar Plexus, you develop a profound appreciation for the unique way you understand and experience (over a period of time) your own multi-faceted emotional nature. You also have a deep appreciation for the depth and complexities of other beings, things and the world itself. You become a deeply patient being.

YOUR WILTING DEFINED SOLAR PLEXUS

When your Solar Plexus Center is wilting, you can have trouble responsibly handling the fullness, intensity and depth of your own emotional life. It can be hard for you to accept how much time it can take you to move from an emotionally turbulent state to a more calm and clear one, where you have a much better sense of who you are, how you feel, what you want, and what you need. You can give into impatience and end up leaping into experiences, commitments and relationships before you're ready.

When you're under the influence of 'negative conditioning pressures,' you can feel so much pressure to make a decision before you're ready. You can habitually learn to not give yourself the space, time and support you need to process your deep feelings. Without even realizing it, you can end up accumulating a lot of emotional triggers, and acting out in ways that can be emotionally unsettling for those around you.

Other possible shadow expressions of your Defined Solar Plexus Center could be:

- decision-making paralysis

- emotional turbulence that just doesn't go away

- excessive perspiration

- being in a state of emotional 'overcharge'—which can lead to expressions of helplessness, violence, aggression, and/or a need to constantly defend, explain or justify how you feel

ROOT

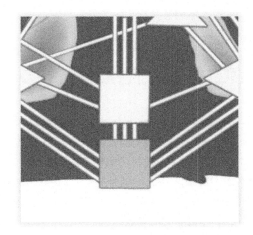

The Root Center is where we experience stress and adrenaline, the pressure or impulse to move, to change, to start things, to need, to desire, to have new experiences. It's where we get the fuel for life itself.

When you have a Defined Root, you are designed to experience a highly-specialized impulse to grow, and a particular way of impacting the world.

YOUR BLOOMING DEFINED ROOT CENTER

From an Integral perspective, the Root is all about the Impulse. When your Defined Root is truly blooming, you dare to follow your intense inner drives, while remaining happy and at ease. You know deep down that you are here to move something into the world in a concrete way, and you embrace this.

The specific Gates activating your Root are going to illuminate your particular way of experiencing your natural impulse to grow and move.

YOUR WILTING DEFINED ROOT CENTER

When your Root Center is wilting, you may not always realize that not everyone is as excited about or motivated by the impulses that drive you. You may end up feeling trapped in an environment that for you feels stagnating or stuck. When you're under the influence of 'negative conditioning pressures,' you can learn that it isn't safe to trust and follow your impulses. Instead of embracing the forces that motivate you, you hold back; you restrain your life force.

Other possible shadow expressions of your Defined Root Center could be:

- deep distress

- feeling strained all of the time

- compulsive tendencies

- being overly 'hyper' or 'on'.

SOME FINAL WORDS ABOUT CONDITIONING

Remember as I shared earlier, this is rarely a conscious process, for anyone involved.

As a child, you simply take others in, from the day you are born—or conceived!—absorbing at a very deep level who 'the others' are, as if _who they are_ is _who YOU are._ Similarly, your parents or teachers aren't necessarily, or intentionally, trying to hurt or sabotage you… unless something went deeply wrong in their own conditioning past. Though there may be a need for healthy boundary-setting, there is no need for blame or shame. This is really about liberating everyone through a path of understanding, empowerment and ultimately, compassion.

#1: Explore Your Openness

Use the Bodygraph on the next page to begin exploring your Open Center/s and the messages you've received through them.

Explore your Openness!

Begin by coloring in your Defined Centers, so that only your 'white' or Open Centers are left.

Take a few minutes to visit each of your Open Centers. Based on what you've learned so far about what each Center represents, write down a few of the main messages you've received through each of your Open Centers.

You might want to have two separate lists for each Center:

● One for the messages that have less positively conditioned you, that have distracted you from your life, or made you doubt, judge or reject your own nature.

● The second for the messages that have nurtured and supported your Openness, the messages that have made you more mindful, reflective and wise.

As you go through this process, notice how often your Open Centers are working together.

An example:

"I better hurry up (Open Root) and come through on all of my promises (Open Ego/Heart), or else people will get mad at me (Solar Plexus), and then I'll be alone and unprotected (Spleen)."

Get the idea?

Write down any insights, thoughts or feelings that arise on the piece of paper in your Blossoming Journal.

For those with no Open Centers

If you have no Open Centers, you are indeed a very rare being, who can have a deep impact on the people around you—since you have more Definition than most. Lucky for you, you still are dealing with conditioning messages all the time, because we're all more open and receptive than we are Defined!

In your case, however, it's likely to be less important that you look into what's coming into you through any given Center. It's even more important to explore what may be coming in through your Open GATES. (Those half white lines that you can see coming out of your Defined Centers.)

It's beyond the scope of this Workbook/Course to go into the Gates of your Design, but that doesn't matter. It's not necessary for you to have all of those details to be able to deepen your exploration into your own conditioning.

For you, I want to start exploring the questions:

- What have I come to think that I'm missing?

- What am I afraid to miss out on?"

For example, "Who do I think I need to be with, what do I think I need to learn, what might I need to feel, or express, or experience, or initiate... in order to be and feel like a whole and complete person?"

On your Bodygraph, I invite you to visit each Center with this flavor of questioning, while looking for the messages you've received about what's missing in relation to each of the Centers. For example:

What have you been taught to think that you're missing, from an intellectual perspective (Head or Ajna) or from an emotional perspective (Solar Plexus) or from a money or survival perspective (Spleen)? What are the fears you have about not having these things or experiences or feelings or capacities? "If I don't find _____, then this might happen." "If I don't experience _____, then this might happen." Or, "If I don't embody _____, then it means this about me as a person." Just write down your thoughts and insights, and see what arises.

 ## #2: Track the Messages

For those with Open Centers

Bring out your Conditioning flower, the one you made in the BE YOURSELF Petal. Place this Conditioning flower next to your Open Centers exploration.

Just take a little time to look at your two explorations.

What do you notice? Do you immediately see similarities? Themes showing up in both places?

Look more deeply at the messages represented by your Conditioning Flower.

(Look for additional messages you might not have thought about when going through your Open Centers for the first time.)

Now see if you can begin to track **which Center** these messages might be coming through.

In other words, what would happen if you cut out each message from your Conditioning Flower, and pasted it directly onto your Nine-Centered Bodygraph. Where would you put each message?

A Few Examples:

- A message in the SUCCESS PETAL that says, "I have to have facts to back up everything that I say and do, otherwise I won't be seen as intelligent."

  ...would be pasted into your OPEN AJNA.

- A message in the BODY PETAL that says, "I have to be thin and in perfect shape, otherwise I won't be desirable to a partner and I'll never have a family."

  ...would be pasted into your OPEN EGO/HEART CENTER.

- A message in the LOVE PETAL that says, "I have to be nice, polite and self-sacrificing all of the time, otherwise people might get mad at me."

  ...would be pasted into your OPEN SOLAR PLEXUS.

Find a way to concretize this. You can use the Bodygraph provided on the next page, this time, placing the messages from your CONDITIONING FLOWER in their respective Centers... by writing them down.

Or, you can actually create a large version of your BODYGRAPH, and create a new collage, where you literally cut out messages from your Conditioning Flower, and paste them into their Open Center homes.

Or, you can do something else! Remember, you can do it however you want. This is your unique and precious life.

Track the Messages!

Some inspiring examples from Designed to *Blossom* participants!

For those with no Open Centers

If you have no Open Centers, you have a lot going on in your Design, a lot of wonderful potential. You also are likely to be really 'felt' by others when you walk into a room (e.g. how you feel, what you're thinking, whether you're feeling satisfied or frustrated, etc.). This is likely to be true, whether you're aware of this or not.

For you, becoming conscious of your impact on others is going to be as big a part of your experiment as learning about how you're specifically impacted by the world. In the end, experimenting with operating in alignment with that intuitive yet emotionally influenced belly of yours is what's going to help you understand and share the gifts that you bring in a way that makes a positive difference in the lives of others. You are obviously someone with so much to offer.

Again, for you, it's less important that you track your Openness in the way I'm encouraging others to do, since you have no Open Centers. However, you can do this same process, looking for messages that seem to really speak to this question of 'missing something.'

Let's say in the Significant Other petal, you see a message like, "Happily Ever After." You can ask yourself, "Have I learned to believe that if I don't have a partner, I will miss out on happiness? That that's the only way for me to achieve happiness? That I can't do it on my own?" That's just one example.

Again, even though the Open Center exploration doesn't apply to you, the Bodygraph does. The themes of each Center, like archetypes, still hold great relevance to you. Feel free to write down (or if you're doing a collage, cut and paste) messages that feel particularly charged for you onto the part of the Bodygraph that feels right to you, based on what you've learned about the Centers and the themes they've carried.

Or, just place the messages intuitively wherever you feel they should be. Do what feels right to you. You don't have to follow any rules here. You've got a strong intuition! As long as the process is interesting to you, and you've got the energy for it, you're on the right track!

#3: Create the Bodygraph of your Dreams!

For those with Open Centers

In each Open Center, write down (or draw, or paint, or collage):

- the most nurturing and positive messages you ever received

- the messages you wish you received, but never did

- the messages you intend to give yourself (or seek out, invite in, or surround yourself with) from now on!

The more energy you put into this process, the more potent this act of self-nurturance will be! I promise!

My thoughts, for example:

HEAD:

I am not responsible for solving every problem.
I can trust myself to know who and what is inspiring and relevant to my life.

AJNA:

I don't have to know anything for sure!
My brain isn't built to be organized! It's built to synthesize!
I don't have to have it all figured out in order to have a great life!

G/IDENTITY:

My life gets to be a grand adventure!
I don't have to know where I'm going.
My job is to reflect my daughter's essence so she can find herself, not to direct her.

SOLAR PLEXUS:

It is OK (and safe) for me to say 'no' sometimes.
I am not responsible for solving every conflict or hurt feeling.
It is safe for me to speak my truth.

If you have no Open Centers, NO WORRIES!
You can create the Bodygraph of your dreams too.

Don't worry so much about what messages belong where. Simply come up with the most healing, supportive and empowering messages you can imagine, and place them wherever you like. This can be a profoundly powerful process. Remember to emphasize the fact that you are whole and complete, exactly the way you are, and that you're not missing anything!

Support Your Life: Petal Five

Your Inner Wisdom Keeper's Unique Truth Compass

Welcome to the fifth petal, called SUPPORT YOUR LIFE! This is one of my favorite petals, because you're going to learn how to trust in your own AUTHORITY—or your UNIQUE TRUTH COMPASS. It's the perfect time to learn this.

OK, so in your everyday life, you are likely to find yourself pulled in a million directions, often away from your own internal sense of what is right for you. Without even realizing it, through those Open Centers, you take in and come to own the values, beliefs and habits of those around you. You walk around with your parents, teachers, peers, bosses, institutions, cultural leaders, even global trends speaking to you through 'shoulds' in your mind, telling you what to do, and why *not doing it* would be a bad, even dangerous idea! Most of the time, the conditioning forces in your life contradict each other, making your task of 'figuring out' what to do even more difficult and confusing.

Of course, as we explored in the last Petal (Synthesize your Parts), just as it is a part of human nature to have a busy monkey mind, it is also in your nature to be influenced, to be penetrable. Your **Openness** is one of your most wonderful qualities. Without the nurturing influence of others, you could never reach your full potential as a unique-yet-interconnected human being. And still, when it comes to the process of making decisions, you can get so lost, and 'under the influence' that you can't feel your truth at all.

What we call *Authority* in Human Design is that place we can turn to for Truth—that part of us that we can trust to make our decisions in life, and to honor our own right timing. Just as we don't all belong to the same flower family, not everyone has the same kind of Authority. Thus, one person's decision-making process can look and feel much different from another's.

Human Design puts each of us in touch with our own unique truth-detecting system, so that in any given moment, we can make the most of the gifts we receive from the outside world without losing ourselves, or our ground, in the process. We can enjoy our Openness, without getting caught by it... or over-identified with it. As we begin to make decisions from our 'Definition,' as opposed to our Openness, we begin to liberate our inner *Wisdom Keeper*. Learning about our Authority shows us how to honor those parts of us that are consistent and trustworthy (no matter what's going on around us). It adds an additional dimension to our self-trust experiment and practice. A super important dimension.

HOW TO DETERMINE WHICH AUTHORITY YOU HAVE

EMOTIONAL Authority

If your Solar Plexus is Defined, you have emotional Definition, and you have Emotional Authority.

SACRAL (GENERATED) Authority

You have Sacral Authority if your Design has these characteristics:

- You are a Generator (your Sacral Center is Defined)
- Your Solar Plexus is not Defined
- You do not have a motor connected to the Throat Center

SPLENIC AWARENESS Authority

You have Splenic Awareness Authority if your Design has these characteristics:

- Your Spleen Center is Defined
- Your Solar Plexus and Sacral Centers are undefined

EGO/Heart Authority

You have Ego Authority if your Design has these characteristics:

- Your Heart Center and Throat Center are Defined and connected
- Your Sacral, Solar Plexus, and Spleen are all undefined

SELF-PROJECTED Authority

You have Self-Projected Authority if your Design has these characteristics:

- Your G-Center and Throat Center are Defined and connected
- You have no other Centers Defined except possibly the Head and/or Ajna

OUTER Authority

You have Outer Authority if your Design has this characteristic:

- You have no Centers Defined beneath the Throat

LET'S DIVE DEEPER!

EMOTIONAL AUTHORITY

The mere fact that your Solar Plexus is Defined, or colored in, automatically tells me that it is your Authority in life. It trumps both of the other awareness Centers—the Ajna, which is a mental awareness, which is never a person's Authority anyway, and the Spleen, which is a primitive, intuitive awareness, as well as the oldest awareness existing in all living beings.

It doesn't even matter if you have all three awareness Centers colored in. If you have a Defined Emotional Center, it'll overpower all of it. That's because the Emotional Center is an extremely powerful motor that operates constantly, and in a wave so great that it can drown out the intuition, which often only speaks once and comparatively softly, and can overwhelm the mind, no matter how hard the mind is working to make sense of things.

The Solar Plexus is that big and strong. It must be respected.

This means that no matter what decision you're making, you must consult with your emotions. Whether you're a Generator making a decision to respond, a Projector deciding whether to accept an invitation, or a Manifestor deciding whether to manifest something or not, you'll need to take your feelings into consideration. You'll very likely need some time to get clear on what—and who—is right for you.

Now, when a Human Design person says, "Oh, you're emotional," it actually means something quite different than what most people assume. What it means in this context is that you are here to know the pain and pleasure of need, passion and desire. You have the potential to be a deeply attractive, warm, sexually exciting person, capable of seeing and experiencing beauty, even in life's most melancholy moments. Through your very presence, you can literally fill up the people around you—especially those who are Open emotionally—with your rich, juicy emotional life, with a deep sense of pleasure, even Spirit.

As I said earlier, you must make your decisions based on how you feel, not what you think. To know what is best for you, you must learn to trust what you feel more than anything else. Your feelings are deeply intelligent.

But here's the tricky thing. You can't necessarily know how you really feel about something or someone right away, as much as you may wish you could. This is because your emotions move in a wave over time. This is how the motor of the Solar Plexus works. It moves in a wave, from hope to pain, from expectation to disappointment, from like to dislike, from joy to despair, from mini-death to rebirth, and back again. Some people experience it as a wave from a whole lot of energy, to exhaustion.

I'd like you to start thinking of your emotional life like a climate. Imagine that you live in a very dynamic, and seasonal climate. You were born totally equipped to deal with the various seasons, the change in weather... like an animal that grows a thick layer of fur in the winter, and then sheds it in the summer. (You may be so equipped to deal with your emotional ups and downs that you don't even realize that they're happening.)

It is because of this constantly changing, moving nature of your emotional life, that your truth can only be revealed **over time**. If you can just learn to wait for emotional clarity before making your decisions, if you can learn to 'play hard to get,' to say things like, "Oh God, that sounds like a great idea, or a wonderful invitation. Let me get back to you when I have a sense of whether I can do it." Or, "I'm contemplating starting this thing, but I feel I need a bit more time. If you don't mind I'd like to sleep on that." Or, "Can I get back to you tomorrow?" Or next week? Or next month?! If you can learn to do that, your life can change dramatically, and for the better.

Emotional beings like you have a different kind of potential awareness than others because of the nature of the frequency of the Solar Plexus motor. Take a Splenic being, for example, someone who has a Defined Spleen, but not a Defined Solar Plexus. This person is designed to grasp everything in the moment. The Emotional being, on the other hand, goes through a **wave process**. The focus of whatever decision or situation you're dealing with remains the same, but the focus goes through a complete spectrum. In other words, you have the potential to actually grasp circumstances and people in a more comprehensive and thorough way than most people. It is what you are made for... **IF** you can resist the impulse to act spontaneously, and give yourself permission to wait for clarity.

The Basics for those with Emotional Authority

● *You never have to make a decision before you're ready!*

(Your mind may instantly grasp this, but your body will likely need time to absorb it. To feel its rightness, whether it's a fit for you.)

- *It's all about distance.* It's about 'physical distance.' You actually get physical distance from a given dilemma (and the kind of 'clarity' that comes with distance) by giving yourself time.

- *Time is your best friend!* With time, decisions that don't really matter, that aren't actually relevant to your life, just fade away. Decisions that do matter either get really calm and clear (one way or the other), or they get increasingly charged.

- *If there's too much charge, chances are very high that you're still not ready to make the decision.* If your environment is pushing you to be ready, then it's a 'No.' If something or someone is truly right for you, it will wait for you.

- *Your emotional life is deeply chemical. It's not personal.* Your emotional wave will have its own movement and cycles within you… all of which are perfectly OK. At different parts of your cycle, you'll be able to feel into different truths. Just like when a woman has a period, she can feel some things more intensely than other times. This doesn't make what she feels at the peak of her cycle any less true. It also doesn't mean she should be making her biggest life decisions during those particularly intense days!

- *You are someone who always needs to take your feelings into consideration when making a decision.* You're happiest when you can make decisions in a way that honors your feelings. You're not a logical decision-maker. At the same time, you aren't meant to make decisions when you're super charged emotionally. It's more about moving through the entire spectrum of feelings in relation to a decision, until the tidal waves turn into little ripples, into calm waters… That's when you know you're ready.

- *Imagine you met an elephant.* A Splenic (purely intuitive) photographer might take one snapshot of the elephant and be done, but you'd be a different kind of photographer. You'd be the kind that walks over to the elephant and takes a hundred pictures. Maybe even a thousand. You'd look at it from every possible angle. You'd probably use more than your eyes too. You'd sense it, smell it, touch it, etc. You'd really FEEL it. You'd have the potential to really grasp the essence of that elephant, from all sorts of perspectives—the pretty to the not-so pretty! In the end, you'd have a very deep appreciation for that elephant. (And be in a much better position to decide what you want to do with it!)

When an emotionally Defined person like you comes to understand this about yourself, when you learn how to wait for truth to reveal itself through your feelings and over time, you become truly powerful beings.

That said, **total emotional clarity about anything isn't in the cards for you.** It's the nature of the emotional realm to always be changing, shifting, moving… If you can be 72% clear, that's good.

Special Word About People with Emotional Authorities and Relationships

To have a Defined Solar Plexus is a real responsibility. It's so important that you learn to understand the power of your emotional aura—whether it is consciously Defined in you (Black), or unconsciously Defined (Red).

It's this simple: When you feel good, the people around you are likely to pick up on your energy and feel good too. When you feel bad, they're likely to pick up on that too. You literally transmit the frequency of your emotional wave out into the world, into your environment. This is quite a powerful thing.

If you push yourself to be social when you're not in the mood, the people around you are likely to feel your emotions—whether you want them to or not, whether you realize it or not. They will take in your emotional state. If they are particularly sensitive to you or Open emotionally, they will not only reflect back to you how you're feeling... but they'll AMPLIFY how you're feeling, and reflect it back 10-fold! (If you're feeling loving, they might fall head over heels in love with you. If you're slightly irritable, they might become enraged at you! And half the time, you'll have no idea what happened.)

You can actually learn a lot about how you're feeling by noticing the way others are responding to you. When you're feeling hopeful, happy and full of love, others (who are taking your feelings in through their Open Emotional Centers, and then amplifying what they receive) can seem twice as joyous and loving. When you're feeling despair, unhappy or bitter, they're likely to double that too.

Patience and surrender are such incredible themes in your Bodygraph… in your life. The more you can learn how to relax into 'what is,' (*including the feelings you have about 'what is'!*), the less you worry about the future or try to get ahead of yourself, the less you get caught up in expectations, the better. (Believe me; that's a spiritual practice right there! To become a witness to your expectations, and to the emotional roller coaster that comes along with being such a full-hearted human being.)

BE SELECTIVE AND TAKE YOUR TIME IN ESTABLISHING RELATIONSHIPS

It's so important that you are careful when taking people into your life, when making friends or entering romantic, professional, spiritual or community relationships.

Although you may have a strong intuition, you can't always just trust in a spontaneous coming together. It's actually very healthy for you to meet people repeatedly, not just so that you can get to know them better, and find your own clarity about whether this is a relationship that you want when you're up, down and in between, but ALSO to see how they respond to you, and your changing wave over time.

For anyone to be truly right for you, they have to be able to accept you, when you're up on your wave, and when you're down, however that happens to manifest in you. You need to know that the people you spend your time with not only appreciate but can handle all of you. That they can provide you with enough room and emotional range to be your full self. This doesn't mean that they have to be crazy about you all the time, or that you have to be crazy about them all the time. It does mean that you have to feel good about being with them, deep down, that the relationship stands the emotional test of time.

Since you're likely someone with a WE-orientation, and a tendency to nurture, support and take responsibility for the people in your life, it's even more important that you take your time before you really commit to someone or a community.

There's no rush.

We don't want you committing before you're ready, and then having a really tough time dis-entangling yourself, because people have come to depend on you so much. Again, this is the case whether you're a Generator, a Manifestor or a Projector.

SLOW DOWN and you won't be sorry. **Time is always on your side.**

An extra few words about the Solar Plexus

You could say that the collective, or combined power of all of the Solar Plexus waves across the planet is literally at the root of all the chaos of the world in which we live today. People—whether their Solar Plexus is Defined or not, don't understand how the emotions work. People who are Defined emotionally usually have very little understanding of how their wave actually works, and how powerful it is. People with an Open Solar Plexus rarely realize just how deeply their emotional lives are being influenced by their surroundings.

So, while half of us are unconsciously leaking our own feelings, the other half are unconsciously amplifying, over-identifying with and over-reacting to those feelings, either with unconstructive fear or violence. Our world and its potential for peace depends on people like you and me understanding the underlying patterns of our emotional life, and learning how to navigate them with grace. Only when we all learn how to witness, metabolize and healthfully release feelings will we be able to transcend them.

Fortunately, because we are all moving through space, this endless emotional wave that I'm describing, is a spiral through which we can learn, not a loop in which we are locked!

SACRAL (GENERATED) AUTHORITY

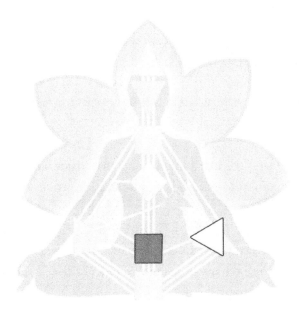

If you have Sacral Authority, you're not built to initiate your life, or to move towards things just because they seem like good ideas. You're not even designed to know who or what is good for you until you're actually there, until the opportunity has presented itself; it's right there in front of you, and your body has a chance to respond to it.

By respond, I mean, to either say, "Hey, yea, I can handle this," or "No, this does not feel right to me." If you're designed for anything, it's to feel deeply frustrated when you're pushing too much, or too hard.

You can pursue any career your mind thinks it wants. You can take any education your mind thinks it wants. You can join any religion or spiritual community your mind thinks it wants. You can make any friends your mind thinks it wants. You can decide to marry any person your mind thinks it wants. You can market your business until the cows come home. You won't know whether any of that is right for you; you won't know if you can commit to that thing with the full force of your creative being; you won't know if this is your own truth…until you're actually there—checking in with your body, for each unique situation, relationship or encounter. Until you're there, feeling and responding to it in your own body.

MORE ABOUT THE SACRAL CENTER

- *It all comes down to the Sacral Center, that big red square, second up from the bottom in your Bodygraph.* That's what makes you the Generator that you are. It's Defined. Any time a person has a Defined, or colored in Sacral, they're a Generator, a creative powerful force on this planet.

- *According to Human Design statistics, over 70% of humanity are Generators.* About 37% of those are Pure Generators, and the rest are Manifesting Generators. I happen to be a Manifesting Generator.

- *We Generators are all here to build and create.* Which is why it's so important that we each come to know and appreciate ourselves. We can then fill this world up with our unique beauty, gifts and joy, instead of the deep frustration we tend to feel when we're not living according to our

True Nature, when we're the slaves of our minds, and the value systems of the people our minds so often represent.

- *Think of the Sacral Center like a giant response machine.* It can respond to anything. It can respond to a person, a question, a flower, a ball of green yarn, a painting, a marketing task, paperwork, a dream, a piece of music, an invitation, an emotion in the room. It can respond to a taste, a sound, a sight, a touch, a smell. It can respond to a course, a job, an environment, a university, a house, a career, the lover of your dreams.

- *It's the seat of vitality itself, of creativity and fertility.* It's like a literal generator inside of you, constantly buzzing, humming, waiting to be asked, waiting to be used, and be used up to a point of satisfying exhaustion.

- *Generators tend to be busy people.* Generators are really not so comfortable being at rest—partly because once their inner engines shut down, it can be hard to restart them. As tired as they can get, it can feel easier to keep the motor going all the time.

- *This partially explains why when Generators hear that they have to "wait to respond," they can start to feel very anxious.* A 'mental concept' is being introduced into an arena that is purely biological. Generators and their bodies are literally wired to be busy… or at least active. Without the knowledge of how they actually work, they don't have a clue that not everyone has this busyness. Being busy is simply the normal state of affairs.

- *It's so important for Generators to understand that at least on one level, they're all about energy.* This body-driven need to be put to work, to be put to good use. This pulsing availability to life, that needs to be honored and channeled properly. When it's used correctly, when their precious energy is used correctly, they know what true, deep satisfaction is.

- *When they do anything with a response, it's not a mental thing.* It's just the Sacral motor itself responding. All the motor is going to say is, "I can handle this." (Or, 'Nah, that's not for me.' If the Sacral is silent, it's saying, "At least not now.") It's like the classic story, <u>The Little Train that Could</u>.

When Generator beings' Sacral Centers do respond, all they know is that they've got the power and energy to participate in whatever is in question—whether it's for a moment or a life time. Or a commitment to a moment, or a life time. It doesn't matter. When the Sacral says yes, it's basically saying, "I can do this and more. This is something that will use my energy correctly."

An Experiment for you if you've got Sacral Authority

Some of the most important things for you to experiment with are your Sacral Sounds. It's time to start letting them out. Start noticing how much they're actually coming out without your even realizing it. If you just pay attention the next time, when you're having a conversation with someone, and are listening to them talk, you'll begin to hear them. You'll hear yourself saying, "m-hm," "ah," "M-hm," "uh" "ooo" "Oh yea." That's your Sacral voice. You can look at (something awful) and find yourself saying, "Ich!" That's your Sacral too. The Sacral is very *very* truthful, uncompromisingly honest. Partly why you can trust it so much.

One of the quickest ways for you to get in touch with your Sacral response is to sit down with a trusted friend (it has to be somebody that you trust, because the Sacral doesn't lie!), and have them ask you all kinds of YES/NO questions—from the mundane, like "Do you like tuna fish?" "Are you in the mood to eat out?" or "Do you want to go with me to see that movie?" To the profound, like "Do you believe in God?" "Are you in love with your partner?" "Do you even want to be in a relationship right now?" "Do you really want to go to Graduate School?" "Are you happy where you're living?"

As your friend asks you questions, let your Sacral respond, and stay open to surprise. Again, you have to be prepared to hear whatever your Sacral says. You might want your friend to preface certain questions with a, "Are you ready for me to ask you a question about...?" "Do you actually want clarity regarding...?" "Do you NEED clarity regarding... right now?"

We're not always ready to hear our own truth, and it's important to respect that.

Sacral Center as a Bank

Earlier I mentioned that when Ra described the Sacral Center, he would use the metaphor of a bank.

Imagine that your Sacral Center is a bank, and that the energy that resides in it is actual money. Your hard-earned cash. You are the guardian of this account, the executor, the one who decides how the money (you've worked very hard to earn) gets spent. Now imagine that someone comes up to you and asks you for something. Maybe they are asking for a favor. Or they want you to join them for lunch. Or they're inviting you to a party, or to some kind of an event. Or they're offering you a job. Or they want you to partner with them. Whatever it is they're asking for, in this scenario, you know that if you say 'yes,' it means you are committing your energy to this thing, whatever it is. You're actually going to have to pay them hard cool cash out of your bank account, in order to say 'yes.'

It's good to play around with this thought, as strange and non-spiritual sounding as it is, when thinking about your energy. You've got to get to a place where you actually 'get' how valuable, how precious your energy is, and how easily you give it away, without even thinking about it. The more you give your energy away on automatic, the less of it is available for those things, relationships and opportunities that will truly bring you satisfaction.

When you don't just 'give it all away,' you're pulling your energy to you. You're building up a potent reservoir or resource. You're actually growing your aura. The bigger your aura, the more likely you are to attract those opportunities and people into your life that will ignite your true purpose. When they come, you'll have more than enough energy to throw yourself in, full force.

If you're constantly and indiscriminately giving your energy away, you can't as easily attract what you need to live a fulfilled life. Even if you can, you won't have nearly as much energy to enjoy and milk the experience for all it's worth.

At first, this can sound very selfish. But ultimately, fulfillment is contagious. The better you get at honoring and using your energy well, the more of a positive impact you'll be able to make on your surroundings. You'll have the energy to really go for what you're meant to do. The force will be with you. It takes courage to say to the world, "Hey, you come to me!" This is what it is to be a Generator, to allow the world to come to you. To demand respect from life, from people. If you dare to do it, you'll find that you get it. You get respect. Opportunities and people come your way.

What and who comes may surprise you. They may not be exactly like, or anywhere near, what you think they'll be. Or what your mind has idealized. When you live out your response, you begin to feel this potential for deep satisfaction that resides in you, how good it is to be a powerful energy being. How clean your energy can be. How good it can feel at the end of each day.

This experiment can be difficult, but it's not impossible. It's about you and you alone. No one can do this for you. Countless Human Design books have been written, many giving you the same advice. But only *you* can slow down enough to start living from and honoring your body's genuine responses. There are times when it's likely to feel very uncomfortable and socially awkward. Not everyone will understand why you say 'yes' to one thing, and 'no' to another. This is your challenge—to learn how to trust your gut, no matter what energies, pressures or conditioning messages you're taking in from your Openness.

Back to the experiment, next time you're trying to make a decision about what to do, ask yourself, "Is this something I'd be willing to pay for?" Even if it's just an invitation to go to a party. If it's not, practice saying "no." See what happens. See what happens when you say 'no' to things, maybe lots of things, that your body isn't so available for. So that you can build up a lot of energy to throw into a good satisfying 'yes.'

SPLENIC AWARENESS AUTHORITY

You have what we call Splenic Authority. This means that your Authority, that place in you that you can turn to for truth, is coming out of your Spleen—that inward pointing triangle on the left of the Bodygraph. The Spleen is our oldest awareness Center as a species. It is at the very core of what it is to be alive in a complex form. Insects, birds, fish, reptiles and mammals do not have a Solar Plexus or Emotional Center, but they all have a Splenic System, a capacity for spontaneous awareness, in the now.

This is what you have. Splenic awareness. It is spontaneous. It is highly intuitive.

It's very yin, very female. For those of us who grow up in this mentally-biased Western world, it can be particularly challenging to trust.

Yet, for you to live your life as yourself, you MUST learn to trust yours.

As hard as it can be to accept with the mind, your Spleen is meant to dictate your life, in the sense that all that you do needs to come out of your Spleen. **Out of your pure, completely incomprehensible intuition.** This is true whether you're a Manifestor, here to manifest your potent intentions based on your in-the-moment animal instincts, or whether you're a Projector, using your in-the-moment instincts to recognize a healthy invitation, one of 'your people,' or an opportunity to engage in something that you love.

- Interestingly, Splenic awareness doesn't even feel like an 'awareness,' in the sense that it's not connected to or coming out of something we understand, know, or even sense. You're basically being asked to trust NOT knowing. That's quite a challenge! That's also exactly what you're meant to do.

- You are not meant to 'make decisions' in the way we usually think about it. Decisions are meant to happen through you, spontaneously. Splenic people like you don't even know how to make decisions. Decisions just happen.

- Many people have Emotional Authority. They have to make their decisions based on how they feel, over a period of time. They're meant to hold on to a particular situation until they can gain enough distance to reach clarity. Their decision-making process can take a long time, and can drive them and everyone around them crazy (because they're often all over the place, when all they want is to be able to be spontaneous like you!). Their process can also be very colorful.

- **You, on the other hand, are an intuitive being.** When you meet someone, and find them interesting, chances are you'll always find them interesting. An emotionally Defined person might meet someone one day and fall in love, and the next day have no idea what they saw in them.

- **You can really trust your intuition.** Here's the thing. While the intuition is extremely trustworthy, it isn't always colorful in the way that feelings are. Intuition doesn't have a 'body' to it. When someone like you is making a decision, it's not like you get all these rich and juicy feelings that vacillate. It's more like something in you just shifts. Either something is right. Or you just get this hit that it isn't quite right. You don't have a clue as to why.

- **This is the Spleen's limitation, or challenge.** You can be walking along a path in the pitch dark. Suddenly, your Spleen says, "There's something wrong here, stop." The Spleen only says this once. It doesn't repeat itself. That's the mind's job. If you don't listen, with your next footstep, you can end up hurling off of a cliff.

- **The Spleen is said to always be right,** unlike the Emotional Center that is always moving, revealing one part of the truth at a time. In this way, the Spleen is infinitely powerful. It's not a motor—like the solar plexus, nor is it always talking like the mind. In this way, it's weak... or soft. This is why it can be so easily ignored, dismissed or overpowered.

- **Another fascinating and challenging thing about the Spleen is that it totally lives in the now.** It's not consistent. It doesn't hold on. It doesn't come back and drive you crazy with its warnings and whining and regrets. It has no situational memory. Remember, think animal. One moment, you manage to avoid the cliff. The next, your Spleen is working on the next Now.

- **Its decisions, your decisions, aren't personal at all. They are health-based. Survival based.** The decisions your Spleen makes can't be understood rationally. They can't be predicted, based on previous decisions. Your Spleen's decisions are completely and only relevant to the very moment you're facing, the question being asked, the opportunity arising, the food plopped on your plate, the person right in front of you, in this very moment. This means that your Spleen might say 'no' to someone one minute, and ten minutes later, might say 'yes' to that very same person, asking about the very same thing. Your mind can't possibly—and shouldn't even try—to understand this. It's not capable of understanding that kind of spontaneous knowing.

- **All your Spleen can tell you is if someone or something (if an invitation or an initiation) is healthy for you in the moment, or not.** Is it going to get in the way of your survival in the moment, or not? That's it. You can't be 'intelligent' or logical about it.

● This also means you can't hold onto your decisions. You can't insist you know why you make the decisions you make, or expect yourself to be able to defend or justify or explain your decisions to others.

All you can do is trust that there is this incredible intuitive intelligence living inside of you, constantly, moment by moment, guiding you towards greater health and aliveness, towards a stronger and stronger immune system.

As hard as it can be to accept this, you actually don't need anything else. As a Splenic being like yourself, your life is meant to be lived, in the moment. That's your incredible gift, if you can learn to trust and accept it.

At the very least, see if you can experiment with it. See if you can start to tune into these very subtle shifts, or knowing, in yourself. More than that, see what happens when you honor them, and then let go. Remember not to expect your Spleen to keep saying 'yes' to the same things, and 'no' to the same things. Free it to do what it's best at, being in the now.

A few extra words about Sacral-Splenic Authority

If you are a Generator, and your Sacral Center is connected to your Spleen (and your Solar Plexus is Open!), we say that you have Sacral-Splenic Authority. What this means is that your responses in the moment will reflect your Splenic awareness about what's healthy for you or not, in the now.

EGO/HEART AUTHORITY

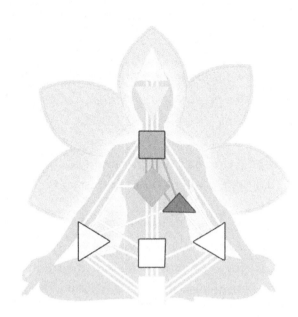

You have what Human Design calls Ego/Heart Authority, in the sense that your Authority is housed in the Ego, or the Heart Center. This means that your Authority resides in your will power. It is your personal Will that you can trust to tell you what is right or wrong for you when it comes to making decisions.

Now keep in mind, that when we talk about Will, we're not talking about an awareness. We're talking about the energetic force of the will power, the courage, the commitment that comes from this part of your body.

Whether you are a Manifestor or a Projector flower, as hard as it may be for you, as forbidden as it may seem, you are literally designed to make your decisions from a self-centered place. The best questions for you to ask yourself, or be asked, when it comes to making a decision regarding an invitation, or an initiation, are, **"What do I really want? What's in it for me?"**

The thing to remember is that you can decide to do all sorts of things from a selfless perspective, or because you feel compelled to satisfy someone else's wants or needs, not your own. That doesn't mean that you have the Will to go through with the thing, or if you DO push yourself through, that you won't suffer—health-wise or psychologically.

This isn't just about your happiness or satisfaction or success. It's about your health. **Your heart literally depends on your doing those things that you have the Will to do, that your 'Ego' wants to do.** Of course, what your Ego ultimately decides to do can be deeply selfless and good for the planet. If your Will isn't with you, forget it.

So many people, women in particular, are conditioned to be selfless, or at least to think of selfishness as a very bad thing, something to be hidden or worked against. When you're a Projector, who is so naturally tuned into other people, or when you're a Manifestor, who without meaning to can threaten people with your independent streak, the pressure to be selfless, to focus all of your attention on the other, at the expense of yourself, becomes even greater.

It can be extremely hard for sensitive we-oriented Manifestor and Projector flowers like you to accept and embrace this aspect of yourself.

Your whole life, you've likely been conditioned to be anything but selfish. If you're a Projector, you've probably spent all of your time learning about others, bending over backwards to please them, so that eventually, they might actually see you, and invite you into their life in some way. If you're a Manifestor, you've probably had to hide your light and do whatever it took not to outshine or make people uncomfortable.

Whatever your story, if you're a we-oriented person, you've probably learned that your success depended in some way on your being self-less, or you were taught to feel guilty whenever you were acting out of your self-interest. The people around you may have felt very threatened by the power of your Will, and they may even have shamed you for it, pushing all of that wondrous power of yours under the surface. Forcing it either to express itself in its less than healthy *Shadow* form, or at least preventing you from feeling the self-love you're designed to feel, and the capacity you have to inspire this same kind of self-love in others.

Many people, when first told that they have ego authorities, can feel awkward and guilty at first. After a little time, you begin to feel this incredible permission, and recognition of something that has always existed in you, and you either knew it, and were forced to repress it, or sensed it. To know that for you to be you, for you to live out your true purpose in life, for you to serve others, you must first be self-centered, in the best possible way. This means being willing to listen to your own desires, and do things (or accept invitations) that ultimately are good for you, can be incredibly liberating. This is my invitation to you.

In the end, there is no separation between the small self and the Big All. When your inner *Wisdom Keeper* is truly liberated, your 'personal Will' will inevitably be aligned with the Divine Will. "What I want" will be the same as what the most healthy expression of "We" wants.

SELF-PROJECTED
AUTHORITY

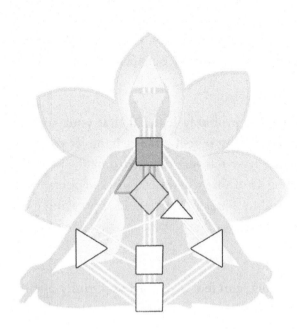

You have what we call Self-Projected Authority. What this means (other than that you are a Projector Flower) is that **your decisions need to come from a place of happiness, or deep contentment, in the core of your being**.

They need to come from who you truly are. Not from what your mind has been conditioned to believe you are, or who you should be. Not from those places that are Open in you, which are often going to be under tremendous pressure from the world around you to work too hard, to hold on to relationships and jobs and situations that aren't necessarily good for you, in order to prove that you are trustworthy and reliable and courageous and loyal and able to come through on all of your promises, or to deal with every emotional need imaginable that arises in any context, or to do everything in your power to make peace in the community, even if it means hurting yourself in some way.

Here's a big Irony. In so many ways you're here for others, to see and understand them, to bring out their gifts, to guide them. For you to discover your own 'selfless' gifts, you need to be quite selfish—or self-oriented—in your decision-making process. This isn't about using your Will. This is about listening to your singing heart.

These are the questions I want you asking yourself when someone has invited you into something, or when you're considering entering an environment or a relationship out of love.

- "Does this person truly see me for who I am?"

- "Will this job actually make me happy?"

- "When I hold this invitation in my hand, do I feel like I come alive as a person? Does my heart light up?"

These questions matter more than anything else when making decisions in your life.

This is not about whether you'll be good at something, or even whether you're needed or wanted. It's about whether an opportunity, invitation or person makes your heart feel warm, happy and toasty inside.

Again, I'm not talking about the 'heart' of the Ego/Heart Center, which is all about Will, loyalty, values and coming through on promises. For you, these are exactly the reasons NOT to enter into something when it comes to your Design.

When we talk about Love in Human Design, we're talking about the Identity, or the G-Center. **This is your Authority. Your love. Your sense of direction.** Your ability to guide and help others find their direction, when invited into the right place by the right people, and *when recognized for who you are.*

- Nothing's worth doing unless it connects you with your joy (in the deepest sense of the word). True joy can be felt even when we're grieving. I'm not talking about giggles and fun necessarily, though I'm certainly not ruling those out either! As a Projector, something you can ALWAYS do is follow your bliss, go and do whatever you simply love. You don't need to wait for anything or anyone to do that. What a gift it is that you have an Authority that gives you such a direct line to your Joy!

- One of the best ways for you to get to a place of clarity about decisions that feel difficult is by talking to those who can be neutral sounding boards. Just by listening to yourself as you speak, you'll be able to hear through the tone of your own voice. You'll be able to hear whether your heart is singing, or whether your mind is busy trying to convince yourself to want something that doesn't really resonate with your essence.

- Another part of your Self-Projected Authority practice will involve learning when and how to use your voice. For people with your kind of Authority, it's been said that "You have nothing to say until someone recognizes you." What does that mean? It means that when someone turns to you in deep recognition of your nature and your wisdom, and you can feel in your heart that they truly want and need what it is that you have to offer, that's the moment when your words will have their greatest power, their biggest impact. **That's when you'll feel your genius radiating out from you and being received with open ears and open arms, without resistance.** That's when you can speak from your true Authority, which is actually not coming directly from your mind, but instead, rising up from your deepest truth, from who you are, your identity.

- You might find that you have your most profound expression when it emerges as a spontaneous verbal release. This can be a sign that it's your true identity talking, not your mind. When you speak, you just naturally give direction to the people around you. When you listen to yourself speak, you have the opportunity to hear your own direction as well.

Now, your kind of Authority—Self-Projected Authority—is different than what we call intuitive Authority, or Splenic Authority. You certainly have a sensitive spleen and intuition, with limitless potential for wisdom in these arenas. I wouldn't be surprised if you actually studied the intuition and became an expert in it, but your Splenic Center is Open, which means that it's always under the influence of your environment. **You can't necessarily rely on your intuition-of-the-moment to always lead you**

in the right direction. Or, you could say that there are other parts of you, like your G- or Identity Center that are even more reliable, because they're operating in you all of the time.

In other words, your Intuition, at least in the way that Human Design defines it, is not your Authority. Intuition, according to the Human Design system, is very animal like in nature. It's connected to the first of our evolutionary awareness Centers. We share it with all species, this capacity to know what's healthy or not, in the split second of the now. It has a very small voice that often gets overridden by the mind and the emotions. It's like a flash, an instinct, a rising hair on the back of the neck. People with Splenic Authorities are here to be spontaneous, to make their decisions based on a subtle instinctual 'non-mental' knowing. Their truth can change completely from one moment to the next.

The frequency of Splenic Intuition and the Identity Center (which is where your Authority lies) may be a bit difficult to distinguish at first. This will be a part of your experiment.

For you, it's about first waiting to be recognized through relationship (especially in relation to the four main life arenas that were addressed earlier). It's about allowing opportunities to come to you through the people your magnetic aura draws towards you. Once the opportunities arrive, you have time to discover your truth.

Your inner *Wisdom Keeper* is often liberated through talking, exploring, feeling into the core of your being as you speak, hearing your own voice, getting more and more clear about what makes you happy.

It doesn't matter what your mind says. Remember, your mind, is here for others. Not for your own decision-making process. Your mind can measure things, but it can't in the end know anything's true value, or anything about timing. When you can enjoy your mind's abilities without giving it the responsibility to 'making itself up,' that's when your spontaneous voice can rise up and speak as your true Authority.

Let's say you're having difficulty with a relationship, and you can feel that you want to talk to that person. First, your mind will do its thing. It'll do its research, its background investigations, by looking at the problem, figuring out what the core of it is, what's bothering you, and what might be bothering this other person. You're probably going to have some preferences as a result of this mental process… or intuitions that make you give more weight to one side, or one plan of action, over the other, and that's all good and natural.

What I'm inviting you to do is to not make a decision yet… To resist the urge, you may feel (and there may be a better example than this one, feel free to use your own imagination) in that moment to pursue that friend, to call them up and say, "I've figured it all out. I know what's wrong with you, or with this situation, and I'm going to tell you right now." Even if your mind is absolutely right, or your intuition is absolutely dead on, there's still a good chance that this person isn't going to be open to what you have to say.

Instead, I encourage you to wait for that person, that friend, that client, that spiritual colleague, teacher or student to come up to you, once they've recognized that there's a problem, and say, "Can you tell me what's wrong?" That's your moment, and whatever comes out of your mouth has the potential to be your true Authority! Whatever comes out in that moment will be your truth, because you've done your research, your mind's information will have given your Identity the necessary background. As you listen to yourself speak, you'll begin to hear what you say, you'll begin to hear yourself as yourself.

OUTER AUTHORITY

You have what we call OUTER AUTHORITY. Whether you are a Mental Projector, or a Reflector, this means that you have no consistent activations beneath the level of your Throat Center. Reflectors and Mental Projectors are very different from each other, but as you'll see here, when it comes to Authority, there are plenty of parallels.

For example, **whether you're a Reflector or a Projector, your entire body (below the Throat) is constantly Open to the energies and conditioning and nurturing of your surroundings.** You can't necessarily count on your body, in any given moment, to be able to tell you what or who's right for you, or what your truth is. You can't do this because your body is always changing.

Let's say you're a Mental Projector (someone whose Ajna and/or Head Center are Defined). BECAUSE your body is always under the influence of either personal energies, environmental energies, or transpersonal transits, you've probably had to rely a great deal on your mind in your life, the only part of you that's consistent. Think of your mind as an anchor in the ocean. You were born to live in the ocean, and your mind was all you had to orient yourself. **Even though your mind was built to be consistent, and to become a fabulous, wise Authority for other people, you always get your best guidance—not from your mind, not from anyone else, but from your environment.**

Just like a Reflector, your Openness is a huge part of your great gift. Your capacity to take so much in is what leads you to your true wisdom. Now remember, your Aura is different than the Reflector's Aura. In a way, you take your environment in even more deeply. You ingest each person you meet through that penetrating, straw-like aura of yours, as earlier described.

If you're a Reflector, **you DIGEST your environments. You take it all in, you sample it all, but (unless your boundaries were violated quite dramatically when you were little) your Aura also has the ability to let it all slide off.**

- The bottom line for both of your kinds of flowers is that your surroundings matter. If you're not selective, you might just end up either identifying with it all, or spending all of your precious body time processing, digesting, metabolizing and reflecting all that you're taking in…to a point of exhaustion.

- One of the most important things for both Reflectors and Mental Projectors is to have a trusted ally, or group of advisers that you can turn to. I don't actually mean people who are going to give you a bunch of advice. You both need people you trust, people who are truly good listeners, people who enjoy joining you in playful, open-minded conversations, where you can have the chance to hear yourself speak.

- When you speak, if you can pay attention, you have the potential to hear your own truth (or at least a part of the truth that you're gathering over time, if you're a Reflector) leaving your lips, and feel it ringing true in your heart with one of the most important questions, "Is this environment correct for me?"

- Remember, you are here to specialize in OUTER AUTHORITY. You're the ones who were born to teach, guide and reflect the rest of us.

Special words for the Mental Projector

I gotta say; it can be challenging to accept the way your truth-gathering process works. **It's often said that there's nothing more difficult than trying to get a Mental Projector, whose mind is literally designed to be an outer Authority, NOT to accept her own outer Authority for herself.**

You Mental Projectors do have a capacity to see things in a way no one else sees things.

It can thus be especially difficult for you to give up the power of your mind as an inner Authority. It may seem at times like there's nothing else for you to listen to than your mind. The opposite is actually true.

Your body is speaking to you ALL OF THE TIME! It's just that your body was built for change. It's designed to be fluid, like water. Water is wonderful for swimming in and enjoying, just as you were built to gather wisdom like a forever-dancing witness.

That said, your body's in-the-moment state can't help you that much when it comes to decision-making. If you think about it, you can't really 'take a stand' on water. You can't just sit by yourself in a room, turn to some inner compass inside of you, and know exactly what to do. You can certainly try, but you may find that the conclusions you come to in that moment fall away or shift as soon as your environment changes, which can be confusing for you, and activate your mind even more.

On the one hand, you're here to be picked out of a crowd and lead. On the other, you can't lead yourself.

All of that said, I want to come back to what matters most: ENVIRONMENT. That's where your body gets its information. **Put yourself in an environment, read it, feel it, and then retreat from it. Unplug from it. Notice the residual energies in your body.** How they move through you, how they make you feel. Does it feel like you've been temporarily poisoned, and the toxicity is leaving your body? Does it feel like you've been energized, that you've come alive, as a result of the encounter with the environment. Talk to people you trust.

Remember, people you trust make up a good decision-making environment for you.

It's all about QUALITY, not QUANTITY.

Where you are and what you do are ultimately less important than who you're with.

How to know if you're with the right person? Allow yourself to explore all sorts of questions about a given situation, one that's troubling you, one that you need more clarity in relation to... when you're with someone. Notice whether you find yourself feeling seen. Visible. Does your outer Authority come alive? Do you find yourself speaking your mind, sharing your truth, in a way that makes you feel safe and welcome? Or do you find yourself stumbling, or trying to prove yourself, or so emotionally overstimulated that you don't know what's hit you? Ask yourself, if this person was a food, would you eat them?

Make sure the people in your life know that you're someone who needs to talk in order to hear yourself, and that you often need to mull over things more than once, and with more than one person, in order to get to your clarity. Generally speaking, the less your listeners are invested in the outcome of the conversation or your decision, the better.

Special words for *Reflectors*

(I definitely recommend that you spend some good time with the Love Yourself Petal. You won't be sorry!)

The right environment is particularly important for you, because you're going to reflect and mirror everything and everyone that surrounds you. If your surroundings don't feel good or right, then you're not going to feel right. Think of that chameleon/canary hybrid flower I mentioned earlier!

Of course, the opposite is true as well. **If the environment feels good, you're likely to feel good.**

Reflectors like you aren't meant to live in caves, even if at times you would prefer to! You're not meant, ultimately, to live an isolated life.

Ideally, early on in life, in addition to being allowed plenty of solitude time, you would have also been encouraged to simply be a part of communities, to be in various environments in the world, so you could become totally absorbed in your environments and thus come to recognize who you are.

Interestingly, Reflector flowers tend to thrive in stable environments, where people play by the rules. When you're in environments that are stable, you're free to scan them, to scan the people around you and the community as a whole, over a long period of time, month after month, moon cycle after moon cycle. Over time, you can actually spot what and who stands out… in the best kind of way.

Even though it's always good to be in communities that love and appreciate your rare Reflector gifts, it can actually be quite healthy for you to be in what we'd call 'normal' environments. We need you everywhere, so you can pull out the unique people that are hidden in the masses, and help set them free, and so, we can all be set free!

Some Reflectors benefit from receiving support in learning to understand the moon, the movement of the stars and neutrinos. Understanding the movements of the cosmos, and how it relates to your unique Design, can help you grasp your life and its own cyclical motions, without being overwhelmed or caught up in how everyone else is doing things. When you can slow down enough to tap into your incredible—even mystical—wisdom, if you can let the moon guide you and keep your ego at bay. If you can resist getting caught up in power trips or trying to prove yourself, then you can know where we all need to go. You're not meant to get yourself there, or get all of us there, on your own.

You need workers around you, creative people who love what they do, to make the most of your innate sense of direction. People who can press the gas pedal, and people who know how to handle the energy required by the trip. You need the right collaborators as well as the right environment.

Like the Mental Projector, you also need good, neutral, patient and loving listeners, people who don't mind hearing you out more than once, people who are neutral and spacious enough for your emerging truth to unfold naturally over time in their presence.

Remember, all people with Open G-Centers are particularly sensitive to their environments. When they are in the right place, they meet the right people. Similarly, when they're with the right people, they're taken to the right place. **Learning to honor your environmental sensitivities (to find and enjoy more and more places that make you come alive) is a huge step in your process of flexible self-discovery.**

A FEW EXTRA WORDS ABOUT THE MIND

The mind doesn't know what's right for us. That doesn't mean it's not intelligent. The mind can be a wonderful tool, as long as it's not the master of our life.

The mind is never our inner Authority, whether it's Defined or Undefined. It has only so called 'Outer Authority,' which means that what we think about and figure out can be inspiring and very helpful for others. Still, we're not here to make decisions from our mind, which can be very tricky… because the mind often second-guesses our true Authority. It skillfully argues for or against anything that serves its agenda. Without our realizing it, the mind hijacks our identity and pretends to be us. We are not our Minds. We have Minds, and our Minds don't have the whole picture.

If you truly want to liberate your inner *Wisdom Keeper*, I really invite you to play with this Petal, and learn to honor your unique Authority. See what happens!

Your Petal Five Invitations

#1: Make a Sign!

Now that you've learned something about your Authority, it's time to start using it!

I invite you to create a simple sign that you can place somewhere you'll pass by every day. On this little sign, write the most important and encouraging reminders you can think of about your Authority. You can put it right next to your computer. Or by the mirror in your bathroom. Wherever you put it, make it easy to access and to read. The more opportunities you have to remember that you have a truth compass, and how that truth compass or truth-finding process works, the more likely you will be to put it into practice. Eventually, this stuff becomes second nature. It can take some time!

#2: Find Your Authority Object!

What I'd like to invite you to do is actually go out and find yourself a concrete object that for you, reflects the essence of your particular truth compass or truth-finding-process. If the object is something you can wear, or have on your body a lot of the time, that would be wonderful.

What's important is that you come to feel like it's with you all the time, especially in the beginning while you are integrating this new way of trusting yourself. You may already have this object in your home. Or, you may need to go out and find it—at a store, in a forest, by the ocean. Your call.

What matters most: Wherever you look, whatever you do, whatever you find... USE YOUR AUTHORITY to find your object.

There will be Authority-specific suggestions for how to approach this process.

Find your EMOTIONAL Authority object!

If you've got Emotional Authority, the first thing I want you to do is take the time you need. If you find an object at a store, for example, don't force yourself to buy it right away. Put it on hold, go home, sleep on it, and when you wake up, feel whether the object still has energy for you.

Let's say you find an object that really speaks to you, but it's in a forest far away from home, and you won't be returning any time soon. If you get a really strong feeling about an object, and it's your only opportunity to decide whether you want it or not, buy yourself as much time as you possibly can within this situation.

Hold the object as you walk around. Sample it on different parts of your body. Put it down. Feel that. Go for a long walk without it. Feel that. See if you discover something even better while you're walking around.

Let yourself walk around with another object. Notice whether you miss the first object. Go back to where you left it. Pick it up again. Feel that. You might want to bring both objects around with you for a while. You get the idea.

Let's say you finally decide which object to bring home with you. Even then, give yourself time to get to know it. Take a picture of it. Draw it. Carry it around with you. See if over time, it continues to resonate as a powerful Authority object. Give it time to feel like a fit. It should relax you, slow you down... not pressure you. It should in some strange way make you feel like you have permission to take your time. It should radiate the art of patience. You should feel like it's a mystery that keeps on giving. If no matter how much time you give this object, it still doesn't feel right, then let it go... and allow another object to find you.

Find your SACRAL Authority object!

If you've got Sacral Authority, trust your gut to find your special object. Let it be red like the Sacral Center, or something that for some reason reminds you of creativity, sexuality and satisfaction! Have someone ask you lots of Yes/No questions to help you hone in on what's right for you. "Is your Sacral object made of stone? Crystal? Is it big? Small? Hard? Soft? Cold? Warm? Natural? Person-made? Can you wear it? Is it solid? Fluid? Can it be bought? Does it have to be found? Do you already have it? etc." When you hold it, make sounds... If you get yummy sounds, you're on the right track!

Find your SPLENIC Authority object!

If you've got Splenic Authority, I invite you to find a symbol that reminds you of your split-second, highly intuitive, in-the-moment, animal instincts! Maybe it's a pendant that has a bolt of lightning. Or maybe you already have a bracelet or key chain with a particular animal totem that for you, represents your keen intuition. Or maybe you spontaneously find a little stone while on a hike. What matters most is that you use your intuition to find your object. Don't second-guess yourself. If you find something and get a 'hit' that it's right, go for it. Don't wait, and don't look back!

Find your EGO/HEART Authority object!

If you've got Ego/Heart Authority, get something that you truly WANT. Make sure it's something that you really like, that you're willing to invest in and commit to... even if your mind doesn't totally approve. Consider spending money on it, or trading something you care about for it. Make sure the object gives you a feeling of strength and courage to be who you are. Let it be bold in some way. If getting this thing feels uncomfortably selfish, you're probably on track!

Find your SELF-PROJECTED Authority object!

If you've got Self-Projected Authority, find something that brings you genuine Joy. Whenever you look at it, or hold it in your hand, or wear it, your heart should sing. Maybe it's a beautiful crystal. Or a conch you found on your all-time favorite beach. Or a tiny puppy key chain. You could even get a symbol of a musical heart!

If you're not sure about which object to choose, talk about this invitation to find an Authority Symbol with someone who really knows you and respects you. Go on an Authority Object hunt together. Make a fun day of it.

While you explore your options, make sure both of you are listening to the tone of your voice as you speak, so that you can discover what's ringing most true for you.

Find your OUTER Authority object!

If you've got Outer Authority, you might want to find a locket where you can put the pictures of people you really trust... your best allies, your most neutral listeners and friends. Or an image of your favorite environment. Or a symbol of the best invitation from someone you've ever received (if you're a Mental Projector). Or a symbol of the MOON, like a moon stone (if you're a Reflector).

If it feels right, string your object around your neck—so at a symbolic level, you always feel that you've got support, and a listening ear, that there's room for you to share about your process and discover your truth in the presence of your people, in your best environment, or in the illuminating light of the moon.

Reflectors, keep your object on or close to your body for at least a full moon cycle before committing to it. You need at least that much time to sense whether you've found the right one. Projectors, there might be an object you've already received from someone who truly sees, loves and recognizes you for all of your brilliance. Be open to re-discovering or re-purposing that as your Authority Object.

Whatever works for you.

Remember, there is power in the concretization of an essence that you're longing to integrate. Giving yourself a constant reminder of your Authority, one that you can touch and hold and roll around in your fingers, can be so helpful...

*Just a few fun examples of Authority Objects
from Designed to Blossom participants!*

Open to Your Path: Petal Six

Gain a New Perspective on your Purpose

OPEN UP TO YOUR PATH!

Welcome to the 6th petal, OPEN TO YOUR PATH. This is a wonderful petal, and a wonderful time to gain a new perspective on your purpose. Now you've got your foundation. You know what kind of flower you are, and the way you're designed to blossom as yourself. You know the places that can easily pull you away from or distract you from who you are. You have a truth compass you can now use when making decisions.

In this 6th petal—we're going to be exploring your PROFILE, an aspect of your Life Purpose, or the unique role that you, as a beautiful unique flower in our planetary garden, are meant to play out in life. Your Profile can also shed light on some of the major themes you are likely to encounter in life, as you move toward living out your true purpose.

At least when it comes to Human Design, your Life Purpose is nothing that you have to go out and try to make happen. It is designed to unfold naturally, as a result of your living your life as your natural self. This isn't necessarily a part of 'your experiment.' There's nothing to do here, other than to receive and enjoy the information—and allow it to plant seeds of openness, insight and self-accepting anticipation.

There are 12 different Profiles in the Human Design system. Each Profile has its own gifts, challenges and set of paradoxes.

Learning about your Profile can actually bring a great deal of relief and permission to be yourself. When I learned about my Profile, one of the first things I learned was that I'm actually designed to constantly experiment, to make lots of mistakes, and to gather skills and wisdom as I go. Wow, what a huge relief that was for me to learn! It was also a huge relief to discover that there was another aspect to my Profile that made me particularly susceptible to other people's projections. That there was a reason that others tended to expect a lot from me, and then get super disappointed when I didn't live up to their expectations.

Just knowing these very simple truths gave me so much compassion for myself. It hadn't been easy being someone who bumbled about and learned as she went, while being watched and assessed, often by those with high hopes for me! I was just trying to be my experimental, weird, clumsy, dive-in-and-get-dirty self. I wasn't trying to hurt anyone, or even impress anyone. But whoa, did I feel devastated when I could just feel myself disappointing, confusing and letting down the people I loved.

Of course, the good news was that through all of my life experiments and explorations, I managed to accumulate a bunch of tools, life experiences and a diverse range of knowledge. Now that I know that that's how I'm actually MEANT to be, I'm much less hard on myself when I don't live up to others' expectations. I know that that's not the role I'm meant to play in life. It's not that I can't have successes or help people out, or occasionally live up to their expectations, but that's not essentially what my life is about. Living successfully up to other people's expectations and projections might be the pleasant bi-product of my living authentically, but it can't be the point. That's just one simple example of how learning about one's Profile can be helpful.

OK...

As I mentioned before, there are 12 possible Profiles—or life roles—in the world of Human Design. Each role or life path style consists of a combination of two numbers. One of the numbers (or LINES) represents your conscious Personality, or the more known aspect of you. The other represents your Design, your body, your genetic make-up, or the less conscious (in Human Design lingo) aspect of you. (Again: The Personality refers to the **BLACK** areas of Definition in your chart, what we call 'the roads,' because they're on the surface and easy to see. The Design refers to the **RED** areas of Definition in your chart, or what we call 'the tunnels,' because they're underground and often obscure.)

> In the context of your Profile, it is the *second* number, or LINE,
> that reflects how change and growth happen in your life.

The numbers we're using when we look at your PROFILE are derived from the 6 Lines of the traditional hexagram from the *I Ching*. Although the meaning of these Lines has been adapted to our modern times, and to the unique synthesis that Human Design is, the *I Ching* is a system for understanding the place of humanity within the cosmos. It's built entirely on two elements—yin and yang.

It's kind of amazing... that just by using these two simple elements, the infinitely vast world and everything inside of that world (you and me included!) are created. The *I Ching* does this by putting the elements together into 64 hexagrams, each one divided into 6 Lines—which are either broken or unbroken. Many people who go very deeply into the *I Ching* and have a serious interest in modern science, have found a surprising similarity between these 64 Hexagrams and the actual structure of human DNA, which has implications for our evolving understanding of chaos theory, among many other things. The PROFILE alone in Human Design is a study in and of itself.

For now, we're going to stick with the basics. All you need to know is that your Profile is made up of these 6 building blocks or Lines.

THE HOUSE

AN OVERVIEW OF THE 6 LINES

Let's start with a fun and simple metaphor used in Human Design circles to describe each of the 6 Lines, and what they represent. After that, I'll share more deeply about each of the Lines. After that, I'll share a simple summary of all 12 of the possible Line Combinations, so that you can better understand the unique synthesis that makes up your own Profile.

OK, so imagine that there's a house with six quite different housemates. Each housemate corresponds to one LINE.

LINE ONE

LINE ONE is the person who lives in the basement. This person does some kind of research but nobody really knows what the research is about, because the person is usually too busy studying to come out of the basement to talk to anyone.

LINE TWO

The second housemate lives in the bedroom on the first floor. This person likes to dance naked late into the night with the lights on, and remains completely unaware that all of the neighbors can see the dance in all its glory. The only reason the neighbors haven't reported this person for indecent exposure is that the dancing is fabulous, despite the fact that this person has never had any formal training.

LINE THREE

The third person hasn't quite found the right place in the House to settle down, so for now has set up a little bed on the landing of the stairs between the first and second floor. This person is often the recipient of bumps and interruptions as other houseguests pass by, which isn't always fun. However, everyone once in a while, an accidental bump leads to a surprisingly interesting connection and an unexpected discovery.

LINE FOUR

The fourth housemate has a room on the second floor with a balcony. This person's favorite activity is standing on the balcony and calling out to friends and members of the community. This person often has a very particular and passionate point of view, thus often succeeds in convincing others to change theirs.

LINE FIVE

The fifth housemate also shares a room on the second floor, but this one isn't as outgoing as the fourth-floor mate. You can often see this person doing things in the room if you stand outside and look up through the window. People tend to have different opinions about who this person is and what they're doing. Many shower this person with their highest expectations and hopes. However, if those expectations and hopes aren't lived up to, or promises are made by this housemate and not kept, it doesn't take long before they're knocked (or hurled) off the pedestal.

LINE SIX

Finally, you have the sixth person, who lives up in the attic and spends a lot of time on the roof! This person isn't unfriendly; they're just a bit aloof. A favorite activity of theirs is sitting and gazing out at the architecture of the next House on the street. Though not a hugely active participant in household activities, if you need to know anything about the weather or general activities on the block, this is the person to seek out... because not much gets past their keen observational skills.

GOING A BIT DEEPER

Now let's take the descriptions of the housemates a bit further. This time I'll include the Human Design-inspired titles for the Lines. (I'll also be making a few tweaks to the official Human Design lingo, which at times can sound a bit ominous.)

Make sure you know which two Lines correspond to your own Profile!

Remember, **the first Line in your Profile is one that is deeply connected to your waking Personality.** This means that either you're very familiar with it, and can easily relate to it, or that it's such a huge part of who you are that you take it completely for granted (while you're off obsessing about all of those exciting Open arenas).

The second Line in your Profile is more connected to your Design, or your body. As mentioned earlier, it also has a lot to do with how transformation happens in your life. You may not feel quite as obviously connected to the description of the second Line (it will depend on other aspects of your chart, and your life experience), but the people who know you well are likely to recognize these tendencies and qualities in you. *(Interestingly, from the Integral Human Design perspective, the second Line is much more essential to who you are.)*

Please remember...

Just because your Profile is made up of two Lines doesn't mean that all of the other Lines don't apply to you or your life.

That's not true at all. For starters, you probably have several if not all of the other Lines represented somewhere in your Bodygraph. Secondly, and more importantly, these Lines represent **archetypes** that reflect aspects of the human experience as a whole. If you're human, you're likely going to relate to all of the Lines at some level. What we're talking about here is more a matter of emphasis. Certain Lines, because of the weight or positions they hold in your specific Design, carry a bit more weight than others. That's all.

According to Ra Uru Hu, the two Lines that make up your Profile represent 70% of the role you're meant to play out in life. Therefore, they deserve extra attention.

As always, I want to remind all of us that this is just a map, not the territory. Take what fits and leave the rest. Remember that your Design is a living, breathing tapestry, weaving together a unique dance between your Flower Family, unique Authority, Definition, Profile, and all of your human experiences... all that you've taken in through your beautiful Openness. Think of your Profile as just another color of paint on the multi-faceted mysterious painting that is you, instead of something that reduces you into a little understandable box.

LINE ONE

If you have a LINE ONE in your Profile, you are a true INVESTIGATOR.

Whether you know this about yourself, or not, you're the kind of person who isn't going to feel truly secure until you've found and established a strong foundation. You can be deeply introspective and a wonderful researcher. You have the ability to look into the core of things and people, and you do this in order to be prepared for what life brings you.

If we were to keep going with the House metaphor, you're the one who is in charge of investigating the building site. One of your main jobs is to make sure that the foundation is solid and worth building on, and then giving your confident go-ahead for the building process.

You really are designed to be deeply dedicated to whatever it is you're learning about. It's healthy and can be very exciting for you to be down at the bottom, on the ground level of a project, or a process... even BELOW ground level.

You instinctively know that something important is under construction, but you don't necessarily know exactly what's being built, or why, or what its future will hold. Especially in the beginning, it can feel a little scary... like you've been called to support a structure that you actually don't know very much about. This partially explains why you're so driven to understand and study that structure, to find out what the heck it is, how it works, why it's there in the first place, and whether it should be there at all.

Also, understandably, you can feel quite insecure if you don't feel like you know what you're doing. This is why study is very important to you, because it allows you an experience of mastery, which is so essential for you. It doesn't matter whether you're studying an academic field, a meditative practice, an artistic modality, an actual relationship with a person you're involved with, or a community you're a part of. What matters is that you have the opportunity to get to the bottom of things. That you get to focus and go deep. That's how you heal and grow. That's how you come to feel increasingly solid and strong in the world.

There are few things that make you happier than finding, exploring and creating a foundation that's worth standing on... than going through a deep process of mastery. This is a huge part of your service to the world, and to the WE. You are here to provide us with the kind of solid ground we can trust.

If you have LINE ONE as your first number, this is a very central part of who you are. It's super important that you learn to embrace it. You might easily relate to the role of the researcher, or the forever-life-student, the one who at some level is always trying to figure something out, to get to the truth, to the bottom of things—whether it's your inner life, your outer partner, or your Life Purpose.

If you have LINE ONE as your second number, you may not always realize just how important getting to the bottom of things and study are for you. In fact, if you're ready for a transformation in your life, a leap into some kind of deep inquiry may be the very thing that will lead you to your next adventure! Be open to that.

Whether your LINE ONE is your first or second Profile number, one thing is true. Fear and insecurity are two of your biggest teachers. They are here to lead you to mastery. Whether you live your entire life painfully aware of your fears and insecurities, or they spring up on you from time to time, you need to learn to embrace these states with all of your love, and be grateful for the gifts they bring.

There may be times when you and your quaking body feel completely overwhelmed by fear. During these times, there's nothing like spending time with someone you trust who can compassionately help you look beneath what's happening. With honest, direct and heart-full guidance, they can help you turn your brilliant Truth-seeking device back towards yourself, so that you can gain more information about what's actually happening for you, deep down.

I wouldn't be surprised if the two of you ended up discovering that your biggest fear is your own magnificent potential! (I invite you to reflect upon that Truth for a while!)

The fulfillment of your Life Purpose is dependent on your willingness to go within, to explore, research, experience and accept—even relax in the presence of—your fears. There will likely be times when you are tempted to sabotage your blossoming by turning your cheek to your own humanity, by repressing your fears and keeping secrets from yourself and others. You may feel afraid to stand up for yourself. For you, running away, avoiding discomfort and hiding from conflict isn't the answer.

There is profound wisdom in the saying, "The Truth will set you free." If you can practice self-love in the presence of Truth, then you're on your way to enjoy yourself, your body and relationships in ways you never thought possible. You're also on your way to becoming a true Mystic, someone with the capacity to embody a deep inner certainty, one that transcends the life's turbulent ups and downs.

LINE TWO

You're like the oblivious but talented dancer in the House. You're happy to just 'do your thing'... preferably in peace!

I wouldn't be surprised if you were also born with a special creative talent, something that others couldn't—and can't—help but see. Make no mistake. You are here to be a natural, relaxed, passionate and creative force in the world. You can also be very shy, with hermit-like tendencies. Sometimes, if it were up to you, you'd just assume dance around naked and have no one ever know about it.

It's impossible for you to be invisible. Invisibility isn't in the cards for you. Just think of the town hermit. Everyone knows about the town hermit! "Oh yea, the hermit lives out in the woods in that little hut!"

This is one of the ironies you're just going to have to accept. No matter how hard you may try to avoid being noticed, your talent is very likely going to find a way to shine through. You would have had to be EXTREMELY suppressed to have managed to keep your light hidden. You were born to receive attention for your gifts, and to attract attention from people who are very likely going to want to call you out. They might say, "Oh, you should do that professionally!" Or, "Wow, you're really good at that. How do you do that? Where did you learn that? Will you teach me?"

Now on the one hand, all of this attention is lovely. On the other hand, you can experience it like a really uncomfortable pressure. A lot of time, you have no idea where your talent came from, or how you got it, or how you came to know what you know, or do what you do. You just know it. You just do it. Even thinking about it too much can mess it all up.

The thing is that we live in a world where we're often expected to be able to explain, justify, credential and legitimate our gifts. In a way, you could say you're similar to the LINE ONE people—in the sense that you can feel really insecure. There may be times when the insecurity gets so great that you feel like you have to study something and get a degree, or a license, or SOMETHING… just to put an end to all of the demands of the world.

Your reason for feeling insecure is different than the LINE ONE.
The antidote for the insecurity and suffering is also different.

Your insecurity and reluctance to deal with the world and all of the pressure that comes with visibility is more about not knowing WHY you know what you're doing, and not being able to explain or justify why you do what you do so well... than it is about the fear of not knowing what you're doing in the first place!

If you do end up engaging in a study, it can't just be about mastery, like it is for the ONES. For you, it has to be more about giving yourself some protection in the world, so that you have the confidence you need to go out there, embrace your gifts and share them without apology. Study can also help you work through some of the confidence issues you may have grown up with, if you were constantly challenged in your gifts.

Becoming an apprentice, for example, to someone who recognizes and respects your natural gifts, can give you the sense that there's some depth and solidity behind the natural gifts.

In the end, what's really going to liberate you isn't study. It's simply owning, acknowledging and embracing your gifts—with utter abandon. Learning that it's OK to know what you know, and to do what you do, even if you can't intelligibly explain a word of it to anybody.

In this way, LINE ONES become free as a result of studying.
LINE TWOS become free when they realize they don't need a diploma
to have the right to use and share their 'Universe-given' gifts!

A Helpful Perspective for LINE TWO people who are open to the idea of reincarnation:

Try to look at your natural gifts as qualities and talents you've actually worked very hard on over many many lifetimes.
If this is true, then your talents aren't coming out of nowhere.
They're coming from potentially thousands of years of experience.
You're worthy of receiving and basking in a well-earned harvest in this life!
(Don't worry. You'll get your share of new challenges too. You might as well enjoy those things that come easily!)

If you have LINE TWO as your first number, this is a very central part of who you are. It's super important that you learn to embrace your natural gifts, as well as your shy nature. You might easily relate to the role of the talented person who can never explain her gifts, or the one everyone tries to yank out of the closet, but is terrified to go out into a world that expects too much of her. You're the one to whom certain things just came easily when you were little. Depending on your environment growing up, this was either celebrated, or a cause for guilt and/or self-doubt.

If you have LINE TWO as your second number, you may not always realize just how naturally gifted you are. You may not even see yourself as shy and introverted. If you're ready for a transformation in your life, it may be time to discover and bring out of the closet an old or hidden gift of yours, perhaps one that was never appreciated or valued in your family, or one you gave up on long ago. It's very possible that by re-uniting with and re-prioritizing something that comes easy to you, your life will take a surprising and very exciting turn!

Whether your LINE TWO is your first or second Profile number, one thing is true. A good way to release yourself from insecurity is to stop hiding, stop feeling like you have to prove yourself to anyone, and start being! Learning to feel safe with visibility, embrace your natural gifts, and to trust yourself when it comes to your innate talent for relating and self-expression, are important steps in your growth process.

Another key to your Life Purpose's unfoldment is your relationship to others. Your relationships are meant to be your mirrors. Just as you have the potential to deny your light and gifts, you carry the potential to deny your hurt and anger by holding others responsible for your suffering. Your hurt and anger may leak (or explode!) out without you realizing it, sending out unsettling ripples into your relationships and environment. When this happens, you may not be seen as the talented one, but rather, the aggressive, superior, provocative one. This can be confusing for you, and feel like yet another projection coming at you from the world that makes you want to hide.

Usually these kinds of reactions from others are pointing to a feeling, need or frustration inside of you that could use some of your compassionate attention. It can be hard to feel like you can escape all of the opinions, investments and agendas that the world has for you. Sometimes the best thing you can do is just relax. Go somewhere where you feel safe to be yourself. Where you don't have to be anything or anyone special. As your shoulders drop and breath releases, you can gently look beneath the rough edges and rumblings the people around you are mirroring and see what's there. Allow yourself to feel whatever guilt or feelings of inadequacy might be there. Just apply a little loving, relaxed openness. Not much more is needed.

As you allow your relationships to reflect back to you your own blind spots, and you find a way to own your anger instead of externalizing it or pushing it under the rug, you'll find that your anger will lead you to your true passion.

One of your big jobs is to learn to see and love all aspects of yourself (especially those parts that you've had to deny in order to survive). As you do this, you will awaken your ability to See beyond the veil of darkness into the brilliance of our shared connectedness. Your relationships with others (with the whole cosmos) will blossom, and a sense of freedom, deep relaxation and un-self-consciousness will permeate all that you do.

Your Life Purpose, ultimately, is about loving people. It's about coming out of the closet as the one that you are, without any pretense, and just being yourself with people. That's what the LINE TWO medicine doctor ordered.

LINE THREE

If you have a LINE THREE in your Profile, you are what we call a courageous ANARCHIST.

You are one of humanity's greatest risk-takers and discoverers. You thrive with diversity. You are here to *learn from experience* more than anything else.

Think of yourself like a sensitive, receptive, and vulnerable being who is designed to blunder your way through life. Without even looking for it, because of your natural attention to details you're often the one who bumps into and discovers that one thing that isn't working. You're like a life scientist who makes breakthrough discovery after breakthrough discovery, because of accidents or 'mistakes' that happen at the lab.

You were probably born knowing that no one and nothing is perfect. You're likely to have had more than a few pessimistic moments in your life. You can be especially hard on yourself too, and have an intimate relationship with shame. It's not easy to go through life, and to bump into so many things and people that don't work. This is especially difficult and painful when living in a culture (and a family) that pushes "mistakes are bad" and "if things don't work out as planned, you're a failure" propaganda.

That said, beneath any pessimism you may experience exists a deep belief that it **IS** possible to find that thing, that vocation, that relationship that can and does work. Beneath any pessimism you feel, is an extremely adaptive, resilient and persevering Spirit, one that allows you to learn from all your glorious life 'mistakes' that have led to the valuable discoveries you've made about life and love.

Let's go back to the House metaphor. You're the one who comes into the House with this tremendous, multi-faceted tool box. This tool box is full of every trick-of-the-trade you can imagine. It reflects all of the lessons, skills and wisdom you've gathered from all of your years living and working in a wide variety of houses.

You've learned so much from your multi-colored journeys and your years of trial and error learning, as well as understanding so much about what works and doesn't work, that you have the potential to know how to fix just about any kind of problem—including personal and interpersonal ones.

In a way, you're like a Universal fixer. You walk around and check things out; you meet the people living in and visiting the House. You just naturally bump into all sorts of things that don't work, both physical things and relational dynamics. If you can find a way to fix the problems you find, you'll do it. If you can see that the House is strong and solid (or at least repairable and worthy enough to expand upon), you'll be the one to give the builders the green light, telling them it's time to build another floor.

HOWEVER! If you can see that the House just doesn't have what it takes, if the roommates just aren't able to work out their differences, if the community's too dysfunctional, if the structure of the House will collapse in an earthquake or a storm, or if for whatever reason, the living conditions aren't going to be sustainable in the long run, you're going to be the one to tear it all down.

Even if you don't enjoy the process, (and you're not always going to enjoy the process! I can say that from personal experience, given the 3 in my Profile!), you're still going to be willing to break a bond, to let go, or to change things that you can see aren't going to work, even if it means starting from scratch.

Some LINE THREE people, because they've had painful experiences, and because they've been so thoroughly shamed for having those experiences, become addicted to breaking bonds, even the good ones. They develop a pervasive pessimism and fear of commitment. They lose their ability to discern between relationships and opportunities that are worthy of sticking around and working through, and those that are best let go. To others they can appear unreliable or evasive. What's most painful is that when they're busy avoiding people and uncomfortable (or seemingly doomed) situations, they are actually abandoning themselves. *They are allowing themselves to become overwhelmed by pressure and feelings of powerlessness, often feelings that stem from their childhood and experience growing up in their families.*

Just because you have a natural love for variety doesn't mean you can't make a home anywhere, or with anyone. There are so many ways to live, love and work with a sense of deep commitment, while making room for adventure and a diversity of experience. To live an exciting, humor-filled, multi-faceted, relationally connected life is your destiny, actually, if you stop blaming yourself and others for your failures (that aren't even failures!), and release yourself from the grips of old shame.

When you come to understand your true gifts, stop buying into our culture's (or your family of origin's) attachment to perfection, and learn to see the whole of humanity as your true family, you can become a powerful teacher of the truth that 'mistakes' and failure simply don't exist. All that exists is life experience and infinite opportunities for discovery. We're all here to simply be who we are. More importantly, we're all in this together.

If you have LINE THREE as your first number, this is a very central part of who you are, and it's super important that you learn to embrace the experimental and experiential way you're designed to learn and the tremendous gift that you bring to the world as a result of your learning. You might easily relate to the role of the risk-taker, the black sheep, the diversity-lover, or the one who seems to move from experience to experience, job to job, relationship to relationship—whether you like it or not.

You might remember learning early on that your parents weren't Gods, and that expecting perfection from life and people is bound to lead to disappointment. Depending on your environment growing up, you may have learned to embrace your experimental nature, knack for surprising discoveries, and resilient, variety-loving Spirit, or to feel ashamed or 'wrong' or like a mess because of it. These are all likely to be recognizable themes for you.

If you have LINE THREE as your second number, **you may not necessarily think of yourself as a risk-taker, or the outsider, or an anarchist**. You may not realize, be very focused on, or value the process of experimentation as a way of life. You may *really* dislike 'making mistakes,' breaking bonds, letting go, and/or tearing down something you've really worked hard to build in order to start over.

If, however, you're ready for a blooming transformation in your life, it may be time for you to take a good hard look at where you are, who you're with, what you're doing... and whether it's actually working... or whether it's time to let something go and move on, even if it feels really hard. If you find that a letting go is needed, you may need some support from someone who respects and believes in you. Shame will likely arise, and the ultimate antidote for shame is permission and a good dose of humor! One of the biggest gifts you can give yourself is permission to feel what you feel, to be what you are, to be utterly, unabashedly human, and laugh. When it comes down to it, we humans are a hoot!

Whether your LINE THREE is your first or second Profile number, one thing is true. For you, there is no such thing as a mistake. Everything that's ever happened to you, every seeming fiasco you've ever participated in and/or witnessed, it's all grist for your UNIVERSAL FIXING mill. You are deeply adaptable, a true alchemist of life, perfectly equipped to surf the imperfectly perfect waves of life.

You are also someone with a deep need for family—whether that family is the one you were born into, or one you've cultivated on your own. For you, there is no healing balm as potent as being able to see, love and laugh at yourself while surrounded by people who love you.

The moment you can let out a giant cosmic chuckle, the moment you can let go of control, the moment you can love and embrace the entirety of your life and its infinite lessons, is the moment you become the archetypal and "Mythical Fool," as Richard Rudd shares. Your true genius shines, and the world gets blown away by your multi-faceted, creative, wise, playful, and flexible and humble Life Purpose!

LINE FOUR

If you have a Line FOUR in your Profile, you are an
OPPORTUNITY-ATTRACTOR!

You are a natural teacher. You are also designed to become a potent messenger, even a wise Prophet if you allow your heart to melt to its fullest potential.

If we go back to the House, you're the person up on that balcony, living on that second floor. You are fully aware of the fact that the LINE ONES and THREES have already been there, building the foundation and making sure it's strong enough for a second floor. You are not so concerned about the building itself. You trust the foundation. You just know that the House is worthy of living in. You don't need to be so focused on the actual House, or the various activities taking place within it.

You're more interested in making sure that everyone outside the House *knows* about the House, and all of the wonderful things that you've found there.

When it comes to this aspect of your role in life, you're not here to get lost investigating all of the facts. You're here to share the facts with others, to get other people excited about the facts, to distribute them first near, then far and wide.

If a LINE FOUR is prominent in your Design, you were designed to share the wealth, to influence people, to make use of the wonderful opportunities life has provided you, so that you can pass your gathered gems on to anyone who is happy to listen, receive and benefit from your knowledge, gifts and influence.

You can be a very friendly person, a wonderful networker, and can end up having a very powerful impact. When you're living your life truthfully, it is all about friendship, romance, sharing and connection. Few things matter more to you than your 'people.'

That said, because of your past, you may carry with you a deep fear of being rejected. This fear may cause you to hide behind a strong, polished or polite persona, to not let people see and feel the tenderness and vulnerability at the core of your nature. This fear of being rejected may also cause you to cling tightly to (and seek validation for) your opinions and convictions in ways that promote division in your surroundings, as opposed to the intimate and authentic connection that your soul longs for deep down. You can end up rejecting others before they have the chance to reject you.

As a LINE FOUR, you have a keen capacity to focus on what you want to get out to the world, and on learning *how* to get it out in the most effective and inspiring way. Unlike LINE FIVES, you tend to have your greatest influence on the people that you know, and the people who know THEM, and so on and so on. The bigger your community, the bigger your network, the more opportunities you'll get to share your enthusiasm about whatever your 'House' stands for.

You can be a true inspiring missionary! What Seth Godin, the author, entrepreneur and marketer, calls a "sneezer"—people who are ultimately responsible for good things going viral! No one can spread the word and teach about something important like you can.

For you to have your ideal impact, it is so important that you learn to relax your mind, open your heart, and hold an embracing attitude. Allow those around you to see and know you, not only in your strength, but in your beautiful vulnerability. Share openly, transparently. Allow them to help you move past your fear of rejection, drop your defenses and down any emotional walls that you've been living behind. Most of all, treat yourself gently, and with kindness, so that you can feel all of your feelings and allow healing to happen where it is needed most.

If you have LINE FOUR as your first number, **this is a very central part of who you are**, and it's super important that you come to see and embrace yourself as a messenger of truth. You may not know exactly which truth you're here to share about, but you're likely to relate to the desire to share something that you really care about with the world, and in a way that makes an impact.

You're likely to see yourself as friendly by nature, and often looking or ready for an opportunity to share, teach or take the next step in your personal or professional unfoldment. You may even experience social fatigue now and then, because people tend to seek you out as a confidant. Depending on your environment growing up, you may have learned to embrace your social nature and strong points of view, or you may have learned to hold back or doubt yourself. Whether you've experienced a lot of friendships, teaching, sharing and/or networking in your life, they're likely to be recognizable themes for you.

If you have LINE FOUR as your second number, **you may not necessarily think of yourself as a super friendly person, or someone who's got a gift for networking, or even as someone who has a strong point of view or message that you can't wait to get out.** You may even have a dislike for 'blabber mouths' who are just spouting out their opinions without anything deep and thoroughly researched behind it, or without having a clue about whether they're being received by an appreciative audience.

That said, if you're ready for a blooming transformation in your life, it may be time to ask yourself whether you're noticing and taking the great opportunities when they come by, or whether you're ignoring or shying away from them. It may be time to ask yourself whether there's something you long to share that you've been holding back. Do you have stronger convictions that you care to admit? Is there a fear that keeps you from entering the limelight in service of a truth, from using your network, or having your impact? Are you rejecting your own magnificent potential, for fear of being rejected by the world?

Chances are you know something that the world needs to know. Chances are that opportunities are all around, and that the place to start sharing is with your own people! (It's actually easiest to let go of something or someone that's no longer serving you when you know and feel that there's a new wonderful opportunity waiting for you, welcoming you with great enthusiasm! So, keep your eyes and heart open for those new opportunities!)

Whether your LINE FOUR is your first or second Profile number, one thing is true. You are here to share something wonderful with the world, in a way that's deeply inspiring to people... that makes them want to share about it too! You need your friends, family, peers, colleagues and students in order to do it.

You also need softness in your heart. You need self-honesty. You need to let go of your masks, so that your people can see (accept and love) you as you truly are. You need to feel, in every cell of your body, your true integrity. In a way, we could say that your ultimate Life Purpose is to blossom into your own best friend, and then from that place, bless the world around you with your contagiously lovable presence.

LINE FIVE

If you have a Line FIVE in your PROFILE, you are—what we say in Human Design circles—a beautiful HERETIC!

You were born to become a true Leader, an Authority who is specifically suited to love and serve humanity, to positively nurture and compassionately condition this world of ours… with simplicity, practicality and Grace.

Back to the House. You are the person who lives up at the top of the House, maybe even the attic. You can be found sitting in your room, with the lights out, peering down onto the street and at the world, through your window and from behind the curtains.

You aren't necessarily wanting people down on the street to notice you, but just like the dancing LINE TWO, everyone down on the street knows you're there. They don't necessarily see you as clearly as they see the talented dancer, but they know you're there, looking down at them and at everything going on. Most of the people on the street carry all kinds of projections about you. Many are positive, since there you are, up there, looking down at the world. They figure you've got some big important perspective, not to mention the insight, capacity and power to solve a good chunk of their problems.

Interestingly, you *do* have the potential to tune into the collective, and to understand many things about this human life. You do carry the potential to bring order and organization where it's needed, just as you do tend to radiate a certain kind of Authority that can draw people to you and have a powerful impact. Unlike LINE FOUR people, who are best suited for influencing their own network, you are actually designed to influence many strangers.

That doesn't mean you're meant to solve every problem or save every soul, or that you always know what's needed in any situation!

You often find yourself on the receiving end of projections, and may find yourself feeling a little wary of people and their tendency to pedestalize you. You can clearly see that they actually can't see *you* very clearly. They're too far away, or you're too hidden. So just because someone seems super impressed by you doesn't mean you trust them, or that they actually SEE you for who you are.

You may be as wary of power as you are projections. Of course, there are plenty of LINE FIVES who out of a deep-seated fear, hunger for and abuse power. They take advantage of the positive projections of others, and use their magnetism to manipulate and oppress, instead of listen and serve.

I'm guessing since you were drawn to *Designed to Blossom* and are a WE-oriented person, that unchecked, dominating and abusive power isn't something you feel comfortable associating yourself with. In fact, you may be someone who is more likely to hold back your intrinsic power, out of fear misusing it. Or even worse, to allow others to misuse their power in relation to you, by constantly placing yourself in disempowering life, love and work situations.

If you have LINE FIVE as your first number, **this is a very central part of who you are**, and it's super important that you come to understand that others are likely to have high expectations of you, whether or not they actually see you for all that you are. Feelings of guilt, the pressure to be perfect, and the fear of letting people down, are all themes you're likely to relate to very deeply. You probably feel very uneasy if someone puts you on a pedestal. It either makes you want to hide, or do everything in your power to stay up on that pedestal, even if it's at your own expense. You are someone who is likely to notice a lot, and can see what's needed in all sorts of situations. You are probably aware of your potential to be an Authority or a leader, even if you're not so keen on taking the risk of 'putting yourself out there.'

If you have LINE FIVE as your second number, you may not necessarily think of yourself as someone others idealize or expect a lot from, but they probably do. You may not go around feeling consciously guilty or paranoid, but there may be an undercurrent of these feelings if you dig a little deeper. You may be very drawn to those in leadership roles, and wish you were more like them, even though you'd prefer to stay out of the limelight. It's possible that you've experienced a loss of reputation in the past that was very painful, or that you've felt like a disappointment to your parents or the people around you. You don't necessarily see that experience as connected to your powerful presence, and the envy and expectations it calls forth from others. Whatever your experience has been up until now, if you're ready for a blooming transformation in your life, it may be time to ask yourself whether you're hiding in some way, whether your desire to stay out of the limelight is keeping you from fully owning your Authority in the world.

I remember when I first learned about my LINE FIVE, I laughed. The last thing I ever identified with was Leadership, Authority or Power. If I embraced those qualities out loud while growing up, I'm not sure I would have survived my childhood… or the enormous amount of guilt I'd have to take on. (I had enough guilt as it was for not living up to the expectations and hopes of others, for not being the perfect, all-loving savior I believed I was supposed to be.)

For me, embracing my LINE FIVE has felt like coming out of the closet. I've had to cultivate an entirely new relationship to and understanding of power. I could only do this by looking honestly at my tendencies towards guilt, feelings of victimization, and the tyrannical nature of my own inner critic. I had to see how lost I could get in the complicated labyrinth of my mind's stories—about myself, others, my family, the world—and how I used those stories to oppress myself (and others, when that was the last thing my conscious mind wanted to do). I thought I was making the world a better place by denying my own inner Authority, by doing everything in my power to avoid misusing it, including repressing it. I wasn't making the world a better place. I was doing the opposite.

As I shared earlier, many LINE FIVES, like me, have experienced being put on a pedestal, only to be pulled down from it. They know the pain of what happens when they fail to fulfill others' expectations, whether those expectations are realistic or not, or fair or not. They carry within them a deep fear of disappointing others. Speaking from experience, this fear can almost become an obsession.

Beneath the fear of disappointing others is often a deeper one, a more tender one.
The fear of being disappointed by others.

You see, if you've lost your reputation or been pulled down from a pedestal, you know what it feels like to feel betrayed, victimized and misunderstood. Your body/psyche may even hold memories of having been 'burned at the stake.' You very likely know the deepest kind of disappointment. The disappointment of being used. The disappointment of not being seen, loved and accepted for the plain old human being that you are, of being set up to fail. The pain of conditional love.

It's understandable if you sometimes feel a little paranoid or untrusting of the very people you're meant to serve. If you feel afraid of failing them, and ultimately, of them failing you. These feelings and thoughts can make you hesitant to come down from the attic, onto the street, and offer your insight, assistance or guidance to people… even when what you have to offer is exactly what the people need.

This doesn't mean, however, that you are not ultimately meant to come down off that attic and share your gifts with others. You are. The key for you is first, to reconnect with your sweet heart. It's been through a lot. Feel your own disappointment fully. Feel the pain of having been conditionally loved. Feel the ways you've disappointed others. Do a little Spring Guilt Cleaning, and then forgive yourself. You're only human. When you forgive yourself, it becomes a lot easier to feel compassion towards others, and to develop the listening skills and clarity you need to be of service to humanity.

Remind yourself, that you don't have to blow people away with universal brilliance every time you come out of the attic. Just see if you can show up with a big, open, receptive ear. When the time is right, offer something simple, practical and helpful. You're never safer than when you've got both feet firmly planted on the ground.

Finally, be patient. It takes time to mature, and to feel truly ready to engage with the world. We want you to feel ready enough to hold projection fields lightly, as they're meant to be held. In the meantime, you might want to ask yourself, "If I weren't so afraid, what would I like to teach or give to this world? Where is my loving heart, clear mind and gift for leadership needed?" Remember there are many ways to lead. Some are much more obvious than others. Trust in your inner *Wisdom Keeper*, and your just right form will unfold.

LINE SIX

If you have a Line SIX in your Profile, you are designed to be an authentic ROLE MODEL.

You are that person who spends most of their time on top of the roof! You're not meant to be constantly focused on the House itself. You've already lived in it. You know all about it. You've been there, done that. In fact, you simply ARE the House. Ultimately, your job is to look over to the next House. At your core, you are a Visionary. You were born to be extremely interested in seeing what's coming next, and to understand, fundamentally, what the purpose of the House was in the first place. There's something very unique about people like you, and the movement of your life.

If you have a LINE SIX in your Profile, you were actually designed to live your life in three distinct phases. The first looks a lot like how the LINE THREES live. Until you're about 30 years old, you're actually supposed to take a lot of risks, to have a lot of experiences, and to learn through trial and error, through your 'mistakes.' In this phase of your life, like the THREES, it's very important that you learn all about what works and what doesn't work in this world of ours.

Unlike the THREES, who are protected by a combination of resilience and skepticism, you can be deeply wounded, even crushed, by some of your early experiences, if you don't understand your nature, or the fact that making and breaking bonds is actually a really positive thing for you, especially in the beginning of your life. It can be especially hard to understand these things, because deep down, in your very core, you are an idealist and optimist.

At some level, whether you know it or not, you're likely always looking for that 'perfect' experience, that 'perfect' truth, that 'perfect' soulmate—and expecting/hoping to find it. Those first 30 years of deeply subjective, often painful learning, can be disillusioning for you, leaving you with your fair share of scars, a reluctance to trust people, and a desire to escape from the messiness of life.

As you approach 30 and move into your early 30's, it is common for you LINE SIXES to leave your experimental, subjective and at times messy life behind, and go as James Taylor sings, 'up on the roof.' During this second phase of your life (your 'roof' phase), even though you still may be participating in life, you're likely to do it from a relatively safe distance.

If your early life was particularly crushing, which isn't unusual, you might find yourself subtly withdrawing from the world during this time, either through physical/literal isolation, or emotional isolation. In an effort to protect yourself from the harshness of reality on planet earth, you can become hard to reach, even dissociated. You can appear aloof, like you don't care… when the opposite is true. It can feel like you're excluded from everyone and everything, from life itself.

It is also during this time in your life, from your early 30's to early 50's, that you have the potential to benefit from all of your previous experiences. You realize, now that you finally have some distance, that you've actually learned a whole lot about life, and about what works and what doesn't. The distance you can enjoy during this period (whether it's obvious to anyone or not, yourself included) also allows you to become a great observer. You have the potential to become a deeply objective person, to maintain the big picture without getting lost in the nitty gritty—or not so relevant—details. Because of this, during this phase of your life, you are likely to be sought out for your wise advice, for your fair and unbiased opinions, and for your sound judgment. You may come to enjoy the Authority and outer success you experience, as well as the safety and relative calm that often accompany this phase of life.

However, you weren't designed to stay up on the roof forever. Somewhere deep down, you likely know this. As you transition into your 50's, whether you like it or not, life begins to pull you back into the adventure.

As a LINE SIX, you are, indeed, meant to return to the undeniably subjective world. During this time, your soul's task is to get back in there, to take some risks, to go through new trials and errors, and to get nice and dirty. If you've managed to make the most of your roof-top years, and if you're true to your unique flower nature and trusting your inner *Wisdom Keeper*, you're not going to crumble or shy away from the imperfections of life. You're going to welcome them with open arms and an open heart.

Whether your LINE SIX is your first or second Profile number, one thing is true. You are like fine wine. You get more alive and radiant with age. You get to live your life as a free agent, as yourself, acting as a true role model for what it is to be and accept who one is, an authentic human being living in a deliciously imperfect world. You are here to embody a combination of subjective experience and objective learning, and end up leading through your example. You are here to walk your talk… and to show the rest of us that it's possible to keep blossoming, for the rest of our lives!

If you have LINE SIX as your first number, this is a very central part of who you are, and you're likely to recognize a deep core idealism living inside of you, as well as this 3-phased pattern to your life. Depending on how old you are, your experience of your LINE SIX, of course, will be different. If you haven't entered your 30's, you're likely to relate to the experience of the LINE THREE people. It's super important that you learn to embrace the experimental and experiential way you're designed to learn, especially during this exciting time of your life.

If you're somewhere between your late 20's and early 50's, you're likely to relate to the desire to distance or protect yourself a bit from the craziness of life. People are likely to come to you for your wise and fair counsel. You may find yourself in a role where your objectivity is often asked for.

If you're moving into your 50s, you may be feeling a pull back into a more juicy, risky life than you've had for a while, and having all kinds of feelings about that. Embrace the pull and the feelings if you can!

If you have LINE SIX as your second number, you're still going to experience a three-phased life, but it may not be quite so easily recognizable. It may be slightly masked or greatly influenced by the first Line in your Profile. If you are a 3/6 or 4/6, your Roof Top time may be much less obvious. 3/6's are designed to always be in the world at some level, having trial and error experiences. Similarly, 4/6's are also designed to be in the world, interacting with all kinds of people, even during their Roof phase. This doesn't mean that the Roof phase isn't happening. It's just likely to be happening more subtly. The questions of 'Who can I truly trust? Who are my true allies? What actually works in this world?' will likely be present for you beneath the surface.

Wherever LINE SIX shows up in your Profile, know that you have the potential to be infinitely wise, emotionally accessible, and deeply in touch with humanity's future. Patience is one of your greatest friends. Not just patience with yourself, but with the world. It will take time for the world to catch up with its potential, a potential you can see so clearly, and feel so intimately. In the meantime, see if you can enjoy being human. Drop into your body. Be here, now. Include yourself in your own life. Let people in. Allow for *what is* here on our humble spinning planet, while staying deeply connected to your vision for all of us. Keep that direct line to Spirit intact, however you do that best. Remind yourself that no matter how things look on the ground, we've got all the time in the Cosmos!

Your Unique Profile

As I've shared earlier, each of us has a unique Profile, and it consists of two distinct (and often very different!) Lines. Together these two Lines form a dynamic duo. I invite you to see them as a reflection of a highly unique inner marriage between what is conscious and unconscious in you, or between those things you were meant to have at least some control over, and the many *many* more things that you weren't.

In a way, your PROFILE is yet another **invitation to think of your body and mind as the ultimate soulmates**—and out of this union, comes the beautiful role you were born to play out in the world.

Soon I'm going to walk us through very simple descriptions of the 12 possible Profile combinations, so you can get a feel for how each pair of Lines can start to sing together.

Before I do that, just a little reminder. While Type reflects the kind of flower you are, your PROFILE says something about how your flower is meant to grow, what role it's meant to play in the garden. Remember, the best way for you to blossom and live out your purpose in a way that fulfills you, is to respect and appreciate your unique flower nature, and to honor your truth finding compass! While you're learning about your Profile, or the way your Blooming process is likely to unfold, there's really nothing you need to do about any of this. Just receive it as a compassion-bringing, self-accepting, insight-enhancing invitation.

(Note: The *Gene Keys* and Integral Human Design provide incredibly rich and expansive perspectives on the 6 Lines and your Profile. I've sprinkled some *Gene Keys* wisdom throughout this section, and Workbook, and will slip in some *Gene Keys*-friendly titles for the 12 Profiles in the pages to come. If you really want to immerse yourself in *Gene Keys* waters, I'll share ways to do that in our final Petal.)

1/3 The Investigating Anarchist

(Or... The Self-Loving, Forever-Discovering, Confident, Truth-Seeking & ... Experimental, Playful, Alchemical, Humorous, Family-loving and Deeply Experienced Being!)

If you have this combination, you are a highly introspective, investigative and deep person who's here to learn by taking risks and experimenting with life! Even if you prefer to focus on securing your foundation by deep study and thorough research, you learn, grow and change through a process of trial and error learning. When it's really needed, you've got what it takes to tear down what isn't working in our world, and to help us all avoid making the same mistakes over and over again. For you, there's nothing more wonderful than finding a foundation worthy of building a life on!

1/4 The Investigating Opportunity-Attractor

(Or... The Self-Loving, Forever-Discovering, Confident, Truth-Seeking & ... Influential, Authentic, Community-Loving, Friendly and Gentle Being!)

You are a highly introspective, investigative and deep person who is designed to attract and make use of wonderful opportunities that naturally come your way! You love to research and study things that matter to you, and are often approached by your friends and professional network to share what you have learned. You can have a very strong point of view. To make sure your perspective is broad and alive, you do really well partaking in a well-rounded and exciting education. You can inspire so many people by taking advantage of opportunities that come your way to share your well-founded messages and truth with the world!

2/4 The Naturally Gifted Opportunity Attractor

(Or... The Relationship-loving, Passionate, Relaxed, Natural, Un-self-conscious, Free & ... Influential, Authentic, Community-Loving, Friendly and Gentle Being!)

Deep down, you are a naturally gifted person who people can't help but notice and want to provide with lots of opportunities to share your gifts. You can be very shy, or private. Solitude is very important to you. It may take you time to know what your real mission in life is. If you pay attention, and learn to feel comfortable being seen for the magnificent person you are, you're likely to discover that you are simply a "natural" at something you really enjoy. You're very likely to be "called out" of your hiding by your friends and community. In the end, you can end up being a true missionary. Once you've been called to share your gifts with the world, and you allow yourself to embrace your God-given gifts, without apology, you can really GO FOR IT, with a zeal that's contagious.

2/5 The Naturally Gifted Heretic

(Or... The Free, Passionate, Relationship-loving, Relaxed, Natural, Un-self-conscious & ... Humanity-loving, Forgiving, Clarity-bringing, Inspiring 'Teacher' Being!)

You are a VERY private person, who is blessed with a powerful gift for leading and helping people in deeply practical ways, when the time is right! You are quite practical in general. You're not here to pontificate about things that don't actually matter or aren't relevant to the people you're engaging with. For you to maintain your place in society, your reputation is important. Even though it can be scary for you to face the world of projections (which is understandable, because you're someone who receives a

LOT of projections—both the true ones, and the false ones), you still have to be true to yourself. There is something you are naturally brilliant at, and you must learn to own and celebrate your brilliance... even though you might be reluctant at first to step out of seclusion and deal with having to live up to the pressures of other people's expectations. In the end, it's up to you to CALL YOURSELF out of your private world and offer a practical solution to the people who need it. When you do, the whole world benefits!

3/5 An Anarchistic Heretic

(Or... The Experimental, Playful, Alchemical, Humorous, Family-loving and Deeply Experienced & ...Humanity-loving, Forgiving, Clarity-bringing, Inspiring 'Teacher' Being!)

You are a deeply experimental risk-taker who is here to solve all kinds of problems in this world, because you've been there and done that! You are one of the great experimenters in life. You're a gifted problem solver, with a scientific knack and courageous heart. Just by being who you are, and going about your daily business, you naturally bump into those things that simply don't work in our society. As long as you embrace your years of valuable life experience—including what might be misinterpreted as 'mistakes,' you have the uncanny ability to find practical solutions to just about any problem. You are a deeply resilient, variety-loving and adaptive person. You're like a brilliant Weeble that wobbles, but it won't fall down. You are a brilliant and brave UNIVERSAL FIXER.

3/6 The Anarchistic Role Model

(Or... The Experimental, Playful, Alchemical, Humorous, Family-loving and Deeply Experienced & ...Allowing, Transcendent, Visionary, Present, Divinity-loving, All-including Being!)

You are a deeply experimental, resilient and courageous person who, deep down to your core, is full of idealism and optimism. You are here to ultimately model for the rest of us what it is to be an authentic, self-embracing, life-loving human being. With your rich and varied life experience, you have the potential to gather some of the deepest wisdom when it comes to the trial and error process of life. As you mature, you are destined to become a living example for how to handle life's challenges, and bounce back even stronger, no matter what twists and turns life throws your way. Beneath it all, you are deeply innocent. It is your purity of heart that equips you for the magnificent, multi-faceted journey of life.

4/6 Opportunity Attracting Role Model

*(The Influential, Authentic, Community-Loving, Friendly and Gentle & ...
Allowing, Transcendent, Visionary, Present, Divinity-loving, All-including Being!)*

You are an attractive, opportunity-attracting and friendly person who is here to show the rest of us how to live and collaborate with others, in ways that truly work and benefit the whole! You are a keen and observant witness, always on some level watching and taking in your social environment. You are one of the great networkers, especially in your immediate community and circle of family and friends. Others see you as friendly and sociable, and they tend to feel comfortable confiding in you. Through your years of participating in families, groups and communities, and watching the people around you, you have the potential to develop wonderful interpersonal skills. Ultimately, you are here to blossom into a role model for that which you have observed works in the world, and amongst people.

4/1 The Opportunity-Attracting Investigator

*(Or... The Influential, Authentic, Community-Loving, Friendly and Gentle & ...
Self-Loving, Forever-Discovering, Confident, Truth-Seeking Being!)*

You are an attractive, friendly and opportunity-attracting teacher. You are designed to be at your absolute best, and to share a very specific and inspiring message in the world, when you're standing on a strong and solid foundation. You are one of our world's most effective and inspiring teachers. You didn't come to the world to change who you are or what you stand for, or to twist yourself into pretzels in order to please or accommodate other people's world views. Your purpose in life is very specific and your unique perspective is needed and wanted by your students. You are here to be respected and valued. If someone can't see or feel the value of what you have to give, they're just not meant for you. There are certainly plenty who can and do!

5/1 The Heretical Investigator

*(Or... The Humanity-loving, Forgiving, Clarity-bringing, Inspiring 'Teacher' & ...
Self-Loving, Forever-Discovering, Confident, Truth-Seeking Being!)*

You are a natural born leader, here to master your fears, stand on a solid foundation and help a lot of people by providing very practical solutions to their very real problems. You are often the leaders, generals and gurus of our world. You just naturally command respect and hold Authority. As a person, you can be very private. When a need arises in the world, you are able and willing to boldly step forward and find solutions for groups of people, organizations, governments and society as a whole. This innate gift of leadership causes others to just naturally expect great things from you. They think you have the answers for them, which can feel like a pressure or a burden sometimes. You can fear that if you don't give people what they want, your reputation might suffer, or they might pull you down from the pedestal they put you up on. Despite this understandable fear, you are meant to stand in your own Authority and serve. The more practical and custom-designed your solutions are, the more likely you are to continue enjoying your positive position in the eyes of others.

5/2 The Heretic Blessed with Natural Gifts

(Or... The Humanity-loving, Forgiving, Clarity-bringing, Inspiring 'Teacher' & ... Free, Passionate, Relationship-loving, Relaxed, Natural, Un-self-conscious Being!)

You are a natural genius, even though you may not know it! You're here—when you're ready—to call yourself out into the world and guide us all—safely and successfully—into the future. You have a natural genius and great leadership potential, but you don't always see it yourself. Others do tend to pick up on this potential in you, and can have very high expectations for what you're supposed to accomplish. When you can sense these high expectations pointed in your direction, you can feel uncomfortable, burdened, even oppressed, and want to retreat into your own little private world. In the end, the world needs you to share your gifts. Under the right circumstances, as you learn to trust and embrace yourself, no matter what anyone is projecting onto you, you can come forward, blossom, and inspire so many others to dare to bloom right along with you.

6/2 Role Model with Natural Gifts

(Or... The Allowing, Transcendent, Visionary, Present, Divinity-loving, All-including & ... Free, Passionate, Relationship-loving, Relaxed, Natural, Un-self-conscious Being!)

You are designed to live your life as a highly authentic role model. You are here to weave together a tapestry of wisdom, and ultimately inspire the rest of us by walking your talk. You glean your wisdom from your early years of subjective experiences, trials and errors, and risk-taking adventures. You then withdraw for a time, to become an objective observer of the world, and to learn how to deal with the kinds of challenges you experienced in your youth. Finally, you descend from the roof and come back into the playing field of humanity, bringing the best of both worlds—your objectivity and subjectivity. You become a living example of a human being who boldly blossoms for the rest of your life!

6/3 Role Model Anarchist

(Or... The Allowing, Transcendent, Visionary, Present, Divinity-loving, All-including, &... Experimental, Playful, Alchemical, Humorous, Family-loving and Deeply Experienced Being!)

You are an eternal optimist, with incredible resilience, humor and a teaching tool box bigger than the sun! No matter what challenges life brings your way, you bounce back. You also move through a three-phased life—from a time of challenge and experimentation, to a time of observation and objectivity, to a time of setting an example for others. In your case, you never truly withdraw onto the roof top. You always have at least one foot in the messy world, experimenting, learning from life's continual challenges and twists and turns. You are built for this! You have the resilient heart and Spirit necessary to blossom even within chaos. For you, there are few things more precious and important than a good sense of humor, and the ability to laugh at yourself, and this crazy human drama in which we're all playing our part!

(Note: Again, there are many places online—both free and paid—where you can learn more about your Profile, from a traditional Human Design perspective, as well as from others, like Richard Rudd. My job for now, as I see it, is to give you enough information to feel good enough about who you are, inspired to start experimenting with your life in a new way, and to keep learning if that's what your inner *Wisdom Keeper* wants for you.)

Your Petal Six Invitation

Dance with the Yin and the Yang!

One of my favorite quotes is by a wonderful man named Wilbert Alix, the originator of TranceDance. He said, "Growth happens in the light. Transformation happens in the dark." I always think about that quote when it comes to Profile in Human Design, and the implicit marriage that exists between what is conscious in us, and what lies beneath the surface.

Remember, in Human Design, we have the more conscious aspects of our nature... what we call the Personality, or what is illustrated through the **BLACK** Gates and Lines in our chart. These are the parts of us that we associate with the activities of the conscious mind, or the character of the soul that one could say exists with or without the body.

We also have the less conscious aspects of ourselves... what we call the Design in Human Design, or the RED parts of our chart. We have the BODY and its in-built intelligence, working all of the time, whether or not our minds are consciously tracking or controlling what it's doing. This, at least in one very real sense, can be seen as the dark or hidden aspect of our nature.

It is often through the body, through its attractions and repulsions, its intuitions or feelings, its cycles and chemistries, that change happens. It is often through the body that we actually draw to us the opportunities, the people—even the thoughts!—that ultimately inspire change. (I'm talking deep, real, life-changing change.)

Very rarely is it our heads and all of the thinking and planning and scheming that they do in the light of our awareness... that bring about the biggest transformations in our lives.

For me, this is yet another reminder that no matter what kind of flower we are, it's all about surrender in the end. Surrender, in so many ways, must include a deep trust in our bodies... in the Dark and hidden Design element of our being.

This is why this week, I'm going to invite you to explore both the LIGHT and the DARK—or HIDDEN—aspects of your Profile. Each LINE holds equal importance.

In this exercise, I'd like you to start thinking about the two LINES in your Profile, in relation to the LIGHT and the DARK I speak of.

1. How does your first Line relate to your personal growth, to what's been 'in the light of your awareness' as you've moved through life.

2. How does the second Line in your Profile relate to the deeper transformations that have taken place in your life? How might this Line speak to the intelligence that's been working underground? How may it have been helping you to let go when you've needed to let go? How might you have given yourself the courage necessary to enter the unknown in order to make an important transition... even when it wasn't easy?

CREATE YOUR YIN YANG FLOWER!

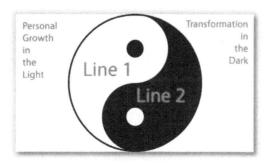

(You can use your journal, or if you are up for it, I also encourage you to work with a larger canvas, so you have as much freedom of expression as possible.)

Start with the YIN/YANG SYMBOL.

- Let the WHITE half reflect the first Line in your Profile—representing personal growth in the LIGHT.

- Let the BLACK half reflect the second Line in your Profile—representing transformation in the dark

Remember you can always do this your own way! You can do this visually, as a drawing, a painting, a sketch or a collage. You can use words, or no words. You can dance the Yin, then dance the Yang, and then synthesize both parts into a single, fluid, back and forth movement. You can create a musical mashup! Whatever you like.

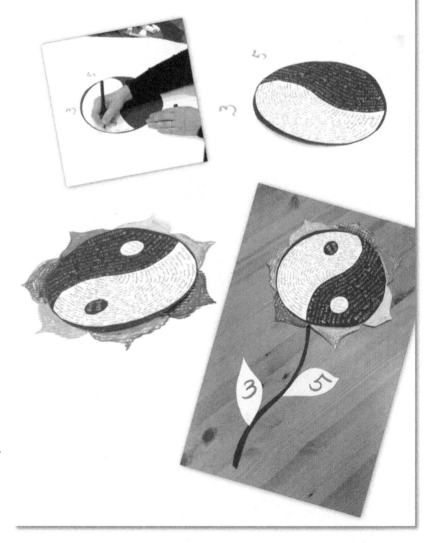

What matters most is that you start to gather insights about how these two LINES (and what they represent) have been at play in your own life... both on the surface, and below.

Now remember, within each YIN, there is a small dot of YANG. Within every YANG, there is a small dot of YIN. Be aware of this paradoxical truth as well. See if you can find a fun way to bring this paradox into your expression.

AN EXAMPLE

I decided to use writing as my main modality of exploration for this exercise. I explored my 3/5 Profile as a YIN/YANG FLOWER journal/poem. I wrote all kinds of memories, stories from my life, and thoughts that reflected the essence of each of the Lines in my Profile, and I placed them on the different sides of the Yin/Yang symbol. It was so interesting to look at my life through this particular lens! Here's a little look at it, to give you just one example of how you could potentially approach this process.

REMEMBER TO PRACTICE YOUR STRATEGY AND USE YOUR AUTHORITY.

Remember to use what you know about your Design as you engage in this process.

If you're a Generator, trust the modality you genuinely **respond** to, and only do this process when you have energy for it!

If you're a Projector, you may want to do this with someone you love, someone who you really enjoy being with.

If you've got an Open G-Center, be sure that you're doing this process in an environment that truly feels good to you!

If you've got a LINE SIX in your Profile, you might want to divide up the Yin or Yang, depending on the position of your 6th Line, into three sections... just for fun and see whether you notice anything about the 3 distinct phases of your life.

You get the idea.

Enjoy!

Move Beyond the Map: Petal Seven

Bask in uncharted, contemplative territory, and expand your family of supporters!

MOVE
BEYOND
THE MAP!

Something I love about Human Design is how it is designed to evolve, just as we are. As this system takes root and branches out around the globe, it is blossoming into a fascinating field of study as well as a profound mystical exploration.

As you know, because of my blended background and alchemical tendencies, I have been drawn to a mix of 'traditional' and 'alternative' when it comes to Human Design. (Feels kind of funny to call any aspect of Human Design 'traditional,' since it's relatively new to the world, and certainly not conventional in any sense of the word, but you know what I mean!)

While I thoroughly enjoyed and completed my analyst training many years ago at Jovian Archive (Ra Uru Hu's official educational hub), I found myself especially drawn to the work of Richard Rudd… even then. I resonated naturally with his poetic and compassionate way of holding Human Design, back in the day when he was still writing Human Design books. I intuitively kept a heart-eye on his web site over the years. With great anticipation, I welcomed and witnessed the birth of the *Gene Keys* transmission.

Immediately, I found the *Gene Keys* to be an incredibly powerful and relevant mythology that amongst many other things, took the most essential aspects of the original Human Design transmission—the 64 Gates, or hexagrams of the *I Ching*—to an entirely new level. I also loved how Richard Rudd, Werner and Laura Pitzal infused traditional Human Design with the frequency-honoring depth of the *Gene Keys*, through Integral Human Design.

Over the years, I continued my personal, communal and spiritual explorations of this boundless transmission. The first virtual Deep Dive and LIVE retreat in Santa Cruz, led by Teresa Collins, Marshall Lefferts and Richard Rudd, was quite the catalytic experience for me.

During that time, I also did a lot of soul-searching in relation to Human Design. I felt a deep resonance with the *Gene Keys*, and a growing desire to integrate it into my professional work with Human Design. I was already integrating the expressive arts and my background in transpersonal psychotherapy into my work with Human Design clients. For me, there was no conflict. However, my choice to 'embrace the whole' publically eventually created a separation between me and the professional Human Design community I cared about and learned so much from. (I still hold the vision that these sorts of divisions will dissolve over time.)

I'd like to share a little more with you here from a blog I wrote a few years back about my process and integration of these two remarkable systems, in case it might help you with yours.

*"I have had a profound experience of the 'trickle-down' effect of a contemplative path. If one sits with an 'essential inquiry' long enough, it will penetrate and transmute every aspect of one's life. This is a deep truth offered by the **Gene Keys**.*

Just as the Gene Keys have felt like a giant shower of golden light pouring down from above and into the cells of my being, Human Design has felt like a warm grass-roots practice, a healthy dose of the 'power of the small,' tickling at my toes, one conscious step at a time. For some time now, these two practices have sung happily in my Generator belly. Not everyone feels this way. We're all so different; we need different things, at different times, often in a different order.

Some need to go as deep as they can possibly go into a system. Some simply need to be initiated with a 'system seed', and then move on. Some need to cycle through systems, going back and forth between them, returning when there is a special need.

*A while back, in an introduction to Integral Human Design, **Richard Rudd** and **Werner Pitzal** shared how 'systems' (like Human Design) are meant to carry us from one place to another. Once we arrive at our destination, they are built to dissolve. I resonate so deeply with that.*

What I've found in my own life, as I've immersed myself in Gene Keys waters, is that my Human Design 'map' hasn't dissolved. It's simply transformed. While I resonate deeply with the vastness, flexibility & Love of the Gene Keys 'territory'...I continue to find the specificity of the (increasingly Integral) Human Design map of myself very helpful as I navigate my way towards my ultimate map-free destination.

Through Human Design, I've learned to track energy and how it moves—both out from me and into me and between those around me. I've learned how to tune into whether/when I (or another) am being energetically seen, recognized, invited, engaged, repelled, etc... or not.

Whether something is coming alive in me (someone else), or not. Whether I am being respected as an authentic being, or not.

Whether my energy (gift) is being used well, or not. Whether I am making choices to avoid uncomfortable feelings or pressures, or not. Whether I'm working too hard with my mind or fear-driven will power, or allowing heart-seeded commitments & relationships to rise up within me naturally, easily, effortlessly... or not.

Especially when I'm feeling flooded or overwhelmed, about to jump into a new life chapter, or relationship, or when I don't have the time and space to delve into a deep contemplation, the Human Design experiment (I prefer the word 'practice') helps me to at least temporarily hone in on the 'now' in an exceedingly practical way. For me, Human Design is an invitation to cultivate the art of micro-discernment. It's like a moving meditation map ... one that ultimately trickles up from the infinitesimally small acts that make up each moment of my life.

The practice starts out small and narrow, and over time, it gets bigger and wider … until it's all about frequency… and the choices are just being made through me as I flow freely through my life and the increasingly wondrous environments I find myself in.

I like to see Human Design as a "choosing meditation"—that if taken to its zenith, won't require any incessant tracking at all. While I don't think Human Design knowledge is necessary for everyone to benefit from the Gene Keys experience (or for everyone in general!), it's certainly helping me practically pace myself, and actually absorb the nourishing 'Slow Down' message of the wonderful 52nd Gene Key. It's also helping me to gently remind myself to take one decision at a time, one new relationship at a time, one environment at a time… and remain true to my energy body."

Today, I remain committed to serving people who are drawn to Human Design, the *Gene Keys*, or some combination of the two. I find that I'm enjoying Human Design in ever-more relaxing and mystical ways, and I remain grateful to all of the teachers, colleagues and students who have inspired me along the way.

I also remain committed to trusting my intuitive Manifesting Generator belly, and to orienting my *Gene Keys*-infused heart towards service, even when it leads me in terrifying directions!

Given my life-long tendency to avoid cameras like the plague, for example, the last thing on earth I ever expected myself to do was create an online course in Human Design, where I basically sat in front of a camera and yapped away for over sixty-five videos! But that's exactly what I did. Thanks to my loving, encouraging and talented videographer husband Kim, I made it through the traumatic aspect of that experience and started having fun creating the online *Designed to Blossom* course, which you now hold in your hands, in the form of a Workbook. It's been an honor to bring together some of my favorite passions in this way, and to now be connected with you!

 AND THEN CAME THE *WISDOM KEEPERS*

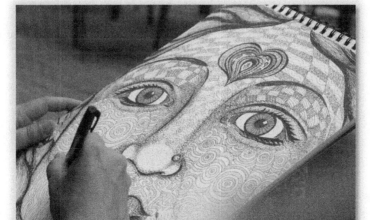

It all began during a particularly stressful time in my life, during the summer of 2014. I yearned to drop in, fret less and play more. I also longed for simplicity, and a way to deal with the despair I felt in relation to the seemingly endless stream of suffering that pervaded our planet.

Little did I know that my decision to spend a little time doodling, as a simple act of self-care, would lead me to birth the *64 Faces of Awakening*, *The Wisdom Keepers Oracle Deck*, an *Inner Guidebook*, a *Coloring Book*, A charitable *Coloring Project*, a Global Video Campaign, and ultimately, a deep involvement with a human rights organization in Uganda! (This is exactly the kind of thing that happens when one's mind is no longer in control of one's life!)

The creative process behind the birth of the *64 Faces of Awakening* (also called the *Wisdom Keepers)* was mysterious, whimsical and deeply intuitive. I began the journey with absolutely no agenda, using nothing more than black ink, white paper and my responsive Generator Belly. My first doodle drawing was completely abstract. My second was the face of a woman. I enjoyed communing with her so much that I decided to keep going.

Over the coming months, I welcomed one face after another. This deeply meditative process not only healed and soothed my stressed-out soul, it allowed me to work through my own grief about the wounded and conflictual state of the world.

Whether the faces came to me through a dream, an encounter, or a vision shared by a loved one, the *Wisdom Keepers* showed me that all of us—no matter where we come from, how old we are, or what religion, ethnicity and nationality we belong to—have the same potential to be fully awake, present, and to live from the heart.

After all of the 64 faces came through (couldn't resist the number for obvious reasons!), and as I spent time with these beings, I found myself feeling increasingly relaxed, trusting, patient and forgiving in my everyday life. I felt invited to become more alive, more empowered and more real.

Just as I had little control over who came through when I was bringing the *Wisdom Keepers* into form, I had little control over what they had to say when it came time to creating *The Wisdom Keeper's Oracle Deck*. Writing the *Inner Guidebook* was also a deeply intuitive process that required complete surrender and trust.

I allowed the *Wisdom Keepers* to reveal their personal stories to me. The most important thing I learned was that each one of them earned their wisdom by not only surviving painful and challenging experiences, but by embracing them, as Jung encouraged us to embrace our

Shadows. I learned that these radiant beings weren't that different from you and me. They were deeply human. I recognized them as keepers and transmitters of archetypal wisdom.

It didn't take long before I saw a profound connection between these beings and my work with Human Design, and especially the *Gene Keys.* I also felt an increasing desire to bring these wise beings into the hands of people through a practical, playful, psychologically insightful and empowering *Oracle Deck.* With care and gratitude, and Richard's permission, I did my best to incorporate the most essential concepts and key words of the *Gene Keys* into the text of the *Wisdom Keepers Inner Guidebook.*

I created the *Wisdom Keepers Oracle Deck* so that it could stand on its own. However, just like the *Designed to Blossom* online course and Workbook, I also intended for it to act as a warm welcome into the world of the *Gene Keys* (and Human Design). What I've learned, as more and more people have begun working with the *Wisdom Keepers* and the *Gene Keys* together, is that there is a profoundly supportive synergy between the two.

These days, my own inner *Wisdom Keeper* is giving me all kinds of fun ideas for how the *Wisdom Keepers* can serve both Human Design and *Gene Keys* communities in the future. I'm cooking up a few fun projects already, including integrating the *Wisdom Keepers* into the *Designed to Blossom* experience! (Stay tuned!)

In the meantime, you can explore the *Wisdom Keepers* as they're being offered today at: *wisdomkeepers.net*

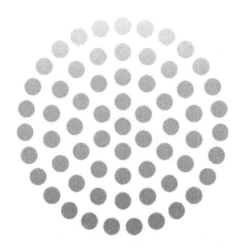

MORE ABOUT
THE *GENE KEYS*

As you've probably gathered by now, the *Gene Keys* is a body of knowledge here to help us transform our core self-beliefs, expand our consciousness and release our individual creative genius into the world. The *Gene Keys: Unlocking the Higher Purpose Hidden in Your DNA* is also an actual book, a contemporary *I Ching,* written by Richard Rudd, a teacher of world mythology, an award-winning poet. It is also a path of self- and cosmic-discovery. There are many, *many* offerings that have grown out of the *Gene Keys,* as well as a worldwide community that is contemplating, experimenting with, refining, and sharing the wisdom of this living transmission.

There are these 64 universal archetypes that lie at the heart of the *Gene Keys.* They correspond to the 64 hexagrams of the *I Ching,* the 64 Gates of the Human Design Bodygraph, the 64 codons of our human DNA, and the 64 *Wisdom Keepers* in the *Wisdom Keepers Oracle Deck.*

Both Human Design and the *Gene Keys* are **massive** syntheses. Human Design brings together modern science (quantum physics, biochemistry, genetics and neuro-gastroenterology—the science of the 'gut-brain') with some of our most ancient systems for understanding the universe and our own nature (the Zohar/Kabbalah's Tree of Life, both Eastern and Western Astrology, the Chinese *I Ching* and the Hindu Chakra system).

The *Gene Keys* is an even more massive synthesis, weaving core aspects of Human Design together with psychology, sociology, mysticism, physics, biology, music and indigenous wisdom. The territory mapped by the *Gene Keys* is infinite. There are different paths that can be explored within the map—the path towards purpose, towards love, towards true prosperity and more. Each path is rich beyond your imagination, and a beautiful way of understanding oneself, life and the universe.

Working with the *Gene Keys* is a very different experience than working with Human Design.

- While Human Design empowers us through a spiritual practice of decision-making, the *Gene Keys* invites us to practice the art of **contemplation**.

- While Human Design is exceedingly practical, the *Gene Keys* is organically transformative.

- While Human Design shows precisely how our conditioning gets in the way of our True Nature, and gives us full permission to go against the grain, the *Gene Keys* helps us learn how to be with the strong feelings that often emerge as we work to liberate ourselves from the grips of our conditioning.

- While Human Design gives us a roadmap for aligning ourselves with our True Nature, the *Gene Keys* helps us understand the beauty, depth and poetry of that nature.

- While Human Design shows us how to become authentic, liberated and empowered individuals, the *Gene Keys* inspires us to embody our gifts and serve the world—with deep breaths, grounded bodies, relaxed minds and softened hearts.

I could go on and on. I couldn't imagine a better match!

If and when your inner *Wisdom Keeper* feels drawn to taking one or more of those paths, there is something called the Golden Path (and so much more) waiting for you at GeneKeys.com. Please, remember to trust yourself and your own timing. Don't overload your mind. Remember to honor the wisdom in your beautiful body.

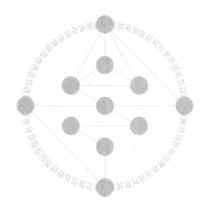

MORE ABOUT RICHARD RUDD'S
SPECTRUM OF CONSCIOUSNESS

One of the main *Gene Keys* concepts that I integrated into *The Wisdom Keepers Oracle Deck*, and that I'd like to share with you now, is what Richard Rudd refers to as the *Spectrum of Consciousness*. Each *Wisdom Keeper* is connected to three essential *Gene Keys* concepts: the *Shadow, Gift and Siddhi*. For Richard Rudd, these define a *Spectrum of Consciousness,* and refer to archetypal states that he correlates with the human experiential stages of *Survival, Service and Surrender*. The *Shadow* has its roots in Jungian psychology, while *Siddhi* is a Sanskrit term used in both Buddhist and Hindu mystical traditions.

SHADOW: When we are worried about our survival, and fear is in the driver's seat, we find ourselves in *Shadow* territory. Our *Shadows* can be expressed in repressive or reactive ways.

GIFT: When we are more oriented towards serving others and honoring ourselves, than protecting and defending ourselves, we more naturally share our *Gifts* with others and feel a sense of belonging in the world.

SIDDHI: When we have entered a pure state (or stage!) of expansion and have completely surrendered our sense of separateness into the Whole, we have entered the realm of the *Siddhi*.

Each of these three stages plays an essential role in our psychological and spiritual development as human beings. There is no *Gift* without the *Shadow*, no *Shadow* without the *Siddhi*, no *Siddhi* without the *Gift*. These states of being (or frequencies) breathe and dance together as we evolve.

Understanding how the *Gift, Shadow* and *Siddhi* are constantly interacting with each other throughout our lives can help us engage with the Gates in our Human Design Bodygraph, the 64 Gene Keys, the 64 *Wisdom Keepers*—and of course, ourselves—with greater compassion and patience. When it comes down to it, this is all about becoming gentler with ourselves, as we begin to notice larger growth patterns at work in our lives.

Even if we've been on a sincere spiritual path for years (since you're reading this Workbook, that probably includes you!), we're still bound to find ourselves moving in and out of *Shadow* and *Gift* territory. We get stuck in the same old ruts, because we're human.

From the perspective of the *Gene Keys* (and many heart-centered, shadow-embracing approaches to healing that are out there today), it's OK to feel sad, afraid and frustrated. In fact, if we can just hang in there without too much self-berating, these states can actually be quite fertile. As we get better at spending time in the *Shadow* realms without resisting, judging or reacting to our feelings, our capacity to unconditionally love ourselves (and each other) grows.

Over time, as our relationship to our emotional life (our Solar Plexus!) becomes healthier, we get more interested in opening up and helping out, than shutting down and protecting ourselves. Our *Gifts* start to come alive. From a Human Design perspective, you could say our Gifts are made up of our Definition, and ALL of the glorious wisdom we've gained through our Openness.

MORE ABOUT THE SHADOW

To confront a person with his shadow is to show him his own light.

~ Carl Jung

As someone with a Jungian and psychotherapeutic background, the *Shadow*-honoring prism of the *Gene Keys* resonated quite easily and deeply for me. I feel it's worth spending a little time exploring how this prism can support your Human Design explorations.

According to Jung and the *Gene Keys,* the *Shadow* holds the key to both our personal and collective transformation.

When we're experimenting with our Human Design, even when we're engaging with the multiple (sometimes conflicting) approaches to Human Design that are out there, the *Shadow* inevitably appears… in us, and in those around us. It is always helpful, no matter what 'system' you're learning, to pay special attention to the *Shadow*, and to understand how it emerges and how best to work with it in your own life.

As we explored through our Conditioning Flower, most of us learn as kids that if we act or feel one way, we get the love, safety and attention we need; and if we act or feel another, we are met with disapproval, rejection or threat.

We depend on the people taking care of us for emotional and physical sustenance, so we quickly and instinctively learn to reject the parts of ourselves that leave us feeling unsafe, unloved or insecure.

This is the essential grist for the Human Design mill. If we don't bring our conditioning experiences into conscious awareness, we'll keep pushing our difficult emotions, natural impulses, and aspects of our True Nature into the shadows. As long as we're doing that, our liberation experiment can only take us so far.

A place to begin… Think back to those areas where you felt like you were 'wilting.' Each of these areas are invitations to explore a *Shadow*.

Whether you feel like you're wilting in relation to a Defined Center, or an Open One, chances are that what you're experiencing is just a distorted version of an innate gift that you have, that you simply haven't fully seen, accepted or honored yet.

THE SHADOW AND HUMAN DESIGN

The shadow is like the nugget of coal that may hide a diamond of great beauty.

~ Richard Rudd

Shadows can be slippery and sneaky. Often, they emerge through our own destructive behaviors and our interactions with the people in our lives. Usually, they show up in the people around us—the people who trigger us the most. Whether we are annoyed by these people or completely in awe of them, they're the ones who are acting out the same impulses, qualities and desires we've been conditioned to suppress.

Let's say, you're a Projector who's been running around like a slave for years. Or you've got an Open Ego Center, and you've been burning yourself out making and keeping way too many promises, never letting yourself off the hook. In walks this person who allows themselves to take 8 vacations a year, or rarely makes a promise, much less keeps one. This person is going to drive you crazy, and is a giant invitation for you to look at a *Shadow*.

What is it that they are allowing themselves to do that you never allow yourself to do?

They allow themselves to take a break, to relax, to let people down, to set limits, to appear flaky, to do what feels right, and not work themselves to a crisp. Perhaps they do it in a '*Shadowy*' way. There's certainly room for you to move a tad in their direction.

That's your *Shadow* work. That's your ticket to liberation.

How can you (healthfully) allow for just a little bit more (for starters) of that which has been forbidden?

Often there can be a correlation between our Human Design charts and the charts of our *Shadow*-people. Sometimes they are Defined where we are Open. Sometimes they are Open where we're Defined. Sometimes, when looking at a Connection chart between two people, we can actually see how a certain dynamic in the chemistry between two people might leave one person feeling extra inspired by the other... or dominated, invisible and victimized.

Whatever our Human Design chemistry may be, the attitude we hold towards our own suffering in our relationships is ultimately what determines whether our *Shadows* serve us, our relationships and humanity, or not. Our capacity to embody and live out the most loving, creative and empowered version of our designs depends on our ability to work honestly and courageously with our *Shadows*. These following questions might assist you in the acceptance and integration of difficult *Shadow* feelings.

Some questions for you to contemplate when experiencing a painful, uncomfortable or forbidden feeling:

- Whether or not the feeling is considered 'yours' from a Human Design perspective, do you push the feeling away? Do you judge it? Do you feel victimized by it? Do you blame others for it?

- Or can you allow it to be what it is?

- Can you let yourself fully feel it—allowing it to wash through you, while keeping your heart open?

- Can you stay, breathe and trust?

There's so much more here… and so many ways to go deeper. For now, I encourage you to follow your own inner *Wisdom Keepers*' guidance, as well as to remember to hold it all just a bit lightly!

Conclusion

Firmly
Rooted
In the
Deep
Dark
Soil,
An
Open
Flower

One of my all-time favorite quotes is the one written by Anais Nin.

"And the day came when the risk to remain tight in a bud was more painful than the risk it took to blossom."

If I have a mission, for myself, for each of you, that pretty much sums it up. To get us to a place where that's our reality. Where it's just a little less scary to blossom than it is to hold back.

Not holding back—or blossoming out loud, living authentically—always involves some kind of risk. It just does. It doesn't matter how far we've come in our 'spiritual evolution' (if such a thing could ever be measured).

We could be some spiritual teacher sitting up on some mountain top all blissed out, and still have some place in us where we have yet to let go, some hidden truth, emotion, secret we have yet to hurl out of the *Shadow* closet. As far as I'm concerned, until we've dissolved into the Cosmos, there is risk.

Since everything can feel like it's going to hell and a handbasket during this time of global transition anyway, there's no time like now to take some real risks. To stop all of the pleasing and the egg-shell walking and the telling of the old story and clinging to the old identities, and to try something new for a change.

I encourage you, as you move forth into the world after this experience, above all else,

to trust yourself and your freshly liberated inner Wisdom Keeper.

And to breathe... a LOT.

To take leaps… even if that means doing things that your mind is convinced are crazy, impractical, stupid and scary. Or downright impolite! I'm not talking about doing any of this in order to be rebellious. Or defiant. (Although that's not always a bad thing for us we-oriented people!) I'm talking about doing these things to be free.

Your mind isn't going to stop judging or threatening you just because you're committed to taking risks. It may even get louder and more obnoxious actually. It may warn you about how you're going to make a fool of yourself. Half the time, it'll probably be right…

Even so, please don't allow that mind of yours to stop you… at least not for long. Give it a big hug and a kiss, let it know that you realize it's just trying to protect you, and that you appreciate its good intentions. Give it some mind candy to look forward to. Tell it you're going buy it a book, or that you're going to let it give someone advice real soon, or that you're going to let it explain something complex and meaningful to someone whose hungry for its brilliance.

Then go do your thing!
*(Which I sincerely hope, at least in some cases,
means doing* **much much less** *than usual!)*

Remember to let this information sink in over time, as it tends to do. Come back to this Workbook/Course again and again.

Over time, you'll find yourself getting increasingly creative with the information, and noticing the interrelationship between the different parts of yourself:

- How your Open Centers influence your ability to be true to your kind of flower and your healthy growth plan

- How your Authority can help you work with Open Center pressures

- How your Open Centers can lead you to your Shadows

- How your Shadows can lead you to your True Nature

- How as you become increasingly true to your inner *Wisdom Keeper*, you find that the *frequency* at which you experience your True Nature, as well as your Openness, begins to change.

How more permission is at the helm, and less constriction. More love, and less fear. More freedom, and less compromise. More flow, and less pressure. More genuine generosity, and less guilt-ridden obligation. More mutual respect in your relationships, and less of the unhealthy, resentment-building kind of sacrifice.

A NICE HEALTHY BALANCE BETWEEN
The ME and the WE!

I tell you; you'll be amazed at how deeply Human Design can influence your life, without your even realizing it. It's slow and deep and soon it permeates everything. Eventually, if you really give this experiment a try, it becomes second-nature. You simply find yourself living from a more trusting place, not making mental decisions, not identifying with all of the stuff coming in from the outside, and being yourself. In the end, you'll experience your Blossoming Bodygraph as a living, breathing, forever-changing map of a mysterious, glorious YOU.

Please stay in touch. As I shared earlier, I have plans to integrate more of the *Wisdom Keepers Oracle Deck* into my Human Design and *Gene Keys* related teaching. I'm super excited about that! I also have done some writing about the connection between the *Gene Keys* and Human Design that (Sacral Center-willing) I'll make available in a Resource Book Form. Keep an eye out for that too!

Lastly, if you think you know people who might really benefit from this Workbook/Course, or the online *Designed to Blossom* Program, please help to spread the word. Consider becoming a referral partner for the online program, so that when your people sign up, you'll receive a gift yourself, as a token of my gratitude.

I want to thank you from the bottom of my heart, for going on this journey with me!
I hope it's not the last time we see each other!

So much love to you,

A final gift of beauty from a Designed to Blossom participant

Resources for You!

For all things *Wisdom Keepers:*
wisdomkeepers.net

For all things *Gene Keys:*
Genekeys.com
Onedoorland.com/genekeys

More places to deepen your love of Human Design:

Integral Human Design
Human Design America
Jovian Archive
Genoa Bliven
Karen Curry
Stephen Rhodes
Richard Beaumont
Chetan Parker
Kim Gould

To learn more about Rosy:
rosyaronson.com

Remember: Wherever you see this icon, there's a free instructional video for you at:
wisdomkeepers.net/DTBvideos

ABOUT THE AUTHOR

Rosy Aronson, PhD, is an Artist, Blossoming Guide and ordained Spiritual Counselor with a Masters in Expressive Arts Therapy and a Doctorate in Intuitive Listening and the Creative Arts. In addition to the ***Designed to Blossom*** Course/Workbook, Rosy has created the ***Designed to Blossom Resource Book***, the ***64 Faces of Awakening, The Wisdom Keepers Oracle Deck, The Wisdom Keepers Inner Guidebook*** and ***The 64 Faces of Awakening Coloring Book*** to reflect essential healing archetypes that lie at the foundation of our universe. Rosy is also the author of ***Walking a Fine Line: How to Be a Professional Wisdom Keeper in the Healing Arts*** as well as ***A Tale of Serendipity***, an archetypal tale for the open-minded, open-hearted child in each of us. Her deepest intention is to provide empowering tools for people to awaken their inner *Wisdom Keeper* and bloom into their authentic selves.

An avid permission-giver, pressure-dissolver and embracer of the unknown, Rosy believes we are literally designed to blossom, and the more each of us radically trusts, honors and expresses our True Nature, the more magic we can create together.